A
Treasury of
North
American
FOLK-
TALES

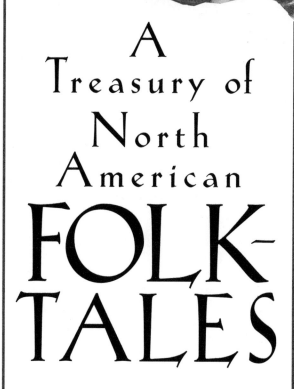

A
Treasury of
North
American
FOLK-
TALES

Compiled and Annotated by
Catherine Peck

Introduction by Charles Johnson

Book-of-the-Month Club

New York

Produced by The Philip Lief Group.

A Treasury of North American Folktales is a publication of Book-of-the-Month Club, 1271 Avenue of the Americas, New York, NY 10020.

Every reasonable effort has been made to trace the original sources for the tales included here. Permission to reprint the tales can be found starting on page 375.

Book design by Monica Elias
Illustrations by Rosemary Fox

Printed in the United States of America

For Hannah and Ellie, with love

Contents

• CONTENTS •

2

TALL TALES, BRAGS, AND OTHER LIES 49

3

LEGENDARY HEROES AND HEROINES 87

• CONTENTS •

4

LARGER THAN LIFE 131

5

LIFE LESSONS 167

Introduction

On the Nature of Tales
by Charles Johnson

A writer sampling the rich offerings in *A Treasury of North American Folktales*, hungrily reading each tale with an eye toward what he or she might learn about the craft of telling a good tale, comes away from this book at once humbled and reminded that folklore is the ancestral foundation for what we—as modern fiction writers—struggle mightily (and usually unsuccessfully) to achieve: a story worthy of being retold over and over for centuries. Like an old, old coin that has traversed continents, picking up something from each one, being passed down through centuries, and bearing the sweat and palm oil of millions who've handled it, these anonymous stories and yarns, legends and myths, distill the collective experience of mankind. They are unquestionably universal. They are timeless. They are, one might say, our human inheritance, for no single man or woman can claim authorship for "Opossum Steals Fire" or "The Yellow Ribbon." Yet modern storytellers as diverse as Vladimir Nabokov, *Twilight Zone* creator Rod Serling, Isaac Bashevis Singer, Alfred Hitchcock, Margaret Atwood, Robert Coover, Ursula K. Le Guin, Charles W. Chesnutt, George Lucas, O. Henry, and far more than I can cite here, have turned to the content and compositional strategies of the folktale to revitalize their own fictions. Reading these stories, carefully assembled by Catherine Peck, one easily understands why.

Tales usually deal with extraordinary events, and with fabulous characters (Brer Rabbit, Pecos Bill, Coyote) whom no one will assume is real. Strictly speaking, the Pecos Bill stories are *yarns*; the stories with animal protagonists are *fables*; and ones like "What Makes Brer Wasp Have a Short Patience" are *myths*. All these share elements of the folktale and are related to fairy tales, parables, and apologues; altogether, with their many variations, they comprise the ancient roots of the modern short story. Often, as in the wonderful story "Tom Dunn's Dance on Rag Rock," the characters are "things not of this world." But reality is never at issue in tales. They can never be "unrealistic" because tales have their own exuberant vision and interpretation of reality. Remember that what we call "naturalism," and sometimes refer to as "social realism," is a literary tradition that has its beginning in the late nineteenth and early twentieth centuries. The tale predates the arrival of these recent "scientific" approaches to fiction by five thousand years and can be found in the oldest African, Hindu, and Asian cultures. As the late John Gardner informed us in his first book, *The Forms of Fiction* (1962): "The laws governing the world of the tale may not be those of cause-and-effect, but even when they are not, they seem natural because they are psychologically and poetically true."

For example, in "Whickety-Whack, Into My Sack," the good-hearted protagonist Jack receives from a mysterious beggar an enchanted sack and drinking glass because it is imperative that he have these magical items later in order to save the king's daughter and capture Death. Or consider "The Haunted House," where a preacher attempts to exorcize a restless spirit and discovers it to be a young woman killed long ago by a lover who wanted her money. Her body, she tells him, is buried in the cellar. Following her instructions, the preacher properly inters her bones, gives her hidden treasure to the church and, with a macabre talisman—"the end joint of the little finger from her left hand"—succeeds in exposing her murderer. In these fantastic narratives, victims of murder walk among us, seeking justice beyond the grave, because—unlike our everyday reality—the dead must never go unavenged. And so phantoms walk. Angels intercede in human affairs (see Bernard Malamud's "Angel Levine"). The logic of the *heart* holds the tale together, fusing realism and fantasy in often profound gifts of the imagination.

Put another way, the reality of the world of the tale is that of a *moral* universe, a place where right and wrong are vividly dramatized, and time-honored ethical principles from the past are applied to present circumstances. Read "La Llorona Teaches a Hippie a Lesson." There, in this remarkable, Native American fiction, the spectral figure of an ancient Indian ghost-woman—La Llorona—appears in the 1970s to foil the stealing of her tribe's food by a hippie named "Bear" who "had some idea he was an Indian" but "didn't have any respect for people who worked hard." In fact, this disrespectful, lazy Californian from a rich family has stolen one of their totemic names ("Bear") as well as Indian dress and rides along the arroyo wearing "this little leather thing like Tarzan, with beads and feathers around his neck and moccasins." No one can catch him pilfering his neighbors' vegetables and fruit or drive him from the village he's plundering until La Llorona's banshee-like howling sends "Bear" scurrying away, terrified, on all fours.

In other words, La Llorona, Stackalee, Paul Bunyan, and Coyote do not have to be recognized as "real" people because they are infused with feelings we recognize in ourselves. More precisely, they are often the distillation of a single trait or emotion. Readers of naturalistic fiction expect writers to provide detailed, physical descriptions for each major character. We've come to expect, and rightly so, psychological realism, a biographical sketch ("back-story"), three-dimensionality, sociological and economic information about the protagonist, a conflict rooted in a performer's historicity, and crisp dialogue that sounds authentic. By contrast, characters in the traditional tale seem *flat*. Even one-dimensional. They are familiar *types*: kings, peasants, beggars, farmers, young men or women.

Notice how all we're told about the protagonist in "The Ghost of Jean Lafitte" is that he is "a young, war-weary Confederate soldier." The hero in "A Pretty Girl in the Road" is as featureless as a mannequin, as ahistorical as the Safe T Man dummies we place in our cars to fool would-be rapists and burglars. Yet there is more to these characters than initially meets the eye. In a haunting work like "The Grouse Girl," we are simply given "two men, the older lame and unattractive, the younger sound and handsome." They do not even have names. But from this spare description flows a complete, compelling "world." Although one man is young and handsome, he treats the Grouse Girl "roughly, and would not let her come near him" in her incarnation as a bird. However, the lame man "drew her fondly to him," and thereby weds his soul with hers, leading the first man to jealousy, then murder, and ultimately to the lonely fate of being "wifeless and partnerless."

Irrespective of their sketchiness, characters in tales do behave in ways we recognize because they are humanized, even supernatural beings like "Aunt Tucky," who "could slip out of her skin and become like a spirit or a ghost or a haunt" but who nevertheless must, after her nature is established, act in ways that do not violate that nature or the story's premise. Just in passing, I must mention that "Aunt Tucky" in particular is a folktale that has proven to be very influential on contemporary African American literature. Her skin-shedding talent is a trait I give to a witch in my first novel, *Faith and the Good Thing* (1974), a novel for which I read over eighty volumes of folklore, and it occurs again in Toni Morrison's third novel, *Song of Solomon* (1977). And how delightfully generous is the unexpected addition of rhyming dialogue in this tale—*Skin, my skin. Let me in* and

Skin, skin, always lucky. Welcome home your Aunt Tucky.

From the tales in *A Treasury of North American Folktales* we see that in order to work their poetically compressed magic, tales must be terse, concrete, telegraphic, and must reveal character through action. (This, I assure you, is a virtue. The French have a word for needless literary padding, *le remplissage*, and you find none of that here.) The tale is *all* plot, like the epigrammatic story of Cain and Abel in Genesis (sixty lines in all), and just as bottomless in meaning as this famous biblical story. Despite this brevity, however, tales need not sacrifice "realistic" description when that is truly needed. We find a precise and terrifying description of the ghost in "The Haunted House" ("Her hair was torn and tangled, and the flesh was dropping off her face so he could see the bones and part of her teeth. She had no eyeballs, but there was a sort of blue light way back in her eye sockets. And she had no nose to her face"), and striking imagery in "The Weeping Woman" ("They always die with their eyes open like they were looking up at something and couldn't stop"), but in stories where such elaborately sculpted details appear the setting may be hazy and vague. The mysterious place of Rag Rock in "Tom Dunn's Dance on Rag Rock," where a demon crew keeps Tom dancing nigh unto death, is barely described at all, leaving us to conclude that the topography of the tale is deliberately ambiguous: moors, islands, wild mountains, dark seacoasts (or the "galaxy far, far away" in *Star Wars*), regions for which our only passport is our limitless capacity to dream. In point of fact, the landscape of the traditional tale shares much in common with and is surely sire of the numberless worlds of science-fiction—the Red Planet of Ray Bradbury's *The Martian Chronicles*, the ape-city of *Planet of the Apes*, and the Morlock/Eloi terrain in H. G. Wells's *The Time Machine*.

Added to the many splendors of these stories, and most important of all, is the authoritative voice of the narrator, which is largely missing in contemporary, naturalistic fiction. It is an oral, storyteller's voice, like that of an African *griot*, the keeper of his people's history, or the compelling voice of our own grandmothers. Often it begins, *A long time ago, all the animals in the jungle got along with each other, except for one* ("Tío Conejo and the Hurricane"), or, *There was once this stagecoach route in Texas* ("The Yankee Peddler"), or, *Well, once upon a time there was two people lived in the world* ("Bobtail and the Devil"), or yet again, *One time there was a fellow a-riding along . . .* ("A Pretty Girl in the Road"), and what we experience in each of these openings is that the very first sentence transports us from here and now to another world, usually in the past. Phenomenologically, these folktale openings force us to suspend for the duration of the story our immediate worries and cares and worldly involvements; they are—as powerful first lines—akin to the slow raising of a curtain in the theater, which quiets down the audience and brings their attention to the stage; or, if you like, the very frame that surrounds the "world" of a painting and sets it off from the rest of a room. Only a fully *voiced* fiction can accomplish this so swiftly.

Such a voice can conjure other delights of language too. In "A Pretty Girl in the Road," it can tell us how a character "hollered a boy out of the barn," for the region of the storyteller clings to his voice, texturing his vocabulary and grammar. And in "Aunt Tucky" it can soar, making a reader feel the teller of the tale is sitting right beside him when she says, "The child would break all four legs! Yes! Four legs. I said that to show you *double* bad luck!" Again and again throughout the folktales in this splendid anthology we encounter *pure* storytelling voices of this sort, confident speakers—sometimes humorous, sometimes moralistic, always compelling—who help us recapture the childhood wonder and awe that makes us hunger for good tales the rest of our lives.

Thus, *A Treasury of North American Folktales* is a book that, I believe, will thoroughly entertain as it enlightens. Whether one simply reads for pleasure, or is an apprentice writer hoping to unkey the technical mysteries of stories that, like the pyramids or Stonehenge, have survived the passage of time, this volume offers inexhaustible treasures. Read it to your children. And as you do, enjoy being a child once again yourself.

Preface

Who are these "folk" who tell folktales? The current definition of a North American folktale includes almost any narrative from the earliest Native American legend to the joke you told at the water cooler this morning. So the first person to tell a story in North America might have been a tribal elder living thousands of years ago whose purpose was to illustrate the origin of the world, and the latest folktale teller might be . . . you. Folktales are an ever renewable natural resource, conceived from the union between past and present human experience, and born of our natural longing to communicate our experiences, insights, and visions to others. Tales are instructive, funny, scary, fantastic, visionary, and factual. They celebrate romance, bawdiness, the hero, the fool, the ordinary, and the extraordinary.

The most important thing to know about folktales is that they are almost always originally *told*. In compiling *A Treasury of North American Folktales* my first goal has been to present versions of traditional stories whose tellers express the richness of our heritage with their distinctive voices. For no single voice can communicate a cultural heritage as deep and broad as North America's. Not only is the continent peopled by almost every cultural group in the world, it also has diverse regions whose traditions have evolved separately from those of other regions. On top of that, the history of North America is a history of rapid change in language, dialect, values, and technology. The wonderful thing about folktales is that, because they represent so many voices, they offer insight into the diversity of human experience among ordinary people on this vast continent.

This collection holds tales both ancient and modern. The voices here are Native American, Latino, African American, French Canadian, Native Canadian, and Mexican. They are also voices of the South, the Midwest, the Northeast, the Northwest, and the West. They are voices from the past, using dialects rarely heard in North America today, and they are voices of the present, with a little modern slang here and there. They are proof that in every era and in every region of North America, fresh voices always have been, and always will be, on hand to make the old stories new.

My second goal has been to provide readers with stories that will entertain as well as enlighten, which has always been the purpose of folktales. I was asked to choose one book's worth of stories out of thousands of possibilities. What a task! Decisions had to be made. My first was to choose primarily tales whose sources are traditional. So while a story might include the exploits of hippies in the Southwest, the purpose of the story is to remind people about the supernatural power of the region's most famous ghost, La Llorona. My second decision was to choose stories whose origins might be vaguely Old World, but whose tellers were firmly rooted on this continent to the extent that the details of the story make it unmistakably North American. Thus while the story of Cinderella is known to have originated in Europe, in the hands of an Algonquin storyteller details are transformed to make the story meaningful to the members of that tribe.

Another decision was to include a number of often-told stories, some of which, like Paul Bunyan, probably originated in print and then moved off the printed page into the rich oral tradition of the North American frontier and into the imagination of almost every American. Yet another decision was to tap into the fieldwork of folktale scholars for stories that have not seen the light of day in many years. There I found contemporary newspaper accounts that formed the basis of heroic legends, personal descriptions of supernatural encounters, and funny stories—brilliantly told—that were languishing in folklore journals on dusty library shelves.

Finally, I decided to call upon modern storytellers who have taken stories that in their original recorded versions had gaps in the narratives or were difficult to understand, and have smoothed out the rough spots in order to bring them to us now in such a way that they will be remembered and retold well into the twenty-first century. These folks are on a mission to keep the stories alive, and I have come to admire them enormously.

I hope you will approach this book as a celebration of voices. I hope you will discover your own voice and read the tales aloud, for they came from the spoken word and deserve to return there. Finally, I hope you will take these stories and continue the folk process; *tell* the tales as they have always been told, by adding, subtracting, multiplying, and dividing details until the stories become your own.

Catherine Peck
Princeton, New Jersey

I

How the World Was Made

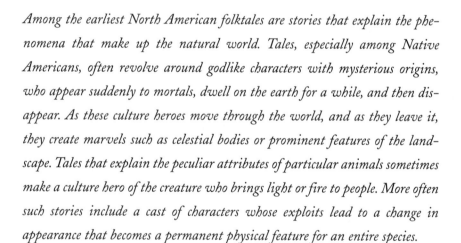

Among the earliest North American folktales are stories that explain the phenomena that make up the natural world. Tales, especially among Native Americans, often revolve around godlike characters with mysterious origins, who appear suddenly to mortals, dwell on the earth for a while, and then disappear. As these culture heroes move through the world, and as they leave it, they create marvels such as celestial bodies or prominent features of the landscape. Tales that explain the peculiar attributes of particular animals sometimes make a culture hero of the creature who brings light or fire to people. More often such stories include a cast of characters whose exploits lead to a change in appearance that becomes a permanent physical feature for an entire species.

Some of the tales in this chapter are taken from stories heard firsthand by folklorists and anthropologists visiting Native American tribes during the latter part of the nineteenth century. Others have been adapted from various sources by contemporary storytellers for a modern audience.

The Boy of the Red Sky

This gentle Native Canadian tale presents an example of how explanation tales weave extraordinary details into a simple story. Many myths around the world have as their central character an unearthly being who appears in the lives of parents who have longed for a child. The magical being's time on Earth is almost always short-lived, and he or she always leaves a magnificent gift.

Long ago a young man and his wife lived near the Great Water in the west. They had no children, and they lived by themselves on an island, far from other people. The man caught deep-sea fish in the ocean and salmon in the rivers. He was gone for many days at a time, fishing. The woman was not afraid, but she was very lonely, looking each day at the gray sky and listening to the sound of the waves on the beach. Day after day she said to herself, "I wish we had children. They would be good company for me when my husband is far away."

One evening she sat alone on the beach at twilight, looking across the water. The sky was gray. Because she was so lonely, the woman said to herself, "I wish we had children to keep me company." At that moment, a kingfisher, with her family, was diving for food nearby. The woman said, "O Sea Bird, I wish I had children like you." The kingfisher replied by telling her to look at the seashells. The next evening a white sea gull was flying above the waves. The woman told the gull that she wished she had children. The sea gull replied, "Look at the seashells," and flew away.

The woman kept wondering about the words of the kingfisher and the sea gull. Suddenly she heard a strange cry coming from the sand behind her. When she came closer to the sound, she realized that the cry was coming from a large seashell lying on the sand. She picked up the shell and inside found a tiny boy, crying as hard as he could. The woman carried the baby home and took care of him. When her husband came home from the sea, he was very happy that she had found the baby. He knew that they would no longer be lonely.

The baby grew quickly. One day the child suddenly said to the woman, who was wearing a copper bracelet, "Please make a bow from the copper on your arm." She wanted him to be happy, so she made a tiny bow and two tiny arrows from the bracelet.

Every day the boy went out hunting. He always returned with his catch: geese, ducks, and small sea birds, which he gave to the woman.

As the boy grew older, the man and woman noticed that his face was becoming the color of his copper bow. Wherever he went, there was a strange light. When he sat on the beach looking toward the west, the weather was calm and there were strange bright lights on the water. His foster parents kept wondering about this unusual power, but the boy would not talk about it. When they asked about it, he was always silent.

Once the winds blew so hard over the Great Water that the man could not go out fishing. He had to stay on shore because the ocean waves beat so strongly on the beach. When the father, worried, said they needed to get fish to eat, the boy said, "I will go out fishing with you, for I am stronger than the Spirit of the Storm." The man did not want to go, but at last he listened to the boy. They went out together to the fishing grounds in the rough sea.

They had not gone far when they met the Spirit of the Storm. He tried hard to overturn their boat, but he could not. He had no power over them because the boy was rowing the little boat. All around them the sea was calm and the waves were still.

Then the Spirit of the Storm called his nephew Black Cloud to help him. But the boy said to the man, "Do not be afraid. I am stronger than he." When

Black Cloud came, he saw the boy, and he quickly disappeared. Then the Spirit of the Storm called the Mist of the Sea to cover the water, because he thought that the boat would be lost if the land could not be seen.

When the man saw the Mist of the Sea coming across the water, he was very frightened, but the boy said, "He cannot harm you when I am with you." Indeed, when the Mist of the Sea saw the boy sitting in the boat, he went away as quickly as he had come. Angry, the Spirit of the Storm also hurried away. And the sea became calm again.

The boy and the man reached the fishing grounds safely. The boy taught his foster father a magic song, which he could use to call fish into the nets. By evening, the boat was filled with fish. As they were rowing back home, the man said, "Tell me the secret of your power." But the boy said, "The time has not yet come."

The next day the boy killed many birds and took off their skins. Then he dressed himself in the skin of one of the birds and flew above the sea. The sea under him was gray like his wings. Then he dressed himself like another bird, a blue jay. This time, when he flew, the sea under him became blue like his wings. He returned to the beach and put on the skin of a robin redbreast. When he flew high above the sea, the waves in the ocean under him turned the bright color of fire, and the sky in the west was a golden red.

The boy flew back to the beach and said to his foster parents, "Now is the time for me to leave you. I am the Child of the Sun. Yesterday my power was tested and I succeeded, so now I must go away. I shall see you no more. But in the evening, I shall often appear to you in the twilight sky in the west. When the sky and the sea are red in the evening, like the color of my face, you will know that there will be no wind or storm the next day. Although I am going away, I shall leave you the power to call me when you need me. Let me know your wishes: make me a white offering, so that I may see it from my home far in the west."

Then he gave his foster mother a wonderful robe. He said goodbye to his parents and flew off to the west. They were left sad and lonely, but the woman still keeps a part of the power he gave her. When she sits on the island and loosens her wonderful robe the wind blows from the land and a storm begins on the sea. The more she loosens her robe, the stronger the storm is.

In the late autumn, when the cold mist comes from the sea, the evenings are chilly, and the sky is gray, she remembers the boy's promise to her. She takes tiny white feathers from the breasts of birds and throws them into the air. They float to the west, and fall to earth like snowflakes that blow westward in the wind. They come to tell the boy the world is gray and gloomy and wait to see his golden face. Then he appears in the evening and stays until the sun is gone. The twilight sky becomes red and the ocean in the west is filled with golden light. All the people know that there will be no wind the next day, as the boy promised long ago.

What Makes Brer Wasp Have a
Short Patience

Not all explanatory tales deal with the grand and sublime mysteries of nature. Some, with great humor, explain the smallest detail of some of nature's most ridiculous aspects. This African American tale was told in North Carolina.

Creatures don't all stay just the way God made them. No sir. With the mistakes made, and accidents, and natural debilitation, and one thing or another, they become different as time goes on, until sometime later they are hardly the same thing at all.

At one time, Brer Wasp looked very different from the way he does today. He was big on company, and he loved to talk, and joke, and cut the fool. He was one person that had to have his laugh.

One day, he was walking on a path, and he met up with Brer Mosquito. Now, Brer Mosquito and his whole family weren't very big at all, but they took themselves mighty seriously. Brer Mosquito and his pa planted a little patch of ground together, but they always called it the plantation. They talked so big about their crops and land and everything that you would have thought that they had a twenty-mile place. Now, Brer Wasp loved to draw Brer Mosquito out on the subject.

That same week, there had been a heavy frost, and all the sweet-potato vines died and turned black and everybody was forced to dig for the early potatoes. And Brer Wasp, after he had passed the time of day with Brer Mosquito, and inquired about his family, asked him about his pa's health and how he had made out with his crop. "We made out fine, Brer Wasp," Brer Mosquito said. "Just too fine. We had the biggest crop you ever have seen!" "The potatoes were big, then?" "I tell you, sir! They were huge! You have never seen such potatoes!" "How big are they, Brer Mosquito?" Brer Wasp questioned him. "My friend," Brer Mosquito said, puffing out his chest and reaching down and pulling his little britches tight around his little leg, "most of our crop came up bigger than the calf of my leg!"

Well, sir! Brer Wasp looked at Brer Mosquito's poor little leg, and as he thought about those "huge potatoes," he had to laugh to himself. Now, he tried to mind his manners, but his chest and face swelled up, and his eye water ran out of his eyes, and he burst out laughing right in Brer Mosquito's face. He laughed and he laughed till his sides hurt him. Whenever he thought he would stop, he looked at that ridiculous leg that stood there like a toothpick, and he laughed more than ever. His sides hurt him so much, he had to hold them in with both his hands and rock himself back and forth.

"What makes you have to do that?" Brer Mosquito asked him. "You had better explain yourself. That is, if you can act sensible!" Brer Wasp gasped out, "Good lord, Brer Mosquito, looking for the biggest part of your leg is like hunting for the heaviest part of a hair! How big those huge potatoes must be, if you say they are as big as that!" And he laughed again till his sides hurt so bad that it wasn't enough just to press them—he had to grab them in both his hands and squeeze.

Brer Mosquito was so annoyed that he felt like fighting Brer Wasp right on the spot. But then he remembered that Brer Wasp was kind of nasty when he got in a row. So he just drew himself up, and stuck out his mouth, and said, "Laugh, you no-mannered devil! Laugh! But take care that the day doesn't come when somebody laughs at you the same no-mannered way!" And he went away so blistering mad that his two little coattails stuck straight out behind him.

But that didn't stop Brer Wasp. All the way to his house he had been laughing so hard that he had to stop now and catch his breath. At last he got home and started to laugh some more and tell his family about Brer Mosquito. Just then his wife got a good look at him, and she hollered out, "For crying-out-loud, Brer Wasp! What's happened to your stomach?" Brer Wasp looked down where his waist had been and he could hardly see it.

He lost all notion of laughing right then. He looked again and he saw what all that shaking, and pushing, and squeezing had done to him. He was almost in two! Even his little hand could reach around his waist. He remembered how big it had been, and he saw how much he had shrunk up, and he was afraid to so much as sneeze.

Then he remembered what Brer Mosquito had said to him. He remembered all those people he had been joking about and laughing at so hard and for such a long time and he thought about how now the others were going to have their turn to laugh at that little waist he had now. He got so that he couldn't get that shameful thing out of his mind. And that is why he has such a short patience! Everywhere he goes he thinks somebody is ready to laugh at him. If anyone so much as looks at him, he gets so mad that he is ready to fight.

And that isn't the worst, because from that day to this day, he can't laugh anymore, because if he does, he will burst in two!

Opossum Steals Fire

Myths explaining how humans first got the use of fire often describe the journey of a culture hero who must steal the fire from a god or, more often, an old woman who hoards it for herself. In Greek mythology Prometheus makes this terrifying journey. His success is met with such anger from the gods that he spends eternity being punished for giving fire to humankind. In most North American tales, the theft of fire explains a feature of the animal who took it. Some describe the journey of a spider whose back remains forever stained red; others say a fox did it, and that is why the fox's feet are black. The following tale is from Mexico.

They say there was an old woman who managed to keep the fire when it had scarcely become separated from certain stars or planets. She was fearless and went to get the fire where it had fallen. She kept it a long time.

Then after a while, people decided that this fire ought to be for everybody and not just for the old woman. So they went to the old woman's house and asked for fire. But the old woman was ferocious. She would not give it to anyone.

Time passed, and word traveled that this old woman had managed to keep fire but would not share it. Then Opossum came along and said to the people, "I, Opossum promise to give you fire, if you promise never to eat me."

Then everyone made fun of the poor creature. But he remained calm and answered them: "Stop making fun of me, because you are only making fun of yourselves. This very evening you will see that my promise has been fulfilled."

When evening came, the opossum went visiting from house to house, saying he was going to get fire from the old woman, so that others might collect as much of it as they could.

When he arrived at the old woman's house, he said to her, "Good evening, Lady Fire. How cold it is! I'd like to stand next to your fire for a moment and warm myself. The cold is killing me."

The old woman really believed the opossum was cold, and she allowed him to come close to the fire. But this was a clever one, and he kept getting closer and closer until he could put himself into the fire. Then he put his tail down, and that's how he was able to catch it. When his tail had caught fire, he ran as far as he could, sharing the fire. And that's why opossums today have a bald tail.

Light

Similar to tales of how fire was brought to the world are stories of the culture hero's quest for sources of light. Like fire, light most often had to be stolen, according to origin stories of Native Americans. In this unusual tale, heard on Kodiak Island, Alaska, around the turn of the century, the hero is the raven, a well-known trickster among Northwestern American tribes. The following tale was recorded by F. A. Golder and published in The Journal of American Folklore *in 1903. Like most folklorists of his day, Golder translated the tale to fit the Victorian literary style of the period.*

Light was not so universal formerly as now. Its cheering influences were then cast over one village only; and even there it depended on the caprices of the chief, who regulated and guarded it jealously. All other villages lived in darkness, although aware of the existence of light in that village. They made many attempts to get possession of it. Some, after a few efforts, gave up in despair. Others, not so easily discouraged, continued a longer time with the same empty result. But one village, owing to the persistent character of its chief, would never own itself defeated, and persevered in spite of past failures.

Here, in the village hall, the people gathered daily to discuss the all-important question of light, and concluded to call for volunteers to go in quest of it. To the fortunate one the following reward was held out: eternal glory and the hand of the chief's beautiful and favorite daughter. Considering the inducements, there were no lack of volunteers at first, but, as none of these returned, not even to tell the story of their failure, the list became smaller and smaller, and after a time weeks would pass without anyone offering himself. What became of these eager seekers after light was a mystery. It was generally supposed that some dropped by the wayside, and the others, on reaching the land of light and finding the task too arduous, decided to remain there always rather than go back without light.

The chief, however, was undaunted, and continued calling the meetings and for volunteers regularly. At one of these the raven was present. He listened attentively to all the speeches, and heard the chief's call for volunteers, and when a considerable time had elapsed without anyone indicating his desire to go, he rose and addressed the assembly. Sad to say, his speech has been lost in the dark ages, except the last and memorable words, "I will bring you light." This was followed by such loud peals of laughter and mocking hoots that the building almost shook. The chief, who was deep in thought during the raven's harangue, was aroused from his revery by this sudden outburst of laughter, and inquired the cause of it. With much derision the speech and boasts of the raven were repeated to him. Although he may have had as little faith in the words of the raven as the others, he was yet too wise a man to let any opportunity, no matter how slim, of obtaining light—the great object of his life—go by unembraced. Instead of joining in the laughter, he mildly reproved his followers, and then addressing himself to the raven, congratulated him on his noble resolution, encouraged him to persevere, and ended by reminding him of the prize that awaited him whose efforts should be crowned with success.

With this the meeting dissolved. The raven, satisfied with the present and rejoicing in the future, flew home to make ready for the expedition. Joyfully he related the events of the day to his grandmother, a woman. "Caw! Caw! Caw! Grandmother, tomorrow I start after the light, and on my return with it I shall marry the chief's beautiful daughter and become famous. Make all things ready, for I leave early in the morning. Caw! Caw! Caw!"

"Ai-Ai-Yah!" she exclaimed. "Better ones than you have tried and failed, and how will you, a raven, get it! Why do you want to marry? Who will marry such a one as you? You smell too strong."

This was too much for him. "You old hag!" he screamed with rage. "Who is asking your opinion or advice! How does my smell concern you? To spite you I will marry, and the chief's daughter at that. Even if I am a raven, I will do what I promise."

Early the next morning he left the village, and after several days of flight in the darkness it lightened up faintly. The farther he went, the lighter it became, and when he reached the village the light was so strong that it almost blinded him. It was a large and cheerful village. The chief's large barrabara, where the lights were kept, was in the center. Close by was a spring of water, and there the raven alighted and eyed sharply the women as they came for water. Not noticing the chief's daughter among them, he began to wish that she would appear. A moment later he saw her coming towards him, and when she had dipped out some water he murmured, "I wish she would drink some of it." The words had barely been said when she bent over to drink. Instantly he changed himself into a tiny piece of down, and, unnoticed, she gulped it down with the water.

She conceived, and in due time gave birth to a son, a raven. Being the first child of an only child, he was fondled and nursed tenderly. The chief was especially devoted to him and loved him even more than his daughter. He was indulged and humored in all his wishes. Whatever he saw he called for; whatever he called for had to be given to him; and if it was not given him immediately, he cawed, cried, pestered, clawed, and pecked until he got it. In this manner he handled everything on the premises that might possibly contain the lights except three little caskets on an out of the way shelf. These he noticed one day and asked for them. The chief was asleep, and as no one else dared touch them, the request was denied. But he would have them, and he commenced such a cawing, scratching, and hawing that the chief awoke. Not waiting to learn the cause of all this disturbance, he shouted angrily, "O, give him anything he wants, and shut him up!" And he went to sleep again.

The caskets were handed him, and he opened them one by one. In the first was night; the second contained the moon and stars, and in the third the sun was shining. He looked at them awhile, and then thrust them aside as worthless. But a few days later, when no one was about, he flew upon the shelf, grasped the two boxes containing the precious lights, and flew out with them. Some of the people outside noticed him, and raised the cry: "A raven flew out of the chief's barrabara with two boxes in his mouth!"

When the chief discovered his loss, the raven was miles away. He flew many days, and each day it grew darker and darker until he was in darkness alto-

gether. After suffering some hardships he arrived in the village, reported himself
to the chief, and requested that the people be called together. When all were
assembled he addressed them, congratulated them, reminded them of the last
meeting, the promises made, and concluded by saying, "I have brought you light."
In the presence of all he opened one of the caskets, and instantly the moon and
stars were visible in the sky. The people and chief were almost wild with joy; and
the latter kept his promise, and bestowed on him his favorite daughter.

On the morrow the raven called on his father-in-law, and asked what he
had to offer for a still better light than even the moon and
stars. "My other daughter," replied the chief.

"Call the people, and you shall have it," said
the raven.

If the villagers were wild with joy on seeing the
moon and stars, imagine their emotions on behold-
ing for the first time the sun. Since that memorable day the sun, moon, and stars have illumi-
nated the whole world. The crow married the
two daughters of the chief, with whom he is
living very happily to this day.

Ojeeg, The Summer Maker

The Ojibwa have a tale describing how summer came into the world. Again, like light and fire, summer must be stolen from powerful supernatural beings. It is from this tale that Longfellow wrote these lines for Hiawatha:

> *He was telling them the story*
> *Of Ojeeg the Summer-Maker,*
> *How he made a hole in heaven,*
> *How he climbed up into heaven,*
> *And let out the summer-weather,*
> *The perpetual summer-weather,*
> *How the Otter first essayed it,*
> *How the Beaver, Lynx and Badger,*
> *Tried in turn the great achievement,*
> *From the summit of the mountain . . .*

Ojeeg was a great hunter. He lived on the southern shore of Lake Superior. Ojeeg had a wife and one son.

Now the son hunted game as the father taught him. He followed the trails over the snow. For snow lay always on the ground. It was always cold. Therefore the boy returned home crying.

One day as he went to his father's wigwam in the cold and snow he saw Red Squirrel, gnawing the end of a pine cone. Now the son of Ojeeg had shot nothing all day because his hands were so cold. When he saw Red Squirrel, he came nearer, and raised his bow.

Red Squirrel said, "My grandson, put up your arrow. Listen to me."

The boy put the arrow in his quiver.

Red Squirrel said, "You pass my wigwam very often. You cry because you cannot kill birds. Your fingers are numb with cold. Obey me. Thus it shall always be summer. Thus you can kill many birds."

Red Squirrel said again, "Obey me. When you reach your father's wigwam, throw down your bow and arrows. Begin to weep. If your mother says, 'My son, what is the matter?' do not answer her. Continue weeping. If she says, 'My son, eat this,' you must refuse the food. Continue weeping. In the evening when your father comes in he will say to your mother, 'What is the matter with my son?' She will say, 'He came in crying. He will not tell me.' Your father will say, 'My son, what is the matter? I am a spirit. Nothing is too hard for me.' Then you must answer, 'It is always cold and dreary. Snow lies always upon the ground. Melt the snow, my father, so that we may have always summer.' Then your father will say, 'It is very difficult to do what you ask. I will try.' Then you must be quiet. You must eat the food they give you."

Thus it happened.

Ojeeg then said, "I must make a feast. I must invite my friends to go on this journey with me." At once Ojeeg killed a bear. The next day he had a great feast. There were Otter, Beaver, and Lynx. Also Wolverine and Badger were at the feast.

Then they started on their journey. On the twentieth day they came to the foot of a high mountain. There was blood in the trail. Some person had killed an animal. They followed the trail of that person. They arrived at a wigwam.

Ojeeg said, "Do not laugh. Be very quiet."

A man stood in the doorway of the wigwam. He was a great manitou [spirit of nature]. He was a head only. Thus he was very strange. Then he made a feast for them. He made very curious movements, so Otter laughed. At once the manitou leaped upon him. He sprang on him, but Otter slipped out from under him and escaped.

The manitou and the animals talked all night. The manitou said to Ojeeg, the Fisher, "You will succeed. You will be the summer-maker. But you will die. Yet the summer will come."

Now when they followed the trail in the morning, they met Otter. He was very cold and hungry, therefore Fisher gave him meat.

Then they journeyed on. On the twentieth day, they came to the top of a lofty mountain. Then they smoked their pipes.

Then Ojeeg, the Fisher, and the animals prepared themselves. Ojeeg said to Otter, "We must first make a hole in the Sky-cover. You try first."

Otter made a great spring. He did not even touch the Sky-cover. He fell back, down the hill, to the bottom of the hill. Then Otter said, "I will go home." So he did.

Then Beaver tried. He fell. Also Lynx and Badger fell.

Then Wolverine tried. He made a great leap and touched the sky. Then he leaped again. He pressed against the Sky-cover. He leaped a third time. The Sky-cover broke, and Wolverine went into the Sky-land. Fisher also sprang in quickly after him.

Thus Wolverine and Fisher were in the Sky-plain, in the summer land. There were many flowers and streams of bright water. There were birds in the trees, and fish and water birds on the streams. Many lodges stood there, but they were empty. In each lodge were many *mocuks*, many bird cages, with birds in them.

At once Ojeeg began to cut the *mocuks*. The birds flew out. They flew down through the hole in the Sky-cover to the Earth-plain below. They carried warm air down with them.

Now when the people of the Sky-land saw these strangers, and their birds escaping, they ran to their wigwams. But they were too late. Spring, and summer, and autumn had slipped down the hole in the Sky-cover. Endless summer was just passing through, but they broke it in two with a blow. Therefore only a part of endless summer came down to the Earth-plain.

Now when Wolverine heard the noise of the Sky People running to their lodges, he jumped down the hole and escaped. Fisher also tried to jump, but the people had shut the cover. Therefore Fisher ran and the people pursued him. He climbed a great tree in the north, and the people began shooting at him. Now Fisher was a spirit; he could not be hurt except in the tip of his tail. At last they shot him in his tail.

Fisher called to the Sky People to stop shooting. But they did not stop until darkness came. Then they went away. Fisher climbed down. He went towards the north. He said, "I have kept my promise to my son. The seasons will now be different. There will be many moons without snow and cold."

Thus Fisher died, with the arrow sticking in his tail. It can be seen there, even to this day.

Powerful Changed

Several African American tales tell why the animals we know today are not as they were originally meant to be. It is usually their own orneryness that got them into trouble and altered what God created. In this story, the great folklorist Zora Neale Hurston recreates a tale-telling session among Southern men.

"Well, you know when de Flood was and dey had two of everything in de Ark—well, Ole Nora didn't take on no trees, so de woodpecker set 'round and set 'round for a week or so, then he felt like he just had to peck himself some wood. So he begin to peck on de Ark. Ole Nora come to him and tole him, 'Don't peck on de Ark. If you peck a hole in it, we'll all drown.'

"Woodpecker says, 'But Ah'm hungry for some wood to peck.'

"Ole Nora says, 'Ah don't keer how hongry you gits, don't you peck on dis Ark no mo. You want to drown everybody and everything?'

"So de woodpecker would sneak 'round behind Ole Nora's back and peck every chance he got. He'd hide hisself way down in de hold where he thought nobody could find him and peck and peck. So one day Ole Nora come caught him at it. He never opened his mouth to dat woodpecker. He just hauled off and give dat peckerwood a cold head-whipping wid a sledge hammer, and dat's why a peckerwood got a red head today—'cause Ole Nora bloodied it wid dat hammer. Dat's how come Ah feel like shootin' every one of 'em Ah see. Tryin' to drown *me* before Ah was born."

"A whole lot went on on dat ole Ark," Larkins White commented. "Dat's where de possum lost de hair off his tail."

"Now don't you tell me no possum ever had no hair on dat slick tail of his'n," said Black Baby, " 'cause Ah know better."

"Yes, he did have hair on his tail one time. Yes, indeed. De possum had a bushy tail wid long silk hair on it. Why, it useter be one of de prettiest sights you ever seen. De possum struttin' 'round wid his great big ole plumey tail. Dat was 'way back in de olden times before de big flood.

"But de possum was lazy—jus' like he is today. He sleep too much. You see Ole Nora had a son name Ham and he loved to be playin' music all de time. He had a banjo and a fiddle and maybe a guitar too. But de rain come up so sudden he didn't have time to put 'em on de Ark. So when rain kept comin' down he fretted a lot 'cause he didn't have nothin' to play. So he found a ole cigar box and made hisself a banjo, but he didn't have no strings for it. So he seen de possum stretched out sleeping wid his tail all spread 'round. So Ham slipped up and shaved de possum's tail and made de strings for his banjo out de hairs. When dat possum woke up from his nap, Ham was playin' his tail hairs down to de bricks and dat's why de possum ain't got no hair on his tail today. Losin' his pretty tail sorta broke de possum's spirit too. He ain't never been de same since. Dat's how come he always actin' shame-faced. He know his tail ain't whut it useter be; and de possum feel mighty bad about it."

"A lot of things ain't whut they useter be," observed Jim Presley. "Now take de 'gator for instance. He been changed 'round powerful since he been made."

"Yeah," cut in Eugene Oliver. "He useter have a nice tongue so he could talk like a nat'chal man, but Brer Dog caused de 'gator to lose his tongue, and dat's how come he hate de dog today."

"Brer 'Gator didn't fall out wid Brer Dog 'bout no tongue," retorted Presley.

"Brer Dog done de 'gator a dirty trick 'bout his mouth. You know God made de dog and de 'gator without no mouth. So they seen everybody else had a mouth so they made it up to git theirselves a mouth like de other varmints. So they agreed to cut one 'nother's mouth, and each one said dat when de other one tole 'em to stop cuttin' they would. So Brer Dog got his mouth first. Brer 'Gator took de razor and cut. Brer Dog tole him, 'Stop,' which he did. Den Brer Dog took de razor and begin to cut Brer 'Gator a mouth. When his mouth was as big as he wanted it, Brer 'Gator says, "Stop, Brer Dog. Dat'll do, I thank you, please." But Brer Dog kept right on cuttin' till he ruint Brer 'Gator's face. Brer 'Gator was a very handsome gent'man befo' Brer Dog done him that a way, and everytime he look in de lookin' glass he cry like a baby over de disfiggerment of his face. And dat's how come de 'gator hate de dog."

"My people, my people," lamented Oliver. "They just will talk whut they don't know."

"Go on, Oliver."

"De 'gator didn't fall out wid de dog 'bout no mouth cuttin' scrape. You know all de animals was havin' a ball down in de pine woods, and so they all chipped in for refreshments and then they didn't have no music for de dance. So all de animals what could 'greed to furnish music. So de dog said he'd be de trumpet in de band, and de horse and de frog and de mockin' bird and all said they'd be there an' help out all they could. But they didn't have no bass drum, till somebody said, 'Whut's de matter wid Brer 'Gator, why don't he play bass drum for us?' Dey called Brer 'Gator but he wasn't at de meetin' so de varmints deppitized Brer Dog to go call on Brer 'Gator and see if he wouldn't furnish de drum music for de dance. Which he did.

" 'Good evenin', Brer 'Gator.'

" 'My compliments, Brer Dog, how you makin' out? Ah'm always glad when folks visit me. Whut you want?'

" 'Well, Brer 'Gator, de varmints is holdin' a big convention tonight in de piney woods and we want you to furnish us a little bit of yo' drum music.'

" 'It's like this, Brer Dog, tell de other animals dat Ah'm mighty proud they wants me and de compliments run all over me, but my wife is po'ly and my chillun is down sick. But Ah'll lend you my drum if you know anybody kin play it, and know how to take keer of it too!'

"'Oh, Ah'll do *dat*, Brer 'Gator. You just put in in my keer. You don't have to worry 'bout dat atall.'

"So de dog took Brer 'Gator's tongue to de ball dat night and they beat it for a drum. De varmints lakted de bass drum so well till they didn't play nothin' else hardly. So by daybreak it was wore clean out. Brer Dog didn't want to go tell Brer 'Gator they had done wore his tongue out so he hid from Brer 'Gator. Course de 'gator don't like it 'bout his tongue so he's de sworn enemy of de dog."

The Star Husband

*As in the Greek myths, Native American gods and goddesses often interacted with peo-
ple, and the story of a human marrying a celestial body is widespread among North
American tribes. This version was told among the Blackfoot and has been adapted here
by storyteller Lynn Moroney. In addition to telling the origin myth, which is its ultimate purpose, the tale includes a warning to be obedient that is similar to the warning
God gave to Eve in the Garden of Eden. It is easy to see why this elegant and compelling
tale survives and is often chosen by modern American storytellers.*

One summer night two girls decided to sleep outside. They left the place
where all the others were camped and walked until they came to a hill. They made
their beds, and after they had lain down, they began to watch the stars. As the sky
grew darker, the stars grew in number and brightness.

"These stars are beautiful," said one girl.

"Oh, look! One of the stars just fell," said the other.

"There in the south is a red star," said one. "And just there, there is a yellow star," said the other.

With the appearance of each new star the girls grew more delighted. They
agreed that sleeping outside was a good idea, for never had they seen so beautiful
a night.

In time, one of the maids noticed one special star. "Sister, see that star,"
she said, "that white star just over there? That is my favorite star. I wish that star
could be my husband. If I married that star, I could go way into the sky and live
with the stars."

The girls gazed at the stars for a while longer, but the night had worn on,
and in time they fell asleep—sound asleep under a sky filled with stars.

The next day, on their way back to camp, the girls found a berry patch.
They started gathering berries, and the girl who had wished for a husband wandered off. As soon as she was alone, she heard a sound. Looking up, she saw a

young man standing before her. He wore a white feather in his hair, and his vest and moccasins were beaded with white and crystal beads that sparkled and glimmered like the stars.

"Do not be afraid," he said. "Last night you wished to marry the white star. I am that white star. I am White Morning Star, and I have come for you. Marry me, and we shall live in the sky world."

All fear left the girl, and she gave her hand to the young man. At once, they began their journey to the sky.

When the other girl discovered that her friend was missing, she ran back to the camp. She told the girl's mother and all the people that she had no idea what had happened to her friend. "We were gathering berries and she just disappeared," she said. Then she began to weep. The people in camp could not understand what could have happened, and for a long time afterward, they waited for the girl's return.

In the meantime, the young couple reached the sky. The girl noticed how much the sky world was like the world below. There were rivers and streams, rolling hills, trees, wildflowers, animals and birds, and all manner of good roots and berries.

The Star Husband presented his new bride to his parents. His father was the Sun, and his mother was the Moon. Moon was the first to speak, saying, "We are pleased that you have come to live with us, and to have you for our daughter." Moon liked her new daughter-in-law, and wanted her to be happy. Then Moon set about teaching the young bride many special things about the sky land.

One day Moon gave her daughter-in-law a magic digging stick. "With this stick you will be sure to find many kinds of roots. Find them and always take as many as you please, but heed this warning: there is one root that you must never dig." Then Moon took the young wife to a place where many prickly bushes and thorns grew. Right in the center there was growing one green plant. "Daughter . . . do you see that turnip plant? You must never dig for that turnip. You must never pull it from where it is growing. Do you understand?" The bride said she understood, and she and Moon went on their way.

Time passed. The Star Husband and his young wife were very happy. She learned much about the sky world. Each day she went forth to gather berries and roots, and always she was careful not to dig around the forbidden plant. More time passed, and the happy couple had a fine baby boy. The sky people brought him gifts and shared their joy.

The baby grew, and the young mother continued each day to gather food, but over time she changed. Instead of avoiding the place where the turnip grew, she passed by it each day. She began having strange thoughts: "I wonder why I cannot have that turnip. Perhaps Moon is just being selfish, and does not want me to have anything that tastes so good."

Each day it was the same. She would sometimes stare at the turnip plant for long periods of time. Soon the young mother began to brood over the plant and wondered, "What kind of turnip plant can it be? What secret does it hold?"

One day, when her baby was at the age when he could sit by himself, the maid again went to the place where the plant was growing. She sat her son down, and this time, slowly and carefully, very carefully, she began to dig around the plant with her digging stick. She poked and dug until the ground was soft. Then she reached down and pulled the turnip up and out of where it was growing. Whooosh! A rush of air came from the hole. She then looked down through the hole and, to her surprise, she could see the Earth below—tall grasses, rolling hills, many buffalo—and she could see the lodges of her people.

That night when her sky family saw the turnip, they scolded her, and Moon asked, "Did you see anything unusual when you pulled the turnip from where it grew?"

The young wife answered, "Oh, nothing unusual, just the Earth, and the lodges of my people."

The Star Husband gasped. "No! You do not know what you have done! Now that you have looked again upon the Earth, you cannot stay here in the sky. You must leave at once. You must take our son and return to your people. When you reach Earth, you must not let our son touch the Earth for fourteen days. If you do, he will turn first into a little puff ball of seeds, then he will turn into a star.

He will not move through the sky, as do other stars. He will remain always in one place."

The Sun Father called one of the sky men to help the mother and child down to the Earth. The sky man took a rope made of spider webs and, tying the mother and child to one end, he slowly let them down through the turnip hole.

Now down on Earth some boys were playing, and they saw the young woman and her child coming down from the sky. Soon she was hanging above the center of camp. One of the boys recognized her and cried out, "Look! It is the girl who disappeared while she was gathering berries." All of the people in the camp ran to her. Everyone was glad to see her, especially her mother, who quickly took her daughter and grandson to her lodgings.

The young woman told her mother all about the sky world, and for the first thirteen days, everything went well. The young mother was ever so watchful over her child, careful never to let him touch the ground.

Then on the fourteenth day, the grandmother asked her daughter to fetch some water. The girl cautioned, "Mother, while I am gone, be sure to watch my son's every moment. He must not leave his bed of blankets, for he must not so much as even touch the ground." Then the girl hurried off to gather water.

The grandmother did not understand why her grandson should not touch the Earth. She watched over the child for a while, but from time to time, she looked away. Then, while her back was turned, the baby boy crawled to the edge of the blankets. Just as the grandmother turned back around, she saw the boy place one little hand upon the ground. Quickly, she swept him up and placed him back in the center of the blanket.

But it was too late. Without a sound, the baby boy crawled inside the pile of blankets that had made his bed.

The mother returned with the water and, not seeing the boy, she was filled with fear. "Where is my son?" she whispered.

"He's down inside the blankets," said the grandmother.

The mother rushed over to the bed and began pulling the blankets away, one after another. She did not find her son. All she found was a little ball of puffy white seeds. She knew what had happened. Slowly she picked up the little puff ball and placed it close to her heart.

That evening the mother went to the top of a small hill. It was the same hill where, many moons before, she had wished for a husband. She watched as, one by one, the stars came into the sky. High in the northern sky, in the place where she had pulled up the turnip, there was a new star. The young mother knew that that little star was her son. That night and all the star-filled nights from then until the day she died, the mother of the star looked into the sky and sent her love to her son.

It was in this way that the fixed star, the star-that-does-not-move, came to be. The star is still there, for the stars go on . . . and on . . .

The Dog-Rib Legend of Ithenhiela

———·•·———

"Dog-Rib" refers to the Chipewyan tribe in northern Canada who told this story to folklorist James Mackintosh Bell in 1903. At that time, the tribe had had almost no contact with white culture. One night, Bell stood watching the northern lights with members of the tribe, and after their return to the Dog-Rib encampment, one of the elders told this fabulous tale. While following the adventures of the culture hero Ithenhiela, the story explains the formation of several important landmarks, including the Canadian Rockies. Of this tale Bell writes, "It was the most beautiful of all the Dog-Rib stories," and he adds a poignant note to the end of the story: "The influx of fur-traders into the Mackenzie River region . . . within the last two years, since my return, has, I believe, very much altered the character of the Northern Indians."

———·•·———

In the great Northwest of Canada there flows one of the mightiest rivers of the earth, known to the whites as the Mackenzie, and to the Northern Indians as the Too-Cha-Tes, or Big Water. On the very border of the Arctic Circle another great river joins the Big Water from the Southwest. This river the Dog-Ribs still know as "the river that flows from the country of the Big Man."

Naba-Cha, or the Big Man, was one of the most enormous men who ever lived. His wigwam was made of three hundred skins of the largest caribou that could be killed on the vast plains far to the northward. It had taken the bark of six huge birch-trees to make the onogan from which he daily ate his meals. And it took one whole moose, or two caribou, or fifty partridges, to feed him each day. Famous indeed was Naba-Cha throughout the whole North Country, and many were the expeditions of war he had made into distant lands to the north, east, south, and west. He had traveled northward to the mouth of the Big Water to fight the Snow-Men or Eskimo, eastward across the Great Lake of Many Slaves to the country of the Yellow Knives, where he had seen the pure copper shining in the sands of mighty rivers, southward away on to the great plains to the country of the Crees, where there were so many large animals. But westward he had never ventured far, because in that direction it was said that a bigger man than Naba-Cha dwelt. Now Naba-Cha was not only big, but he was also cruel and wicked, especially to a young Wood-Cree boy whom he had brought back from the South once when on the warpath, and who had neither father nor mother nor sister nor brother to help fight. Ithenhiela, the Caribou-Footed, as the boy was called, had, however, one great friend at the wigwam of Naba-Cha. This was Hottah, the two-year-old moose, the cleverest of all the northern animals. Truly he was clever for he had traveled all the distance from the mouth of the Too-Cha-Tes to the wigwam of Naba-Cha in three days, and this was very far indeed. Now Hottah had long thought of a plan by which he might help Ithenhiela. He knew that far to the westward, much beyond where Naba-Cha had ever gone, flowed another river almost as great as Too-Cha-Tes, and that safety for a hunted man or beast lay on its farther side, because there dwelt Nesnabi, the Good Man.

One day Hottah came to Ithenhiela and said to him, "We will go away. You get a stone, a clod of earth, a piece of moss, and a branch of a tree, and we shall escape from the cruel Naba-Cha." Ithenhiela got what he was told to get, and soon they were ready to be off. Hottah took Ithenhiela upon his back, and before long they were out on the great plains which lie many days beyond the Too-Cha-Tes. Hardly had they started when they saw coming behind them Naba-Cha on his great caribou. Then said Hottah, "Fling out behind you your clod of earth." [Ithenhiela] did so, and immediately there rose up behind them, and between them and Naba-Cha, great hills of earth so wide and so high that it was many days before Naba-Cha again came in sight. And during this time Ithenhiela ate the ripened berries, while Hottah chewed the sweet grass which grew beyond the hills.

When Naba-Cha once more appeared in sight, Ithenhiela flung out behind him the piece of moss, and a great muskeg-swamp lay behind them. And for days the great man and his caribou foundered in the thick sphagnum. Meanwhile, on and on towards the country of the Setting Sun passed Hottah and Ithenhiela. And when once more Naba-Cha appeared, Ithenhiela dropped the stone, and great indeed were the high rocky hills which intervened between them and Naba-Cha. Up to the very clouds rose the hills, white with snow, and magnificent, such as had never been seen before. Long it was before the fugitives again saw Naba-Cha and the great caribou, and far had they gone towards the West before Ithenhiela had to throw the branch of the tree from him. Then arose a great and mighty forest of which the trees were so thick that Naba-Cha could not pass between them, and had to cut his way through, while the caribou was left behind because his horns had stuck in the branches, and he could not pass on. All this delay helped Ithenhiela, and when he once more saw the cruel Naba-Cha, he and his moose-friend had already crossed the Great Western River which they had tried so hard to reach. Away into the Northwest wound Tes-Yukon, through the high rocky hills to the northward, foaming as it flowed. Soon came Naba-Cha to the other side of the Tes-Yukon, and called aloud, "Help me, Hottah, across this mighty river. Help me to reach the country that lies beyond, and I shall do no harm to Ithenhiela." Then across for him went Hottah, and as he brought him back across the great Tes-Yukon, he overturned him, and down he swept through the swirling rapids of the river and was lost. This was the last of the wicked Naba-Cha.

Then came Hottah to Ithenhiela standing upon the bank, and, turning to him, he said, "Ithenhiela, I must leave you now, and return whence I came. Go you and follow this great river, and soon you will come to a great tepee. This is the home of Nesnabi, the Good Man. Great indeed is he, and far has he traveled into our country to the eastward, among the golden rivers lost in mountains to the southward; to the great water which has no ending to the westward; and to the silent plains, all snow-covered to the northward, where live the Snow-Men. He, like Naba-Cha, is big, but he is not cruel, and he harms no one. He will aid you."

Then departed Ithenhiela, and following the bends of the great Tes-Yukon through the high spruce forest, he came to the wigwam of Nesnabi, who stood silent beside his home.

"Whence have you come, young man," said he, "and where are you going!"

At this, up spoke Ithenhiela, "Great Chief, I have come from far. I have neither father nor mother nor brother nor sister. My home was with my own people away in the South Country, and there I lived happily until the coming of Naba-Cha, who took me away with him to the cruel North Country, where the snow lasts long in winter by the sweeping waters of the Too-Cha-Tes. Hard indeed was Naba-Cha to me, and many a season passed I in misery with him, until I came away with Hottah, the two-year-old moose who brought me to your country, O Great Nesnabi, and but now has he left me."

To this answered the kind Nesnabi, "Ithenhiela, I have long known that you would come to me. Stay with me as long as you like, but if at the end of the week you wish to journey away, I will then prepare you for your journey farther into the West Country."

Thus it was that Ithenhiela stayed at the wigwam of Nesnabi. But when the week was done, he came to his protector, and said to him, "I must now leave you and travel farther. Give me that preparation for my journey that you have promised me."

Then took Nesnabi seven arrows from his wigwam, and said to him, "This is enough to help you, Ithenhiela, but should you shoot at any bird or beast in a spruce-tree and the arrow stick in the branches, take you care that you go not after it, for if you do, surely something will happen to you." Hardly had Ithenhiela left the good Nesnabi, when he saw a squirrel in the branches of a red spruce-tree, and, raising his bow he shot an arrow at it. Down fell the squirrel, but the arrow lodged in the branches. At once, Ithenhiela, forgetting what Nesnabi had told him, started to climb after the arrow. As he mounted, the arrow went up, too. Up, up, they went, until at last they came to the sky, and the arrow passed through, and he after it.

Great was Ithenhiela's surprise when he entered the Sky Country. It was so different from what he had expected. He had imagined a glorious country, where the sun always shone, and where herds of musk oxen, caribou, and moose roamed at large in plenty, with many of his own people camped in large wigwams here and there. But instead, the air was damp, dreary, and cold; no trees or flowers grew; no herds of animals ran on the silent plains; the smoke of no wigwam greeted his anxious eyes; the war-whoop or hunting-cry of no Indian of his own people was heard. Only, far in the distance against the sky shimmered a great white mass, like a pile of snow, when the sun shines upon it in the early summer. Towards this great white thing ran a winding path from the very spot where Ithenhiela stood.

"I will follow it," thought he, "and see what I come to and find out what lies in that blazing wigwam over there." As he passed along, he met an old woman who said to him, "Who are you, and where are you going?"

"I have come from far," said Ithenhiela. "I am the Caribou-Footed. Can you tell me who lives over there in that big white wigwam?"

"Ah," said Capoteka, "I know you, Ithenhiela. Long have I thought you would come here. But you have done wrong; this is no country for man. In that great wigwam over there lives Hatempka, and unhappy is he because he has lost his belt of medicine, and until he gets it again, no one will be happy in the Sky Country. The belt is at the tepee of the two blind women who live far beyond the wigwam which shines so white, and no one can get it from them. Whoever finds it, and gets it from the bad blind women, will have the daughter of Hatempka, the beautiful Etanda, for his wife." Off then started Ithenhiela, and, traveling hard, soon came he to the home of the two old blind women.

As he entered the wigwam, he saw hanging upon the side the belt of Hatempka, and many indeed were the skulls which hung about it, for many had gone to seek the belt, but none had returned. The blind women bade him welcome and said to him, "When you leave, Ithenhiela, tell us so that we may bid you good-bye."

Now Ithenhiela had noticed that each of the two old women had behind her back a knife of copper, long and sharp. "Ah," thought he. "When I leave they mean to kill me." For one sat on either side of the door in readiness. "But I shall fool them."

In one part of the wigwam lay a muskamoot, a bag of bones and feathers. To this he tied a string, which he pulled over the pole above the door. Then said he, "I am going now, blind women. Remember I am old and fat, and when I leave,

I make much noise." At this he pulled the string, and towards the door passed the bag of bones and feathers.

Immediately the two old blind women stabbed, but striking only feathers, the long knives passed through them into each other and both were killed. Then took Ithenhiela the belt of medicine, and went he unto the shining white home of Hatempka and said to him, "Great chief, be you happy now, I have brought to you your healing belt. Give me now my wife, your daughter, the beautiful Etanda, that I may leave you."

Then said Hatempka, "Oh! Much pleased am I, Ithenhiela. You have saved my people. Now shall the sun shine again. Now shall musk oxen, caribou, moose, and bear live once more in our country. Again shall we see the smoke of many wigwams. Once more shall we hear the voice of many hunters. Take you now my daughter, the fair Etanda, but leave me not. Stay with me, and be a great man after me." So Ithenhiela remained at the shining white home of Hatempka.

Hence was derived the name and country of the Big Man. Still, the Indians in that distant country, when the northern lights flit across the sky, see in them the fingers of Ithenhiela, beckoning them to the home he has found for them so far away.

Man, the Burro, and the Dog

This tale from the Hispanic Southwest of the United States is a fanciful explanation for the aging process that is a natural part of human life. Hispanic tales in North America have their roots in Mexico, and ultimately in Spain. The following tale is from a collection heard in New Mexico and southern Colorado.

When God created the universe, He also created man to rule over the earth. At the same time, He decided to give man two friends. So He first made man, and then He created the burro and the dog. Then, as the three stood before him, God spoke these words to the man:

"Your name is man, and you shall rule over everything. You will have dominion over the earth, and you will live sixty years. During this time you will see good days and bad days, but there will be more good days than bad."

The poor man thought sixty years was a very short time to live as ruler of the earth, but he agreed.

Then God turned to the burro and said:

"Your name is burro, and you will be subject to the law of man. You will live thirty years, and in that time there will be good days and bad days, but the bad days will outnumber the good days."

"Oh," said the burro, "if my life is to be so hard, I don't want that many years. Take away ten of those thirty years."

The man, who was carefully watching the proceedings, spoke up:

"Those ten years, Lord, give them to me!"

So God added those ten years to man's sixty. Then He spoke to the dog and said:

"Your name will be dog, and you will be man's best friend, and you shall live according to his law. You will live twenty years, and during your lifetime you will see good days and bad days, but there will be more bad days than good."

"Oh," the dog wailed, "if my life is to be one of torment, I don't want so many years. Please take away ten."

"Lord, give those ten years to me!" begged the man.

So God added twenty years to the man's life so that man would live to be eighty.

And that is why man lives the life of a donkey from sixty to seventy, and also why he lives the life of a lowly dog from his seventieth year on!

Possum, Turtle, and the Wolves

Contemporary storyteller Doug Elliott shows us how the simple desire to explain a small feature of the natural world can lead to a ripping good story. Elliott believes that the following tale, which he adapted from a Cherokee tale heard in the late nineteenth century, has African origins. It seems only logical, since there is a clear relationship between Turtle's adventure and Brer Rabbit's famous trip to the briar patch. But there is also an element here of "The Brave Little Tailor," a widely told fairy tale from Europe.

Possum is sort of a slow critter, not fast like a rabbit. He just ambles along, looking for things to eat, making a living as best he can. He can climb a tree but not quickly like a squirrel. He climbs slowly and carefully as you or I might.

Possum had a friend who was even slower than he was. His name was Turtle. Bright and early one morning Possum said, "Come on, Brother Turtle, I want to take you out to my favorite tree." So he and Turtle ambled on over to a big persimmon tree. The tree was loaded with persimmons, and they looked very ripe. They were a rich orange color, and their skins were soft and wrinkly. Possum carefully tasted one of them. They didn't have any of the mouth-drying puckery taste that unripe persimmons are famous for: They were as soft and sweet as sugar plums.

Turtle said in his slow deep voice. "Well, they look pretty good, Brother Possum, but how am I gonna get some? I can't climb a tree."

"Don't worry, Brother Turtle," Possum said as he started up that tree. "I'll climb up and throw some down to you."

He got up in the tree, climbed out on a limb, and started eating some of the persimmons and tossing others down to Turtle. He'd eat one and toss one down, then he'd eat another and toss another down to Turtle. They felt like they were having a picnic.

"Keep 'em coming, Brother Possum," Turtle shouted (as well as he could with a mouth full of persimmon). "They sure are good!" Possum continued throwing them down, and the two friends were having a wonderful time of it until all of a sudden, out of the bushes came a great big wolf. Now, Possum knew he was up in the tree, where the wolf couldn't get him. Turtle knew that he could pull into his hard shell, where the wolf couldn't get him. But that wolf still ruined the picnic by standing right over Turtle and catching and eating all the persimmons that Possum was trying to throw down to Turtle. Possum threw them all around, thinking the wolf would miss some, but that wolf jumped up and caught them all before they even hit the ground. So Possum tried throwing the persimmons down very fast, one after the other, in rapid succession, but the wolf still managed to catch every one.

Possum didn't know what to do. That wolf might never leave them alone! Then he looked up higher in the tree, and there he saw a huge persimmon that was almost as big as a grapefruit. And that gave him an idea. First he started throwing down the small persimmons as fast as he could. That greedy old wolf had his jaws open wide so he could catch every one. When Wolf's jaws were flapped open as wide as they could be, Possum heaved down the giant persimmon as hard as he could, and the wolf caught it right in the throat. That persimmon stuck there, and the wolf soon keeled over dead. As Possum climbed down the tree, Turtle remarked in his slow deep voice, "That sure was good thinking, Brother Possum. I didn't think that wolf would ever leave us alone." They stood for a moment and looked at the big dead wolf. Then Turtle said, "I didn't tell you, Brother Possum, but I'm about to go on a long journey, and the one thing I need for my traveling bag is a couple of spoons. Then if somebody offers me a meal along the way, I could use the spoons to eat with, and I could also use them for ladling water out of streams when I get thirsty."

"What has that got to do with a dead wolf?" Possum asked.

Turtle replied, "I just figured out where I'm gonna get those spoons. I'm gonna cut that wolf's ears off and make wolf-ear spoons." And that's just what Turtle did. He cut those ears off, took them over to the stream, scrubbed them out, and laid them on the rocks to dry in the morning sun.

As the sun shone down, those ears dried out, and as they dried, they curled up. It wasn't long before they looked a lot like spoons.

When the ears were all dried out, Turtle tucked them into his traveling kit and started down the trail. "See you later, Brother Possum. Thanks for that delicious 'simmon breakfast." And down the trail he went, just a-walking and a-hiking and a-walking and a-hiking. And for a turtle, he traveled quite far that morning.

As the noon hour approached, he started to get hungry, but he couldn't find anything to eat. There weren't any persimmon trees, and even if there had been, his possum buddy wasn't there to climb them for him. There were no berries or worms or snails or anything else that turtles like to eat. So he just kept on a-walking and a-hiking, getting hungrier all the time.

Soon he came to a village, and as he walked by, some people came out and said, "Hey there, Turtle! It looks like you've been traveling. Do you want something to eat?" Turtle said that, indeed, he was hungry, so the people invited him into a lodge to have a bowl of hominy.

They put the hominy in front of him and said, "Now just a minute, Turtle. We'll get you a spoon, and you can have all you want." Turtle replied, "That's all right. I've got my own spoon, thanks." And he reached into his traveling bag, pulled out one of his wolf-ear spoons, and started eating that hominy. Nobody thought anything about it at first, until someone noticed what Turtle was eating with. They started whispering among themselves, "What's that turtle eating with?"

"It looks like a wolf's ear!"

"A wolf's ear! Where would a turtle get a wolf's ear?"

"Could he have killed a wolf? I didn't think a turtle could kill a wolf."

Right then, somebody came into the lodge and heard just the last part of the whispered conversation. "Killed a wolf? Who killed a wolf! That turtle kills wolves? I'm getting out of here!" Soon the rumor was spreading through the village like wildfire. "There's a wolf-killing turtle on the loose, and he's right here in our village!" Those foolish people were thrown into a panic, and they all ran to the woods, hid in the bushes, crawled into hollow logs, or climbed up in trees.

Turtle continued eating his hominy. He didn't know why everybody had disappeared so fast. When he finished, he crawled out of the lodge and looked around. There was no one in sight, so he called out, "So long, folks. I'll be on my way now. Thanks for the meal." And down the trail he went, a-walking and a-hiking and a-walking and a-hiking.

In the meantime the people came back to the village and congratulated one another for their quick escape from the dangerous wolf-killing turtle. Everybody was talking about it. Every boy told every girl, every girl told every mama, every mama told every dad, every dad told every grandpa, told every grandma, told every dog, told every cat, told every mouse, told every rat, told every frog, told every bird, told every squirrel, told every rabbit, told every fox, told every snake, told every bug, and soon the forest was buzzing with the rumor of the wolf-killing turtle. Turtle didn't know a thing about it—he just continued slowly and steadily down the trail, just a-walking and a-hiking.

He traveled along for several more hours, and the sun was beating down. He was getting very thirsty, but he couldn't find any water to drink: not a spring or a stream or even a puddle. He came to another village, and as he approached, some people came out and said, "Hey there, Turtle, it sure is hot today. Aren't you thirsty?"

"I sure am," said Turtle.

"Well, come on over. We just made some fresh sumac lemonade. It's right here in this pot. We'll get you a ladle, and you can scoop out all you want."

"Oh, that's all right," said Turtle, "I've got my own little ladle right here." And he reached into his traveling bag, pulled out one of the wolf ears, and started slurping away. Nobody thought anything of it until they noticed what Turtle was using for a ladle.

Now, we all know that turtles travel pretty slowly. However, rumors travel a whole lot faster, and would you believe that the rumor about the wolf-killing turtle had gotten to this village long before Turtle himself had arrived? Of course, everybody figured it was just a silly rumor, and nobody believed it, because how could a little turtle kill a great big wolf anyway? It just couldn't be true.

But when they saw Turtle pull out that wolf's ear, they knew that the rumor must be true, and in an instant this village too was thrown into panic and fear. Soon everybody was running to the woods, climbing up trees, hiding in the bushes, or crawling into hollow logs.

Turtle kept on slowly slurping away at the sumac drink. When he stopped and looked around, he noticed that everyone was gone. "Now, what got into them?" he said to himself. "This bunch of humans is even stranger than the people I met in that last village." He drank his fill of the tangy juice and felt very refreshed. "Thanks for the drink, folks, wherever you are," he shouted over his shoulder as he started down the trail, a-walking and a-hiking.

Before too long the people came out of hiding and started talking excitedly among themselves, and soon the rumor of the wolf-killing turtle had spread to every corner of the forest. Turtle just kept trudging slowly along. He didn't know anything about the rumors that were being spread about him. But he did notice something peculiar as he traveled. He would hear the birds singing and the squirrels and chipmunks scurrying around ahead of him on the trail, but as he got closer to them, the woods would become absolutely quiet. All the critters were hiding because they had heard about the wolf-killing turtle, and they were afraid that he might kill them too.

It made Turtle uneasy not to hear all the other animals around him as he walked, especially as he neared a thick dark place in the woods. He just kept on slowly, a-walking and a-hiking. Suddenly, out of the bushes came a whole pack of wolves, and they surrounded him. Everywhere he looked, all he could see was growling wolves and sharp teeth. He blinked and said, "Uh oh . . ."

The leader of the pack swaggered up. "All right, Turtle," he snarled. "So you're the one who's been killing our brothers!" And he reached into Turtle's traveling bag and pulled out the wolf-ear spoons. He held the ears up to the other wolves and howled in rage. "Look. Brothers, what more proof do we need? This is the wolf-killer, all right!"

"But . . . but," Turtle protested.

"No buts about it," the wolf leader rudely interrupted. "We're gonna put a stop to this wolf-killing right here and now."

"Let's build a fire," one of the wolves suggested, "and throw him in it and burn him up. What do you think of that, Turtle?"

Turtle knew what to say. "Well, you just go ahead and throw me in that fire. I wouldn't mind at all. No sir. I'd just roll around in that fire with my hard shell and put your fire right out."

The wolves muttered among themselves. "We'd better think of something worse than that." Then one of them barked, "I know—let's get a big clay pot of water. We'll put him in it, build a big fire under it, and boil him."

Turtle said, "Go ahead and try to boil me. I wouldn't mind that at all. I'd just kick around in that old pot and hit it with my hard shell, and it would crack your pot. Then the water would come out and drown your fire—and you'd have a broken pot besides."

The wolves began talking among themselves, trying their best to think of something worse, when one of them said, "I know, let's take him to the river. We'll throw him in, and he'll drown!"

Turtle thought to himself, "I wouldn't mind that. I'm a good swimmer." But he was a smart turtle, and this is what he said: "No! Don't throw me in the river. That would be the worst thing you could do! Burn me or boil me, if you must, but please, oh please, don't throw me in the river!"

Those foolish wolves said, "If that's the worst thing we can do, let's do it." And they marched Turtle straight to a river bank high up over the water. One of those wolves grabbed his front legs, and another grabbed his back legs, and they started swinging him. One, two, three! They threw him off the river bank.

Turtle sailed through the air, end over end, down toward the river until—wham! He hit a rock and splashed into the water. When he felt the cool water all around him, he knew that all he had to do was swim across the river, and he would be home free. But as soon as he began to swim his first stroke, he felt a sharp pain. "Oh, my aching back," he moaned.

He had really hurt his back when he hit that rock. In fact, he could hardly swim at all, so he ended up having to half-swim and half-limp. Slowly, slowly he made his way across the river. When he reached the other side, he found a sloping sandbar that was overhung with wild plants and bushes. He pulled himself up on the sandbar and crawled up under the bushes to rest.

His back hurt so badly that he didn't even want to look at it. But he knew he had to, and when he finally did look, he saw that his shell was all cracked and broken. He didn't know what to do. Then he noticed some of the plants that were growing around him. They were medicinal herbs: mint and willow and comfrey and even backache root. Turtle sniffed the mint, chewed the willow bark, and rubbed the comfrey and the backache root all over his sore, broken shell.

That night he sang medicine songs and prayed to the Great Spirit, and soon he was fast asleep. The next morning when he woke, he felt much better, and when he looked back over his shell, all the pieces had come back together, and the cracks had healed. And to this day you can still see the cracks in Turtle's shell.

Getting Common Sense

Anansi, the trickster-spider who was imported in folktales from West Africa during slave times, is responsible for all manner of mischief in the world. But like the trickster of Native American tribes, Anansi is sometimes also responsible for creating things humans need to survive. In this tale the spider is up to his usual tricks. When they backfire, the world gains what Anansi loses. The nonsense line at the end of the tale is a marker of the sort used by traditional tale-tellers in many cultures to indicate the end of the story.

Once upon a time, Anansi thought to himself that if he could collect all the common sense in the world and keep it for himself, then he was bound to get plenty of money and plenty of power, for everybody would have to come to him with their worries, and he would charge them a whole lot when he advised them.

Anansi started to collect up and collect up all the common sense he could find and put it all into one huge calabash. When he searched and searched and couldn't find any more common sense, Anansi decided to hide his calabash on the top of a very tall tree so that nobody else could reach it.

So Anansi tied a rope around the neck of the calabash and tied the two ends of the rope together and hung the rope around his neck so that the calabash was on his belly. He started up the tall tree, but he couldn't climb very well or very fast because the calabash kept getting in his way. He was trying and trying so hard when all of a sudden he heard a voice burst out laughing in back of him. And when he looked he saw a little boy standing on the tree's root: "What a foolish man! If you want to climb the tree front-ways, why don't you put the calabash behind you?"

Well, Anansi was so angry to hear that big piece of common sense coming out of the mouth of such a little boy after he had thought he had collected all the common sense in the world that Anansi took off the calabash, broke it into pieces, and the common sense scattered out in the breeze all over the world. Everybody got a little bit of it but no one got it all. It was Anansi who made it happen that way.

Jack Mandora, me no choose none.

Ouiot and Frog

———

Of all the mysteries confronting humankind, death is the most perplexing and profound. Almost every culture has accounts of the origin of death among the tales explaining the glories of the universe and the smallest details of the insect world. The following tale explains not just how death came into the world, but also the reason some animals are used for food and the divine nature of the moon. Collected from the San Luiseno tribe in California in 1906, it may seem somewhat incomplete because the missing aspects of the story would have been understood by the hearers. Yet it is a graceful story, with its own integrity and beauty.

———

While they were all living at Temecula, there was a man among them, Ouiot, who was very wise and who knew more than anyone living. He taught the people and watched over them and made provision for their needs. He called them all his children.

It was a custom for all the people to take a bath every morning. Among them was a beautiful woman whom Ouiot had especially admired. She had a beautiful face and long hair that fell down to her feet, completely covering her back. She always went down to the water when no one else was there and would bathe when no one could see her. Ouiot noticed this and made it a point to watch her one day. When she jumped into the water, he saw that her back was hollow and flat like that of a frog, and his admiration turned to disgust.

The woman, Frog, observed Ouiot and read his thoughts. She was filled with anger against him. When she told her people of his feelings towards her, they conspired together saying, "We will kill him." So the four of them, Frog, Earthworm, Gopher, and Water Animal, decided to destroy him by witchcraft. As soon as they had finished their witchcraft, Ouiot fell sick. He tried in vain to ease his pain. He sent north, south, east, and west for remedies, but nothing could help him. He grew so much worse that he lay helpless, unable to rise. Frog and her helpers came and jeered at him, and because he lingered so long in his illness, they gave him the name Ouiot.

Then a man, named Rattlesnake, arose and said, "What is the matter with all you people? You call yourselves witches, yet you cannot cure our sick brother." So Rattlesnake, who knew everything, searched north, south, east, and west, trying to find some way to help Ouiot, or to learn what was the matter with him. But it was all in vain. After him another man, Horned Toad, equally great, went about searching for a remedy, trying his best, but without success. Next Roadrunner stood up. He examined Ouiot and searched about among the people to see if any of them had caused his illness. But he could discover nothing. Next came Little Bird. He did the same thing. He examined Ouiot and told the people that someone had poisoned him and that he was going to die.

Ouiot was getting worse all the time, and he called his best friend, Kingbird, a great captain and a very good man, and told him that he had been poisoned and named the four who had caused it and told him why they had done it and that he was soon to die. To Kingbird alone he revealed the truth that he would return. "Look towards the east for my coming in the early morning," he said. Thus Kingbird knew the secret. Then Ouiot summoned all the rest of the people that he might give them his final commands. When all had gathered together, some of his children raised him in their arms so that he could sit up and address them. The tears began to run down his cheeks. Coyote, Bluefly, and Buzzard crowded about him, wanting to eat his body. Coyote began licking his tears. Then Ouiot said that his death might come in the first month or in the second part of the first month. But this time passed and he was still alive. "Perhaps I shall die next month or in the second part of the next month." This also passed. So he predicted his death in each successive month, only to linger through until the last. In the last month, he died, and death came into the world. No one had died before.

There was a man, Kangaroo-Rat, who made a carrying-net in which to lift Ouiot. They sent to all four points of the compass for wood, the sycamore, black oak, white oak, tule, hemlock, and cedar, in order to build the funeral fire. They got a hollow log, and on the lower half they laid the body. Then they put the other half of the log above it for a lid. After the pile of wood was ready and the fire lighted, the men carried the body in the net, and after circling the fire three times laid it on the flames.

Coyote, who wanted to eat the body, was sent away. He ran off but looking back, he saw the smoke of the burning fire rising up to the sky. So he turned and came running back with all his might. They took sticks and tried to drive him away, and they stood in a circle close together about the fire to prevent him from approaching it. But Badger was only a little man, and Coyote ran at him and jumped over his head. He snatched the heart, the only part of the body that was not consumed by the flames, and ran off with it, devouring it.

There was a man among them named Little Squirrel, and when Ouiot was burned he stood up and addressed the people. He called the clouds from the mountains to come, and the clouds and fog from the sea to gather, and to fall in showers upon the earth to blot out all tracks that Ouiot had made when he moved upon the world. He asked that none be left. So the clouds came, and it rained heavily.

Ouiot had told them that in time to come they must have fiestas for the dead and that they must begin to kill and eat for food. Until this time they had never eaten flesh or grains, but had lived on clay. They discussed the matter, questioning who should be killed first. One man after another was chosen, but each refused in turn.

Ouiot had said that Eagle must be killed at the time of every fiesta, and Eagle did not like this. To escape, he went north, south, east, and west. But there was death for him everywhere, and he came back and gave himself up. Hummingbird said that he would like to take Eagle's place. He felt that he was a person of importance. But the people said, "No! You are a little man, not fit for that." And they would not let him.

Ouiot had also said they could eat Deer. They talked about killing Deer. "He is a nice-looking man. He would be good for meat." Lion was a strong, powerful man, and he said, "Why do you delay and discuss? This is the way it should be done." So he fell on Deer and killed him, and the others that had been selected to be animals were killed at the same time. They turned into different kinds of animals and different kinds of grain, and all the things we see now in the world.

When they killed Deer, they took the small pointed bones of the leg to use as awls for making baskets. A fine basket was made, and the bones and ashes of Ouiot were placed in it. They buried the basket in the ground. While they were burying it, they sang solemn words with groans and they danced. This was the first time there had been singing or dancing for the dead. Rabbit was the man who sang first, and Crow and Wild Goose danced first.

After the fiesta was over, they had a big meeting at Temecula, where they were still together. They had found out that death had come into the world and they didn't know what to do. They discussed the matter. All those that are now stars went up into the sky at this time, hoping to escape death in this manner. And all things that live in the ground, worms, insects, and burrowing animals, went underground to hide from death. But others decided to stay on earth. They figured that it might be possible to live for a certain number of years and then to go back and be young again. Then they all left Temecula and scattered all over, just as it is today. Now that Ouiot was gone there was no use staying in their first home. They no longer had a guide and teacher there.

No one knew that Ouiot was to come back, except Kingbird. Early in the morning he would go to the housetop and call out, "Ouiot is coming back."

"What does he say?" the people wondered. They did not understand, until Ouiot rose as the moon in the east. They saw the moon rise, and they knew it was Ouiot. It was the first time the moon had ever come, but it has risen ever since.

2

Tall Tales, Brags, and Other Lies

~

Americans didn't invent the tall tale, but they certainly have embraced the concept and improved on it. The ability to produce "lies" at will, to make the most outrageous story appear true, is still considered high art in North America. But what makes a tale "tall" is not just that the facts are exaggerated. The key is the teller's ability to exaggerate with a straight face. Some "liars" will pepper any conversation with one-liners beginning, "That reminds me of the time . . ." Others will begin long yarns based on one exaggeration, then add to it every other lie they can think of. Then there are those who have whoppers on the tips of their tongues all the time. I once asked my friend Don McCleod whether his new woodstove was any good at drawing air. He didn't miss a beat before he said, "It draws very well. Sucked the cat right up the chimney the first day we had it." It seemed perfectly effortless, and he never smiled.

Tall-tale telling flourished after the opening of the frontier, when early settlers sent back tales of fantastic plants, superhuman creatures, and astonishing feats of strength by ordinary men and women. Such stories entered the popular imagination, providing fertile ground for yarn-spinners and glib "liars." Most rural communities harbored a local "character" known to be "downright windy," or "a real wit," who was highly respected and popular at parties. Greenhorns heading West, or blundering into any isolated part of America, were at the mercy of the local wit, and new tall tales evolved just to describe the gullibility of outsiders.

Tall tales are widely dispersed throughout North America. They were originally passed by word of mouth along railroad lines and stagecoach trails and told as though the unbelievable had occurred at the last stop down the line. Newspapers on the American frontier entertained readers with pages of outrageous lies, which further spread the tales. As time went on tall tales became a part of the national literature, Mark Twain being only one among many writers who used them as a jumping-off point for their work. Today, many a storyteller and stand-up comedian stakes his or her fame on the audience's willingness to be roped in by a yarn.

How to Tell a Story

Not just anyone can spin a yarn, for the successful tall tale depends entirely on the teller's ability to think of something utterly outrageous and "tell it for the truth." To help make this principle clear, Mark Twain obliges us with instructions.

I do not claim that I can tell a story as it ought to be told. I only claim to know how a story ought to be told, for I have been almost daily in the company of the most expert storytellers for many years.

There are several kinds of stories, but only one difficult kind—the humorous. I will talk mainly about that one. The humorous story is American, the comic story is English, the witty story is French. The humorous story depends for its effect upon the manner of the telling; the comic story and the witty story upon the matter.

The humorous story may be spun out to great length, and may wander around as much as it pleases, and arrive nowhere in particular; but the comic and witty stories must be brief and end with a point. The humorous story bubbles gently along; the others burst.

The humorous story is strictly a work of art—high and delicate art—and only an artist can tell it, but no art is necessary in telling the comic and the witty story; anybody can do it. The art of telling a humorous story—understand, I mean by word of mouth, not print—was created in America, and has remained at home.

The humorous story is told gravely; the teller does his best to conceal the fact that he even dimly suspects that there is anything funny about it; but the teller of the comic story tells you beforehand that it is one of the funniest things he has ever heard, then tells it with eager delight, and is the first person to laugh when he gets through. And sometimes, if he has had good success, he is so glad and happy that he will repeat the "nub" of it and glance around from face to face, collecting applause, and then repeat it again. It is a pathetic thing to see.

Very often, of course, the rambling and disjointed humorous story finishes with a nub, point, snapper, or whatever you like to call it. Then the listener must be alert, for in many cases the teller will divert attention from that nub by dropping it in a carefully casual and indifferent way, with the pretence that he does not know it is a nub.

Artemus Ward used that trick a good deal; then when the belated audience presently caught the joke he would look up with innocent surprise, as if wondering what they had found to laugh at. Dan Setchell used it before him. Nye and Riley and others use it today.

But the teller of the comic story does not slur the nub; he shouts it at you—every time. And when he prints it, in England, France, Germany, and Italy, he italicizes it, puts some whooping exclamation points after it, and sometimes explains it in a parenthesis. All of which is very depressing, and makes one want to renounce joking and lead a better life.

Let me set down an instance of the comic method, using an anecdote which has been popular all over the world for twelve or fifteen hundred years. The teller tells it in this way:

THE WOUNDED SOLDIER

In the course of a certain battle a soldier whose leg had been shot off appealed to another soldier who was hurrying by to carry him to the rear, informing him at the same time of the loss which he had sustained; whereupon the generous son of Mars, shouldering the unfortunate, proceeded to carry out his desire. The bullets and cannon-balls were flying in all directions, and presently one of the latter took the wounded man's head off—without, however, his deliverer being aware of it. In no long time he was hailed by an officer, who said:

"Where are you going with that carcass?"

"To the rear, sir—he's lost his leg!"

"His leg, forsooth?" responded the astonished officer; "you mean his head, you booby."

Whereupon the soldier dispossessed himself of his burden, and stood looking down upon it in great perplexity. At length he said:

"It is true, sir, just as you have said." Then after a pause he added, *"But he TOLD me IT WAS HIS LEG!!!!!"*

Here the narrator bursts into explosion after explosion of thunderous horse-laughter, repeating that nub from time to time through his gaspings and shriekings and suffocatings.

It takes only a minute and a half to tell that in its comic-story form; and it isn't worth the telling, after all. Put into the humorous-story form it takes ten minutes, and is about the funniest thing I have ever listened to—as James Whitcomb Riley tells it.

He tells it in the character of a dull-witted old farmer who has just heard it for the first time, thinks it is unspeakably funny, and is trying to repeat it to a neighbor. But he can't remember it; so he gets all mixed up and wanders helplessly round and round, putting in tedious details that don't belong in the tale and only retard it; taking them out conscientiously and putting in others that are just as useless; making minor mistakes now and then and stopping to correct them and explain how he came to make them; remembering things which he forgot to put in in their proper place and going back to put them in there; stopping his narrative a good while in order to try to recall the name of the soldier that was hurt, and finally remembering that the soldier's name was not mentioned, and remarking placidly that the name is of no real importance, anyway—better, of course, if one knew it, but not essential, after all—and so on, and so on, and so on.

The teller is innocent and happy and pleased with himself, and has to stop every little while to hold himself in and keep from laughing outright; and does hold in, but his body quakes in a jelly-like way with interior chuckles; and at the end of the ten minutes the audience have laughed until they are exhausted, and the tears are running down their faces.

The simplicity and innocence and sincerity and unconsciousness of the old farmer are perfectly simulated, and the result is a performance which is thoroughly charming and delicious. This is art—and fine and beautiful, and only a master can compass it; but a machine could tell the other story.

To string incongruities and absurdities together in a wandering and sometimes purposeless way, and seem innocently unaware that they are absurdities, is the basis of the American art, if my position is correct. Another feature is the slurring of the point. A third is the dropping of a studied remark apparently without knowing it, as if one were thinking aloud. The fourth and last is the pause.

Artemus Ward dealt in numbers three and four a good deal. He would begin to tell with great animation something which he seemed to think was wonderful; then lose confidence, and after an apparently absentminded pause add an incongruous remark in a soliloquizing way; and that was the remark intended to explode the mine—and it did.

For instance, he would say eagerly, excitedly, "I once knew a man in New Zealand who hadn't a tooth in his head"—here his animation would die out; a silent, reflective pause would follow, then he would say dreamily, and as if to himself, "and yet that man could beat a drum better than any man I ever saw."

Ab Yancey's Squirrel-Hunt

Stories of "The Marvelous Hunt" abound throughout North America. In some, the miraculous events are added to the exploits of well-known characters such as Davy Crockett. In this whopper, though, the teller wants his hearers to believe that he is the one who had the great day out.

"Wal, gentlemen, when I was a young-un powder an' ball was high an' hard t' git, so we allus had t' make ever' shot count. I recollect one time I was a-tryin' t' git two red squirrels lined up so's I could kill both of 'em with one bullet. Thar was four of 'em a-runnin' 'round in a chinkapin tree, an' I reckon I must have sot thar twenty minutes afore I got 'em set to suit me. When I pulled trigger I seen both of 'em fall, but jest then I heerd turkeys a-yoikin', an' it warn't but a lee-tle ways off I seen seven hens an' a gobbler a-settin' in a tree. Seems like that 'ar bullet done skittered over thar some way, an' split the limb they was a-settin' on, an' ketched their feet in th' crack.

"Wal, sir, I clumb up t' git them turkeys an' wring their necks afore they could bust loose on me, but just as I was a-comin' down I lost my holt an' fell slap-dab into a bresh-pile. Thar I was a-scramblin' an' a-rollin', an' afore I could git out I'd smothered a hull gang o' quails an' two big swamp-rabbits! I jest tied them eight turkeys an' them forty-one quails an' them two swamp-rabbits all t'gether with pawpaw bark, an' back I went a-packin' 'em t' whar my squirrels was at. One o' them squirrels had fell in th' creek, so I waded in atter him. Hit was deeper'n I figgered on, an' th' water was kinder riled up an' dingy like. . . . When I got out on th' bank ag'in, danged if my pockets an' boot-tops wasn't jest chuck full o' fish—mostly perch an' goggle-eye!

"Whilst I was a-stringin' them fish I retch back t' scratch a chigger bite, an' my ol' shirt was too dang-tight anyhow, so one o' th' buttons popped off'n it. I seen th' dang thing go a-whistlin' off into a bunch o' hazel bresh, an' I aimed for t'

hunt it up soon as I got my fish strung t' suit me. D'rectly I heered a turrible scuf-flin' round an' gaspin' an' gurglin' in them bresh, so I drapped th' fish an' snuck over whar I could peek in. Thar was a big buck a-rollin' round, an' he was a-dyin', too, but danged if I could see what kilt him. Hit kinder skeerd me. But I just cut his throat anyhow, t' let him bleed right good, an' thar was my ol' button stuck in his wind-pipe! He must of opened up his mouth for t' belch, I reckon, an' that 'ar but-ton jest flipped in thar an' shut his wind plumb off! Hit shore was th' biggest one-bullet huntin' I ever done, seen, or hearn tell of. . . . Thar was one deer, eight turkeys, two swamp-rabbits, forty-one quails an' maybe fifty pounds o' fish, an' Pappy shore was proud when he seen me draggin' of it all home.

"Hit was a sad day at our place, though, on account of Uncle Hen. Uncle Hen was a purty good feller, but he didn't have no sense, an whut did he do but up an' call me a liar when I was a-tellin' how I got that 'ar buck. 'Liar' allus was a fightin' word in th' Yancey family, so I just naturally had t' kill him. Pap hisself said he couldn't make out t' blame me none, but it shore did gravel him t' see his own brother a-layin' thar all butchered up an' gutted that-a-way. . . . I done it with my ol' huntin'-knife, gentlemen,—same one you-uns see a-stickin' out o' my boot-top right now!"

Tall Hunting Tale

Few subjects in rural America inspire more lying than hunting does. Here is another hunting tale, told in the first person, with an outcome similar to the previous tale, but with a very different beginning.

Once upon a time I bought me a dog. I give three bushel of dried apples for him—sold the dried apples and then bought the dog. Well, the feller I bought him from said he would tree coons. So I took him a coon huntin'. He begin barkin' about ten o'clock, out on a high knob. We went up to see what the dogs was barkin' about. I looked up on a cliff about thirty feet high. The dog was lookin' up the cliff. I looked up in a tree and about ten feet above the last limb a coon was stickin', a coon on a little knot. I asked him if he couldn't climb up and catch it. And he nodded his head. So he backed off about thirty yards and clim' up on another cliff about forty feet high. I asked if he could jump from one cliff to the other, and he nodded his head. He backed off about four hundred yards. He started to jump. And he got out about halfway and saw he wa'n't aimin' to make it, so he turned around and come back.

Well, I thought it was smart of him, you see. He went ahead and I shot the coon and it rolled off the cliff. I picked it up and we took on off to the house. We got down to the creek, and my brother was with me. We started across the creek on the swingin' bridge and I dropped my flask of carbide down in the water, river about twenty feet deep. I told him I'd go down and get my carbide, if he'd wait for me, and he said, "No," said, "you've had a cold. I'll go down and get it," said, "it'd make you sick."

He dived down and was gone about thirty minutes. And I dived down to see what he was doing. He was settin' there on a log, stealin' my carbide, takin' it out of my flask, pourin' it in his'n. I asked him what he was doin', and he said, "Nothing, I just needed a little carbide and I was takin' it out of your flask—I seed you had plenty of it."

Well, my dog, see, I was gone about thirty minutes and my dog he got worried. So he come down to see what I was a-doin'. He run around to the end of this log where we was settin' and he begin barkin'. I looked in and saw an old boar hogfish and a gang of little shoats. I nodded my head and he went in after 'em. He shook his head. He couldn't make it. I kindled me up a far at the other end and I smoked them out. I smoked and smoked and smoked. About thirty minutes here they come. And the water run out of their eyes, I'd smoked 'em so much. My brother said, "How did you kindle a far?"

I said, "I jerked a few slabs off the log we was settin' on and struck me a match, and that's all there was to it."

Well, we caught the fish and come on up to the top. I had a rifle-gun, had one round of ammunition. I looked out in front of me and there laid a rattlesnake about twelve feet long. Well, I started to shoot it and about that time I heard a noise down the river. I looked and there was 5,000 wild ducks comin' up the river. Well, I didn't know which to shoot, the ducks or the rattlesnake. About the time I started to shoot the ducks I heard another noise up the river and I looked and there was 5,000 wild geese. Well, I shore didn't know what to do then. I knowed I couldn't kill the geese and the ducks, all, and the snake. So I said to myself, "I'll kill the snake and try to catch a goose as she passes." I pulled the trigger. The barrel busted. Half of it went down the river and killed 5,000 wild ducks. The other half went up the river and killed 4,999 wild geese. The gun flew all to pieces. I didn't have nothing left but the stock.

I gathered up all my ducks, killed the snake, gathered up all my geese and started across the swingin' bridge. I looked over in the corner and saw my gun locks, stickin' there on a rail, had that other goose hemmed. I walked over and picked her up and wrung her neck. Well, I had all them geese and ducks and started across that bridge, and the bridge broke with me. Down I went twenty feet deep in the water. I swimmed, I kicked, and I paddled, and when I finally got to the bank and got out I had 300 pound of fish in my hip boots. And I went on to the house and told my wife I thought I had purty good luck. And that was all of it.

The Dog Who Could Walk on Water

If hunting brings out the liar in men, competition to have the best hunting dog brings out the braggart. The following Cajun tale from Louisiana was told by Revon Reed not about himself, but about two people he claims to know. Note that the winner in this competition is the man with the wittiest remark, not the one with the miraculous dog.

You know, the typical Cajun is a terrible liar, and naturally likes to brag. And it's natural, in a way. Let's say you have a good hunting dog. Mine will always be a little better. I don't care how good your dog is. And there's a little story that I tell like that about two old guys who were always arguing about dogs and ducks. One always had a better dog than the other.

One day, one [named Olide] struck oil on his property and became a millionaire. He decided that he would travel around the world to find a dog better than Pascal's [his neighbor's] dog. And he finally found a dog which had been trained to walk on water, a retriever, but it didn't swim; it walked. It ran so fast that its feet just barely touched the water. So he bought the dog. He paid ten thousand dollars for it. Just to prove to Pascal that he had a better dog than him.

So when he came home, he said to Pascal (he told him nothing about the dog), "I found myself a dog, so," he said, "wouldn't you like to go duck hunting tomorrow!"

"Oh yeah!" he said. "You have a dog!"

"Yeah."

"He's not nearly as good as mine, eh!"

He said, "We'll see."

So they went hunting. Pascal shot first. A duck fell on the water. His dog quickly started swimming. It went to get the duck. It came back tired.

Olide said, "Look here! Watch what my dog can do!" Another duck. He shot. Fell on the water. The dog jumped out of the boat and started running on the water.

Pascal watched this. The other one watched, too, to see if this would impress him. So it came back, it brought the duck back. It was hardly wet.

He said, "What do you think of my dog now!"

"Well," he said, "I don't see that it's one bit better than mine." He said, "All I can say is that it can't even swim." He said, "I don't see where it's such a good dog!"

Old Gawge and the Ninety and Nine

Hunters affectionately gave names and personalities to their guns and made claims about them to rival the lies they told about their dogs. The punch line of the following whopper, told around New England, is a favorite among the nation's best liars.

Old Gawge took a heroic draft of lemonade. "Ah-h-h!"—he smacked his lips. "I ain't had a drink like that since the Spring my brother John come offa the drive an' fell over the cow-yard fence." Then he settled down to business:

"Wal, sir," he said, "they wan't nary shotgun in the back country whar I was riz. My fambly was addicted to the old Winchester 44-40, which were, an' still is, a great gun fer deer an' b'ar. But when it come to ducks, I fixed me up a scattermaran that had the old 44-40 skun forty ways fer Sunday. She was a old Revolutionary War flintlock musket with the bar'l sawed off half way betwixt the muzzle an' britch. My load was a handful or so of powder, paper waddin', an' as many rocks, dried beans, nails, and sech like as I could cram into her.

"Course, she wouldn't allus fire when you pulled the trigger, 'specially if the weather happened to be a mite damp, but when she did go off—gracious Peter! It took the rest of the forenoon fer to tote the ducks home!

"Wal, sir, this partic'lar mornin' I'm a-tellin' you about, I riz long before the sun, did the most of my chores, loaded up ol' Betsy Ann, an' traipsed down to the lake an' rowed out to a island while 'twas still dark. 'Twas early in the Fall an' they was consid'rable of a mist, which put me to some trouble fer to keep my powder dry.

"Without makin' no more noise than a weasel in a chicken coop, I pulled the boat up on shore an' crep' across that island to a leedle small cove on t'other side, whar the ducks held their lodge meetin's.

"Gosh all hemlock you should of see the sight which met my eyes! The sun was jest beginnin' fer to rise, an' that thar cove was fuller of ducks than a Grange hall on a strawberry festervule night! They was young ones, old ones, big ones, leedle ones an' meedjum-sized ones: all colors, shapes an' descriptions!

'Jeepers!' thinks I, 'I'm goin' to need help luggin' them ducks home, sure as leedle green apples'll give you the tummy-ache!'

"Cautious as a tomcat at a dog show, I creeps a leedle closter, kneels down, pours a leedle powder in the pan, an' aims right spang into the middle of them ducks. Then I braces myself, closes my eyes, and pulls the trigger.

"Nawthin happens.

"I wait a leedle while an' nawthin still happens, so I opens my eyes an' takes a peek at Betsy. The powder in the primin' pan ain't went off. I snaps the flint a couple times an' she sparks all right, but it seems like that ain't enough fer to set the powder off 'cause she's mebby a leedle mite damp.

"But this don't bother me a mite. I aims ol' Betsy again an' scratches a match an' holds it onto the pan. Z-z-z! The primin' percolates fine an' dandy this time, but it don't set off the charge. So I fills up the pan an' tries again. I kept tryin' till my primin' powder was all gone, but 'twas no use."

Here Old Gawge favored me with a meaning look: "But I didn't git on the rampage an' begin cussin' an' threatenin' like some folks I knows on. Nossir, I had too much sense fer that, even if I was leedle more than a boy. I jest riz onto my feet an' quietly went back to my boat and started to row fer home.

"Wal, sir, I hadn't got more'n a few rods offa that island when I hears a sizzlin' noise. I looks down at my feet an' thar is ol' Betsy Ann jest a-smokin' an' a-frothin' at the mouth, a-rarin' to go! The sun had riz by now an' out on the open water it had been hot enough fer to dry that powder charge out.

"Judas Priest! Now I want to tell you, mister, the way I turned that boat round and rowed fer that island again was a caution! I knew ol' Betsy was a-goin' to speak her piece right plumb sudden, an' I wanted to git her aimed at them ducks afore she started talkin'.

"I beached the boat an' run across that island to the cove so fast, the trees looked like a card of matches, an' all the time ol' Betsy Ann was a-splutterin' away like as if she couldn't hold in no longer.

"Wal, sir, to make a long story short, I jest did manage to git back to that thar cove an' draw a bead when 'Boom!' ol' Betsy Ann let a roar out of her an' a peck of rocks, dried beans, nails, and lead-foil from tea packages scattered in amongst them ducks, while I went rump-over-tea kittle in the opposite direction, on account of not havin' a chancet to git set fer ol' Betsy's kick.

"Purty soon I got myself picked up, found they was no bones busted, an' begin a-countin' of them ducks. I counted ontil my fingers was all used up an' then begun a-countin' on my toes ontil they was all used up too, when I begun all over ag'in."

Suddenly Old Gawge halted and poked a club-like finger into my chest. "I'll bet you couldn't guess how many ducks I got with that one shot if'n you was to go to Tophet fer it," he said.

"One cripple scared to death by the noise and another paralyzed just by seeing your face," I replied, just a bit sarcastically.

Old Gawge sniffed disdainfully and turned to Paxton. "S'pose yea guess," he invited.

Paxton thought a moment. He takes games very seriously, Paxton does. Once he won first prize of a fifty-cent cigar lighter in a charades contest. "Seven?" he asked hesitatingly.

Old Gawge spat disgustedly. "Nossir!" he snorted. "They was ninety an' nine ducks layin' dead in that cove when the smoke rolled away!"

Paxton and I stared open-mouthed for sixty seconds. Then I reached for and downed a liberal libation. A lemon seed choked me and it was several more seconds before I could recover my breath. "Why," I inquired of Old Gawge when I could talk again, "why didn't you call it a hundred?"

The old sinner assumed an expression of injured dignity. "I said ninety an' nine 'cause that's jest prezactly how many I counted," he said firmly. "Do you think fer one minute that I would up an' make a liar out of myself jest fer one measily duck?"

Uncle Swain

———— ·•·· ————

Swain Lupton was a classic local "character" of a type that has all but died out in North America. Admired and prized among men for his wit and strength, he was good-naturedly scorned by women who hated to see him coming, they said, because when he got around, the men quit working and sat out under the tree swapping yarns. Uncle Swain lived in the eastern-most region of North Carolina, where the barrier islands known as the Outer Banks begin. He died in 1910, so I never met him, but I spoke at length to his nephew Worth Harris, who narrated his deeds.

———— ·•· ————

Oh, he was a character. And there was no amount to what he could eat. Had legs as big around as nail kegs.

One afternoon in particular he went to my house and my mother said to him said, "Uncle Swain, have you had any supper?"

"Ah . . . Nah . . . Ain't struck none."

Well she went to work. She'd already cooked for the rest of us. So she went to work and it was a devil lot of trouble, cause she cooked on one of them woodstoves. Went to work fixing up his supper.

The following day she went over to the neighbor's. She said, "Well I had Uncle Swain for supper last night." Neighbor said, "YOU had him for supper. Well we did, too." And one of the ladies who lived right close to the dock where the boat stopped said, "My God, did he eat to your house. He ate to my house, too."

That was three suppers he ate that one evening.

Yeah, he went to hollering, "Ah . . . Ah . . . Ain't struck none!"

My God! Tales like the day he'd be going somewhere . . . used canoes around then, dugouts. Said he tied his canoe to what he thought was a stake and turned out to be flounder's eyes. Just such tales as that. Somebody'd tell about seeing a big flounder—eighteen or so pounds—and he'd come up and tell that one. So big, he tied the skiff to his eyes. And pretty soon the flounder started to submerge and just about sunk his boat.

Another one he used to tell, said he was going deer hunting one time. And his wife's named Margaret. Says, "Marg—have I got any shot left?" "No, got no shot left, Swain." Says, "Ah . . . What am I going to do? I'll load her down with these peach pods." So he said he soaked her down with peach pods. So said he went in the woods. It wasn't long he said one of his dogs run a real big buck right by. He blazed away right into his side. He said he didn't kill him though.

Disappointed him to death. And went and told Marg, "Well I missed my first deer." Anyhow he said that the following year he went back to the same woods again and saw this peach tree in bloom. It was moving round through the bushes! "Well," he said, "I'm getting old. I'm seeing things. I gotta get out." Said when he got a little closer look—it was that deer he'd shot—that deer he'd shot with those peach kernels. He said a tree was growing out of his side that was IN BLOOM!

Said there was an uncle of his [of Swain's] shooting loons in the fall. Yeah, loons going south. They'd go on the Outer Banks and shoot loons. And Swain said there was Uncle so-and-so would always get to shoot the first one that came by. Said he and another boy went and found this uncle's gun—unbeknownst to him—poured out the shot and rammed it down with feathers. Said they went on and started waiting. Waited, and by and by he said they saw one a-coming.

Said, "Uncle so-and-so, SEE A LOON COMING BY. YOU GET READY NOW!" Old man put the gun up like this here. WHOOM! And did the whole world turn to feathers up there. Said the old man looked at the loon he thought he'd hit but was still flying and said, "Old fellow, it is a good thing you're going South. Because as many feathers I shot out of you, you'll freeze to death this winter!"

To tell you the truth, there's nobody comparable to him. Nobody even close who tells stuff like that. He went up until he died. He was on his death bed. He didn't have but one grandson. Called him—said, "Robert, come 'ere. Something I want to tell you."

Said, "Grandfather, what is it?"

Said, "I'm leaving you a fortune."

The boy, he thought he was leaving something valuable of course. He began to get excited and asked him what it was.

"Ah . . . Ah . . . I'm leaving you the whole world to make a living in."

Just such nonsense as that.

The Trained Trout

Among American tall-tale tellers, the characters who inhabit the area of Maine known as "Down East" are far and away the best known for keeping a straight face while "sawing off a whopper." This story is so movingly told, it is hard not to be roped in.

The sage of Beaver Camp sat sunning himself on the bench beside the cook camp, the bench so widely known as the scene of countless weary hours of that perpetual toiler. He seemed to be smoking an old black pipe, whereas he was only dropping matches into its empty bowl at intervals of three minutes, agreeable to the terms of his contract with the American Match trust.

As he so sat and pondered, the writer, at the time a recent arrival, approached and said: "Mr. Grant, I wish you would give me the true history of your wonderful success in taming a trout. I have heard of it in all parts of the world but I have always longed to hear the story direct from headquarters."

"Well, it really ain't so much of a story," replied the famous chronicler. "It was this way. Nine year ago the eleventh day of last June, I was fishin' out there in the pads, and right under that third yaller leaf to the right of the channel—yes, that one with the rip in it—I ketched a trout 'bout six inches long. I never see a more intelligent lookin' little feller—high forehead, smooth face, round, dimpled chin, and a most uncommon bright, sparkling, knowin' eye.

"I always allowed that with patience and cunning a real young trout (when they gets to a heft of 10 or 15 pounds there ain't no teachin' them nothin') could be tamed jest like a dog or cat.

"There was a little water in the boat and he swims around in it all right till I goes ashore and then I gets a tub we had, made of the half of a pork barrel, fills it with water and bores a little small hole through the side close down to the bottom and stops the hole with a peg.

"I sets this tub away back in a dark corner of the camp and every night after the little fellow gets asleep I slip in, in my stockin' feet, and pulls out the peg softly and lets out jest a little mite of the water. I does this night after night so mighty sly that the little chap never suspected nothin' and he was a-livin' hale and hearty for three weeks on the bottom of that tub as dry as a cook stove, and then I knowed he was fit for trainin'.

"So I took him out o' doors and let him wiggle awhile on the path and soon got to feedin' him out of my hand. Pretty soon after that when I walked somewhat slow (I'm naturally quite a slow walker some folks think) he could follow me right good all round the clearin', but sometimes his fins did get ketched up in the brush jest a mite and I had to go back and swamp out a little trail for him; bein' a trout, of course he could easy follow a spotted line.

"Well, as time went on, he got to follerin' me most everywhere and hardly ever lost sight of me, and me and him was great friends, sure enough.

"Near about sundown one evening, I went out to the spring back of the camp, same one as you cross goin' to Little Island, to get some butter out of a pail, and, of course, he comes trottin' along behind. There was no wind that night, I remember, and I could hear his poor little fins a-raspin' on the chips where we'd been gettin' out splits in the cedar swamp. Well, sir, he follered me close up and came out onto the logs across the brook and jest as I was a-stoopin' down over the pail I heard a kee-plunk! behind me and Gorry! if he hadn't slipped through a chink between them logs and was drowned before my very eyes before I could reach him, so he was." Here a tear started from the good old man's eye on a very dusty trip down his time-stained cheek.

"Of course I was terrible cut up at first—I couldn't do a stroke of work for three weeks—but I got to thinkin' that as it was comin' on cold (it was in late November then) and snow would soon be here and he, poor little cuss, wasn't rugged enough for snowshoein' and he couldn't foller me afoot all winter no how, and as he couldn't live without me, mebby it was jest as well after all he was took off that way. Do you know, Mister, some folks around here don't believe a word of this, but if you'll come down to the spring with me, right now, I'll show you the very identical chink he dropped through that night, so I will. I've never allowed anyone to move it. No, sir! nor I never will."

Here the old man dropped match number thirty-seven into his pipe and sucked at it hard in silence, while I crept softly away on tiptoes. I never could bring myself to speak of it again, after seeing him so deeply moved—I never could.

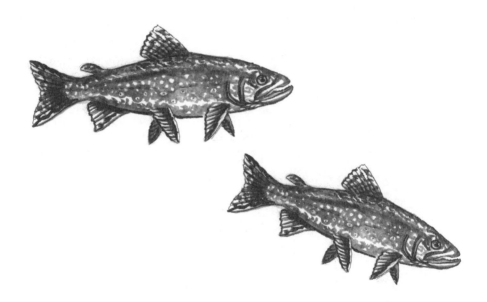

A Trip to the Moon

Tall tales make the best entertainment for children, and skillful tellers keep stories handy so that when questions come up such as, "What is the moon made of?" the answer is at the ready. The proof of the moon's famous composition is given here by Mrs. Casto (Elizabeth) Wallace of Sparta, Tennessee.

When I was a child I'd always heard, you know, that the moon was made of cheese; so I decided I'd see. There was a large mountain close to where we lived and I could see the moon as it would come up at night. It just come right over that mountain, and I thought I could just reach right over and touch it. And I'd heard people say that you could. So I decided that I'd go to that mountain and see.

Well, I started out walkin'; packed me a little lunch, you know, and put it on a stick across my shoulder. I walked and I walked, and oh, I got so tard. And I come to a pasture, and there was an old gray mar' grazin' thar in the field. So I had a rope in my pocket that I could tie to a tree so that when I jumped off on the moon, if I didn't land thar it would hold me, you know, and I wouldn't fall and kill myself. Well, I put that on the old gray mar' and made me a halter out of it.

I got up on her and went to ridin', and not far from the foot of this mountain, why, her back broke in two. I got off and I cut me a hickory limb and stuck it each way in her back and shoved it up her backbone and that fixed 'er up, you know. And I got back up on her and I rode to the foot of this mountain.

And I started up the mountain, and when I got almost to the top I saw a b'ar a-comin'; and Lawd, you can't imagine how fast I finished a-goin' up that mountain! But just as I got to the edge of this bluff, why, that b'ar was right thar behind me. And I grabbed hold of its tail and turned that b'ar wrong side out. And that b'ar went back down that mountain just a-laughin' itself to death, because all that fur was ticklin' it on the inside.

And about that time, why, here come the moon. And it was close enough that I tied my rope to the tree, you know, and as it came by I jumped off on it and

I got up on thar. And in a little bit, why, I thought how far that I was from it [the bluff]. And it was a little farther the next night, and the next night; so I knew that, well, maybe I couldn't never get back on that rock anymore.

And I soused [plunged] my fingers down in the moon, and found out it was really cheese. And it was just full of skippers—like cheese skippers [insects], you know, that gets in old cheese—it was so old. Well, those skippers, they were larger than any huge rats we have here. I set about skinnin' those skippers, and I skinned, and skinned, and skinned. And then I tied those skippers together until I made a rope long enough that I skinnied down it, and come back to Earth!

The Snake-Bit Hoe Handle

This time-honored tall tale has been adapted by contemporary storyteller Doc McConnell, who grew up in Tennessee "listening to stories in his family's cabin home and around the potbellied stove at John Mauk's General Store." It is one of the many fantastic stories settlers told to exaggerate the size and scope of the American land and the creatures who inhabited it.

When I was growin' up, it seemed like all I ever done was hoe corn. I'd hoe corn from mornin' to night. One day, I was out in the field a-hoein' corn and, as I was lookin' outa the corner of one eye, there in that corn patch was a great big ol' copperheaded rattlesnake. You'd never seen such a snake in your life. He rared back at me, and I rared back at him with my hoe.

I took a swing at that ol' snake, missed 'im, and hit a rock and broke the hoe outa the end of my hoe handle. That ol' rattlesnake sunk them teeth into the grain of that hoe handle and held on for dear life. Down through the cornfield we went. I would shake him awhile, and he would shake me awhile. We got clear down to the end of the corn patch before I finally shook that ol' snake offa the end of my hoe handle.

I ran to the house, threw that ol' hoe handle down at the garden fence, and said, "Pa, you won't believe what's happened to me out there in the cornfield. I jist seen the biggest snake up there on that ridge as you've ever seen. He bit my hoe handle, and I hit a rock and broke my hoe offa the end of my hoe handle, and I ain't a-goin' back into that cornfield no more."

Pa said, "Son, I know what you're a-tryin' to do. You're jist tryin' to git outa hoein' corn. You jist go out there and git that hoe handle and bring it to me and I'll put you a new hoe on the end of that handle."

Well, I went out to the garden fence and started to pick up that hoe handle, and you ain't a-goin' to believe this. Where that snake's poison had soaked into the grain of the wood of that ol' hoe handle, it had done started swellin' up. It commenced to swellin' and swellin' and swellin' from the poison until that hoe handle was as big 'round as a baseball bat—and ten feet long. I couldn't believe it.

So, I took that ol' hoe handle to show Pa and he said, "Why, we'll jist have to make some kindlin' wood outa that hoe handle. Run out and git the axe."

By the time I got back, the hoe handle had kept a-swellin' and a-swellin' and a-swellin' so that it was as big 'round as a water bucket.

Pa said, "We'll jist have to saw that ol' hoe handle up for firewood. Git the crosscut saw."

So I went over to the woodshed to git the saw, and by the time I got back, that hoe handle was as big as a wagon wheel—and over seventy-two feet long.

"Why," Pa said, "there ain't nothin' to do now but to take that hoe handle down there to the sawmill and have it sawed up for lumber."

It was so big now that we could barely git it in our wagon. And as that ol' team of mules pulled that log to the mill, that hoe handle drug a big trench right down the middle of the road.

Well, they sawed all day Friday and 'til dinner on Saturday. And when they was done, they had sawed 746,362 board feet of lumber from that ol' hoe handle. It jist kept on a-swellin' and a-swellin', and by the time we got that lumber stacked up, we had twenty-two wagonloads of lumber. We hauled that lumber home, and Pa sat out there and looked at that pile of lumber and thought and thought.

Finally on Monday mornin', he said, "You boys git outa bed. We're a-goin' to build a chicken house."

Well, we commenced to sawin' and hammerin' them boards, and when we was done, we had one of the finest chicken houses in Tucker's Knob. It was a purty structure—twenty-two foot long, seventeen foot deep, and nine foot high in the front. We had boxes for layin', and little poles for roostin'. It was a nice-lookin' building.

And as we were standin' back admirin' our new chicken house that afternoon, Pa said, "Son, that chicken house needs one thing before we've completed our job. We need to put a good coat of paint on our new chicken house. Run and git us some paint."

So I went down to John Mauk's store and bought five gallons of the purtiest striped paint that you've ever seen. We commenced to paintin' that chicken house, and we painted way up into the evenin' 'til it was jist gittin' dusky dark. And when we finished, we stood back to admire our work, and all of a sudden, we heard this creakin' and moanin' and groanin' and that chicken house commenced to shakin' and movin' 'round.

You see, I had mixed some turpentine in that paint, and that turpentine that I'd used to thin the paint was such good medicine that it started takin' the swellin' outa that lumber. And that chicken house went to shrinkin' and shrinkin' and shrinkin'. And when it got done shrinkin', it wasn't no bigger than a shoe box. And it's a good thing we hadn't put our chickens in it, 'cause they'd ever' one been killed, I know.

Uncle Billy Hallock's Yarn

In every region of the continent people make it a point of pride to claim the largest, fiercest, most determined mosquitoes. This story was recorded at the turn of the century on Long Island. Uncle Billy Hallock would go to any lengths to prove that mosquitoes "in those days" were much bigger than "in these days."

A generation ago, when the box tree post office was in use here, travelers were wont to while away an hour between stages by listening to Uncle Billy Hallock. One of his stories ran this way:

"No, there ain't no 'skeeters here now; there used to be 'skeeters, but arter we got tu puttin' 'em on the farm for manure we used 'em all up. One summer I was kinder short of manure for turnips and I hitched up the ox cart, loaded up the old flintlock and druv down tu the beach. When I got thar I backed the cart under a beach plum bush—beach plum bushes used to grow taller than they du now—and fired the old flintlock. Talk about skeeters; I jest slaughtered 'em; the cart was full and I had tu shovel 'em away from the wheels before them blamed oxen could start the load.

"I druv hum and spread the dead 'skeeters onter the turnip patch and then I made tu more trips tu the beach and got tu more load of the 'skeeters, and put 'em on the patch. Well, I sowed the seed and yu could see them turnips grow if yu'd been thar. I use't watch 'em grow, an' I seen 'em grow an inch a minute by the watch. By the first of September they was six feet high an' still growin'.

"One dark, foggy night long toward the last of September my oxen got out of the yard an' I couldn't find 'em. I didn't think of huntin' for 'em in them turnips, but I spent a week huntin' for 'em on Quogue plains.

"I druv up tu Moriches and got Captain Smith tu lend me his deer hounds tu hunt with and blamed if them hounds didn't find them oxen in them turnips an' run 'em all day long without ever driven' the oxen out. The turnips was so high that I couldn't see the oxen and only knew they was in thar by the barkin' of the dogs.

"That night there cum on a reg'lur old-fashioned southeaster. It was one of the hardest blows I ever see—I think like a'nough yu've heard uv it—we used to call it the September gale. Well, that gale blowed every darn leaf off of them turnips and the next day I started them hounds again. Well, I could jist see the top of them darned oxens horns over the top of them turnips and made out to find 'em then.

"How big was the turnips, did you ask? Well, I couldn't measure them because they was bigger than my bushel corn basket and I had tu cut 'em up in the patch before I could handle 'em. No we don't have no 'skeeters to 'mount to nothin' nowadays."

I Wish I Could Tell a Lie

Like mosquitoes and other creatures, the weather in America has always provided a rich body of lore for use in tall tales. Seafarers, of course, had bragging rights when it came to knowing what bad weather meant, and they became famous for their ability to exaggerate "a little."

This rhyming tale was reportedly told by a sea captain in Newport, Rhode Island.

I stood one day by a breezy bay
A watchin' the ships sail by,
When a tired tar said—with a shake of his head
"I wish I could tell a lie.

I've seed some sights that would jigger your lights
And have jiggered me own—in sooth,
But I ain't worth a darn at spinnin' a yarn
That wanders away from the Truth.

We was off on the brig—the Rig—A Gig,
A mile and a half to sea,
When Captain Snook with a troubled look
He comes and he says to me—

'Hey! Bos'n Smith, make haste forthwith
An' hemstitch the for'ard sail;
Accordion pleat the dory sheet
For there's goin' to be a gale.'

I straightway did as the Captain bid
And no sooner the job was thru,
Than a North wind—Whoof! bounded over the roof,
An' sufferin' lights she blew!

She blowed the tars clean off the spars,
The spars clean off the mast,
While anchors 'n sails, 'n pails 'n nails
Went by on the wings of the blast.

And before we could look—she blowed the cook
Straight out o' the galley bin,
While pots 'n pans and kettles 'n cans
Went rattlin' after him.

She blowed the fire from the galley stove,
The coal from the galley bin,
Then she whizzed a pace past the Captain's face
An' blowed the beard off his chin.

'Now whizzle me dead,' the Captain said
An' the words blowed out of his mouth
'We're lost I fear, if the wind don't veer
An' blow a while from the South!'

An' whizzle me dead—no sooner he said
Them words that blowed from his mouth,
Then the wind veered 'round with a hurricane sound
And blowed straight in from the South.

An' we opened our eyes with wild surprise
With never a word to say,
For in changing her tack, the wind blowed back
The things that she'd blowed away.

She blowed the tars back onto the spars,
The spars back onto the mast
Back came the sails, an' the pails an' the nails
That into the ship stuck fast.

An' before we could look—she blowed the cook
Back into the galley coop;
Back came the pans an' the kettles an' cans,
Without even spillin' the soup.

She blowed the fire back into the stove
Where it burned in its proper place,
An' we all of us cheered as she blowed the beard
Back onto the Captain's face.

There's more of my tale—said the Mariner hale,
That would jigger your lights in sooth,
But I ain't worth a darn at spinnin' a yarn
That wanders away from the Truth."

Remarks Made at the Hatchet Club

"Liars' clubs" became popular during the nineteenth century, where people sat by the hour swapping tall tales, brags, and generally trying to outdo one another in exaggerating the truth. These liars' bench gatherings took tall-tale telling out of the country store and turned it into a more formal type of public entertainment.

"Talking about hard blows out west," said Mr. Lewis, of the Detroit Free Press, at a meeting of the Hatchet Club, "talking about heavy winds, why I saw a man out in Michigan sitting quietly on his doorstep eating a piece of pie. Suddenly, before he could get into the house, the wind struck him. The gale first blew the house down, and then seized the man, carried him through the air a hundred yards or so, and landed him in peach-tree. Soon afterward a friendly board from his own house came floating by. This he seized and placed over his head to protect himself from the raging blast, and—finished his pie." (Sensation.)

"That was a windy day for Michigan, I presume," said Mr. Wm. Nye, of Laramie, "but that would not compare with one of our Laramie zephyrs. Why, gentlemen, out in Laramie, during one of our ordinary gales, I've seen boulders big as pumpkins flying through the air. Once, when the wind was blowing grave-stones around, and ripping water-pipes out of the ground, an old Chinaman with spectacles on his nose was observed in the eastern part of the town seated on a knoll, calmly flying his kite—an iron shutter with a log-chain for a tail." (Hear, Hear!)

"That was quite windy," said a Boston man, who had just returned from Nevada. "We had some wind out there. One day as I was passing a hotel in Virginia City, the cap blew from one of the chimneys. It was a circular piece of sheetiron, painted black, slightly convex, and the four supports were like legs. The wind carried it down street, and it went straddling along like a living thing."

"Well, what was it?" asked a member.

"Why, it turned out to be a bed bug from the hotel, and, by George! I never saw anything like it," then he added, "outside of Boston." (Sensation.)

"You have seen some strong winds, gentlemen," observed Eli Perkins, "but I have seen some frisky zephyrs myself, and, as tonight is the 22d of February, the birthday of the patron saint of the Hatchet Club, I will tell you about them.

"Once, out in Kansas, they told me the wind blew a cook-stove eighty miles, and came back the next day and got the griddles. (Wonder and applause.)

"A reporter of the Kansas City paper was standing out in the street looking at the stove as it floated away, when the wind caught him in the mouth, and turned him completely wrong side out. (Sensation.)

"In Topeka," continued Mr. Perkins, "post holes were ripped out of the ground and carried twenty miles (hear, hear), and careless citizens who ventured out were blown right up against brick walls and flattened out as thin as wafers (Sensation, and a voice, 'that's too thin'). Yes, thousands of citizens," continued Eli, "'were thus frescoed onto the dead walls of Topeka. The next day after the wind subsided, Deacon Thompson went around with a spade and peeled off a wagon load of citizens, and—"

"What did he do with them?" gasped the members of the Club.

"Why, gentlemen, if I remember rightly, he shipped them to Texas and sold them for circus posters and liver pads."

"Arise and sing!"

Frontier Brags

Bragging began as the spontaneous eruption of the overripe, Wild West ego in the saloons and on the streets of frontier towns. A peculiar form of American tall-tale telling, brags eventually became a form of entertainment and were "performed" at liars' clubs and other venues. In the first example below, notice the reference to "grinning the bark off a tree." It is the braggart's challenge to the famed Davy Crockett who makes political hay from the same claim in Chapter 3.

BILLY EARTHQUAKE

As we were passing by the court-house, a real "screamer from the Nob," about six feet four in height, commenced the following tirade: "This is me, and no mistake! Billy Earthquake, Esq., commonly called Little Billy, all the way from No'th Fork of Muddy Run! I'm a small specimen, as you see, a remote circumstance, a mere yearling; but cuss me if I ain't of the true imported breed, and I can whip any man in this section of the country. Whoop! won't nobody come out and fight me? Come out, some of you, and die decently, for I'm spileing for a fight, I hain't had one for more than a week, and if you don't come out I'm flyblowed before sundown, to a certingty. So come up to taw!

"Maybe you don't know who Little Billy is? I'll tell you. I'm a poor man, it's a fact, and smell like a wet dog; but I can't be run over. I'm the identical individual that grinned a whole menagerie out of countenance, and made the ribbed nose baboon hang down his head and blush. W-h-o-o-p! I'm the chap that towed the Broad-horn up Salt River, where the snags were so thick that the fish couldn't swim without rubbing their scales off!—fact, and if any one denies it, just let 'em make their will! Cock-a-doodle-doo!

"Maybe you never heard of the time the horse kicked me, and put both his hips out of jint—if it ain't true, cut me up for catfish bait! W-h-o-o-p! I'm the very infant that refused its milk before its eyes were open, and called out for a bottle of old Rye! W-h-o-o-p! I'm that little Cupid!

"Talk about grinning the bark off a tree!—'tain't nothing; one squint of mine at a bull's heel would blister it. O, I'm one of your toughest sort,—live for ever, and then turn to a white oak post. I'm the ginewine article, a real double act-ing engine, and I can out-run, out-jump, out-swim, chaw more tobacco and spit less, and drink more whiskey and keep soberer than any man in these localities. If that don't make 'em fight . . . nothing will. I wish I may be kiln-dried and split up into wooden shoe-pegs, if I believe there's a chap among 'em that's got courage enough to collar a hen!"

THE PURPLE BLOSSOM OF GINGHAM MOUNTAIN

"Let all the sons of men b'ar witness!" sings this gent, as he goes skatin' stiff-laig about in a ring like I relates, arms bent, an' back arched; "let all the sons of men b'ar witness; an' speshully let a cowerin' varmint, named Sam Enright, size me up an' shudder. I'm the maker of deserts an' the wall-eyed harbinger of deso-lation! I'm kin to rattlesnakes on my mother's side; I'm king of all the eagles an' full brother to the b'ars! I'm the bloo-eyed lynx of Whisky Crossin', an' I weighs four thousand pounds. I'm a he-steamboat; I've put a crimp in a cat-a-mount with nothin' but my livin' hands! I broke a full-grown allagator across my knee, tore him asunder an' showered his shrinkin' fragments over a full section of land! I hugged a cinnamon b'ar to death, an' made a grizzly plead for mercy! Who'll come gouge with me? Who'll come bite with me? Who'll come put his knuckles in my back? I'm Weasel-eye, the dead shot; I'm the blood-drinkin', skelp-t'arin', knife-plyin' demon of Sunflower Creek! The flash of my glance will deaden whiteoak, an' my screech in anger will back the panther plumb oft his natif heath! I'm a slay-er an' a slaughterer, an' I cooks an' eats my dead! I can wade the Cumberland with-out wettin' myse'f, an' I drinks outen the spring without touchin' the ground! I'm a swinge-cat; but I warns you not to be misled by my looks! I'm a flyin' bison, an' deevastation rides upon my breath! Whoop! whoop! whoopee! I'm the Purple Blossom of Gingham Mountain, an' where is that son of thunder who'll try an' nip me in the bud! Whoop! whoopee! I'm yere to fight or drink with any sport; ary one or both! Whoopee! Where is the stately stag to stamp his hoof or rap his antlers to my proclamations! Where is that boundin' buck! Whoopee! whoop! whoop!"

California

As statehood came to the Western Territories, so did state pride. Since inventing whoppers had already grown into a national sport, the practice lent itself perfectly to yarn-spinners who went back east and were called upon to describe the state in which they lived.

The wear and tear of this covered-wagon life on the plains discourages many, although (who can doubt it?) we are journeying to a land unexcelled in all the world—even if there isn't a single nugget of gold within its boundary lines! This is illustrated by the yarn of a man who had lived in California, until he had reached the interesting age of 250 years. In most countries a man that old would be pretty feeble and decrepit, but not in California—Oh no! In fact such were the exhilarating, life-giving, and youth-preserving qualities of that climate that our hero at 250 was in the perfect enjoyment of his health and every faculty of mind and body. But he had become tired of life. The perpetual responsibility of managing a large fortune made him long for a new state of existence, unencumbered with this world's cares, passions, and strifes. Yet, notwithstanding his desire—for which he daily and hourly prayed to his Maker—health and vigor typical of residents of California clung persistently to him. He could not shake them off. At times he contemplated suicide; but the holy padres (to whom he confessed his thoughts) admonished him that that was damnation; being a devout Christian, he would not disobey their injunction. A lay friend, however, no doubt the heir to his estate, with whom he daily consulted on this subject, at last advised him to a course which, he thought, would produce the desired result. It was to make his will and then travel into a foreign country. This suggestion was pleasing to our California patriarch in search of death, and he immediately adopted it. He visited a foreign land; and very soon, in accordance with his plan and his wishes, he fell sick and died. In his last will and testament, however, he required his heir and executor, upon pain of disinheritance, to transport his remains to his own beloved country and there entomb them. This requisition was faithfully complied with.

His body was interred with much be-candled pomp and ceremony in his own California, and prayers were duly rehearsed in all the churches for the rest of his soul. He was happy, it was supposed, in Heaven, where, for a long series of years, he had prayed to be; and his heir was happy that he was there. But who can safely mock Providence? Being brought back and interred in Californian soil, with the health-breathing, youth-preserving, Californian zephyrs rustling over his grave, the energies of life were immediately restored to his inanimate corpse! Herculean strength was imparted to his frame and, bursting the prison-walls of death, he appeared before his chapfallen heir reinvested with all the vigor and beauty of early manhood! He submitted to his fate with Christian resignation and determined bravely to live his appointed time.

3

Legendary Heroes
and Heroines

Folk heroes are made, not born. That is, the measure of a hero's fame is not nec-
essarily what he has done, but how many stories and songs have been generat-
ed about him among the people. Take the case of such well-known heroes in
North American folklore as Annie Oakley and Casey Jones. Though they pos-
sessed remarkable skill and talent in their chosen fields, they actually led rather
ordinary lives—she as a performer and he as a railroad engineer. But the body
of lore that surrounds their memories has made them legends. Others, such as
Davy Crockett and Johnny Appleseed, certainly led extraordinary lives. But
even so, their exploits might have died with them had not people kept on
inventing tales and ballads about them long after they passed away.

The question of what makes a hero becomes a thorny one when we con-
sider how many stories and songs have been created about people who would
otherwise live in infamy—real criminals like Stackalee and Belle Starr who
became legends thanks to the folk process. When a master tale-teller takes the
core of a story about a real human being and adds to it all manner of exagger-
ation, then the person, who may in fact have been only remarkable, becomes a
hero. So while the following tales are usually based in truth, they are heroic folk-
tales by virtue of the fertile imagination of the North American people.

Annie Oakley Makes Her Name

Annie Oakley was born in 1860 in Ohio, and by the age of six she was using a rifle to hunt for food. At the age of twenty-five she joined Buffalo Bill's Wild West Show and traveled throughout the United States and Europe demonstrating her uncanny talent as a markswoman. Thrilling tales of her exploits with the rifle vary in the details, as proper folktales always do. In some stories about Annie's contest with her future husband, Frank Butler, the element of mystery about her gender is missing. This story, though, is much more entertaining than those.

Late in the afternoon on a day in spring of the year 1865 the manager of the Gibson House [in Cincinnati, Ohio] waited impatiently as Jesse Jago tossed the lines, sheathed his rifle and began his impressive descent from the Martin and Chenowith stage. The ritual over, he approached the driver.

"Jesse," he said, "is that A. Oakley still up in Greenville?"

"Yep," Jesse said. "Be sendin' more quail any day now, from what I hear."

"Never mind about the quail, can you get him up here?"

"What for?" Jesse asked.

In answer, the manager produced a four-sheet poster announcing in circus-style letters the appearance of, "FRANK BUTLER, WORLD'S CHAMPION RIFLE SHOT."

"Ever hear of this fellow?" the manager asked, gesturing to the poster.

"Reckon I have," Jesse said.

"You know he has a standing offer of a hundred dollars to anybody who can outshoot him?"

"Has he now?" Jesse said, stroking his chin.

"That's right. And what's more I've already bet him another hundred dollars that I know a fella who can beat him. Word's all over town. Everybody's betting on that Oakley fella. Can you get him to come up?"

"What sort of a match?"

"Rifle. Best out of a hundred."

"I'll fetch A. Oakley, providin' one thing—the match goes on regardless of Oakley's age or size or looks."

"I don't care what he looks like. He can shoot, that's all we care about."

"Oakley'll be here Saturday."

Never was there such a crowd on hand to greet the Greenville stage as there was that Saturday. Quail shot through the head had been the talk of Cincinnati for months. Word of it had passed up and down the river and now it seemed that everyone was at the Gibson House for the coming out of A. Oakley.

No one waited for Jesse Jago's ceremonious descent. Eager hands pulled open the coach door. There were two passengers, an alert, athletic-looking man and a young woman. Quickly the male passenger was hoisted to several pairs of broad shoulders. Necks were craned and excitement ran high as the crowd closed in. It was some time before the protesting stage passenger could explain that there'd been some mistake. He was Oliver Toth, correspondent for *Leslie's Weekley*, and what was going on anyhow?

The lithe, willowy girl who had also come in on the stage approached the center of excitement. A plaid skirt hung nearly to her ankles. A sunbonnet framed her finely chiseled face. There were tiny crow's feet alongside a pair of extraordinarily bright hazel eyes. The young lady addressed the man who was making the most commotion.

"I beg your pardon," she said, "I reckon I'm the one you're lookin' for. My name's Annie Oakley."

A roar of protest went up from the crowd. The quick-thinkers rushed to cover their bets, the others surged around the manager of the Gibson House demanding that the match be called off.

Jesse Jago came up then, and for once he had forgotten to sheathe his rifle. He handled it casually, almost carelessly. The hubbub died.

Jesse spoke softly, as he always did.

"One of the conditions of this match was that it goes on exactly as scheduled, no matter what A. Oakley looked like."

There was a sharp protest but it died quickly as Jesse made a particularly careless gesture with his rifle.

"Get your gun, Annie," he said.

The rest of the story is still told on winter nights when men are fondly cleaning their favorite rifles. The little girl from backwoods Ohio fired shoulder to shoulder with the world's champion rifle shot, scoring hit for hit. On the last round, the one hundredth, Frank Butler missed. Annie Oakley never missed.

Davy Crockett

Having grown up with little formal education in the backwoods of Tennessee, Davy Crockett became interested in politics in the early part of the nineteenth century. He served as a state legislator, and then as a U.S. congressman before he was killed at the Alamo in 1836. His exaggerated eccentricity led to many tales being generated about him. But, in fact, Crockett was a self-made legend since he was responsible for making up most of the stories about his outlandish deeds. It has been difficult to decide whether he should be included here among our heroes and heroines, or among the rogues' gallery of liars in Chapter 2. But there can be no question of his authenticity. He is as much a hero for his ability to entertain as for his courage.

GRINNING THE BARK OFF A TREE

American politicians have used the fine art of braggadocio in stump speeches almost from the beginning of the nation. No one, however, has ever done it better than Davy Crockett.

That Colonel Crockett could avail himself, in electioneering, of the advantages which well applied satire ensures, the following anecdote will sufficiently prove:

In the canvass of the Congressional election of 18—, Mr. ***** was the Colonel's opponent—a gentleman of the most pleasing and conciliating manners—who seldom addressed a person or a company without wearing upon his countenance a peculiarly good humoured smile. The colonel, to counteract the influence of this winning attribute, thus alluded to it in a stump speech:

"Yes, gentlemen, he may get some votes by *grinning*, for he can *outgrin me*—and you know I ain't slow—and to prove to you that I am not, I will tell you an anecdote. . . . You all know I love hunting. Well, I discovered a long time ago that a 'coon couldn't stand my grin. I could bring one tumbling down from the highest tree. I never wasted powder and lead, when I wanted one of the creatures. Well, as I was walking out one night, a few hundred yards from my house, looking carelessly about me, I saw a 'coon planted upon one of the highest limbs of an old tree. The night was very *moony* and clear, and old Ratler was with me; but Ratler won't bark at a 'coon—he's a queer dog in that way. So, I thought I'd bring the lark down in the usual way, *by a grin*. I set myself—and, after grinning at the 'coon a reasonable time, found that he didn't come down. I wondered what was the reason—and I took another steady grin at him. Still he was *there*. It made me a little mad; so I felt round and got an old limb about five feet long, and, planting one end upon the ground, I placed my chin upon the other, and took a *rest*. I then grinned my best for about five minutes; but the cursed 'coon hung on. So, finding I could not bring him down by grinning, I determined to have him—for I thought he must be a droll chap. I went over to the house, got my axe, returned to the tree, saw the 'coon still there, and began to cut away. Down it come, and I ran forward; but d—n the 'coon was there to be seen. I found that what I had taken for one was a large knot upon the branch of the tree and, upon looking at it closely, I saw that *I had grinned all the bark off, and left the knot perfectly smooth*.

"Now, fellow-citizens," continued the Colonel, "you must be convinced that, in the *grinning line*, I myself am not slow—yet, when I look upon my opponent's countenance, I must admit that he is my superior. You must all admit it. Therefore, be wide awake—look sharp—and do not let him grin you out of your votes."

The Colonel Swallows a Thunderbolt

———

Davy Crockett was capable of playing the back woods rube to the hilt. The following tale, though, shows that behind the act he was a sophisticated humorist, as well.

———

Thar ar a grate menny kinds of larning. I found it out when I went to Kongress. That ar your mattymatticks, your jommytrees, your sighentifficks, and your axletrissity. I nose nothin about the other wons, but the axletressity is a screamer. Thar war a feller in Washington that put the thunder and litening into glass bottles, and when a feller had the roomatiz, or the Saint Vitals dance, he would put the axletressity into his corpse jist like pouring whiskey into a powder horn, and it cured him as clean as a barked tree. So I seed how 'twas done; and intarmined whenever ennything aled me to try it, only I didn't keer about the bottles, for I thort I could jist as well take the litening in the raw state as it cum from the clouds. I had been used to drink out of the Massissippy without a cup, and so I could take the litening without the bottles and whirligigs that belongs to an axletressityfying masheen. It fell out that sum two yeers arter I had ben to see this axletrissity, I got a leetle in love with a pesky smart gal in our cleering, and I knowed it war not rite, seeing I war a married man. So I combobbolated on the subject and at last I resisted that I would explunctificate my passions by axletrissity, so it must be done by bringing it rite on the hart and driving the love out of it. So I went out into the forrest one arternoon when thar war a pestiferous thunder gust, I opened my mouth, so that the axletressity might run down and hit my hart, to cure it of love. I stood so for an hour, and then I seed a thunderbolt a cummin, and I dodged my mouth rite under it, and plump it went into my throte. My eyes! It war as if seven buffaloes war kicking in my bowels. My hart spun round amongst my insides like a grindstone going by steem, but the litening went clean through me, and tore the trowsers cleen off as it cum out. I had a sore gizzard for two weeks arterward, and my inwards war so hot that I use to eat raw vittals for a month arterward, and it would be cooked before it got farely down my throte. I have never felt love since.

David Crockett Meets a Bear

———

Sometimes Davy Crockett told the truth, and sometimes he didn't. This story, unlike the previous tales, has the ring of authenticity about it and is one of the stories that helped make his reputation for bravery.

———

In the morning I left my son at the camp, and we started on towards the harricane [a stretch of timber felled by a hurricane]; and when we had went about a mile, we started a very large bear, but we got along mighty slow on account of the cracks in the earth occasioned by the earthquakes. We, however, made out to keep in hearing of the dogs for about three miles, and then we come to the harricane. Here we had to quit our horses, as old Nick himself couldn't have got through it without sneaking it along in the form that he put on to make a fool of our old grandmother Eve. By this time several of my dogs had got tired and come back; but we went ahead on foot for some little time in the harricane, when we met a bear coming straight to us, and not more than twenty or thirty yards off. I started my tired dogs after him, and McDaniel pursued them, and I went on to where my other dogs were. I had seen the track of the bear they were after, and I knowed he was a screamer. I followed on to about the middle of the harricane, but my dogs pursued him so close, that they made him climb an old stump about twenty feet high. I got in shooting distance of him and fired, but I was all over in such a flutter from fatigue and running, that I couldn't hold steady; but, however, I broke his shoulder, and he fell. I run up and loaded my gun as quick as possible, and shot him again and killed him. When I went to take out my knife to butcher him, I found I had lost it in coming through the harricane. The vines and briers was so thick that I would sometimes have to get down and crawl like a varment to get through it all; and a vine had, as I supposed, caught in the handle and pulled it out. While I was standing and studying what to do, my friend came to me. He had followed my trail through the harricane, and had found my knife, which was mighty good news to me; as a hunter hates the worst in the world to lose a good dog, or any part of his hunting tools. I now left McDaniel to butcher the bear, and I went after our horses, and brought them as near as the nature of case would allow. I then took our bags, and went back to where he was; and when we had skin'd the bear, we fleeced off the fat and carried it to our horses at several loads. We then packed it up on our horses, and had a heavy pack of it on each one. We now started and went on till about sunset, when I concluded we must be near our camp; so I hollered and my son answered me, and we moved on in the direction to the camp. We had gone but a little way when I heard my dogs make a warm start again; and I jumped down from my horse and gave him up to my friend, and told him I would follow them. He went on to the camp, and I went ahead after my dogs with all my might for a considerable distance, till at last night came on. The woods were very rough and hilly, and all covered over with cane.

I now was compel'd to move on more slowly; and was frequently falling over logs, and into the cracks made by the earthquakes, so that I was very much afraid I would break my gun. However I went on about three miles, when I came to a good big creek, which I waded. It was very cold, and the creek was about knee deep; but I felt no great inconvenience from it just then, as I was all over wet with sweat from running, and I felt hot enough. After I got over the creek and out of the cane, which was very thick on all our creeks, I listened for my dogs. I found they had either treed or brought the bear to a stop, as they continued barking in the same place. I pushed on as near in the direction to the noise as I could, till I found the hill was too steep for me to climb, and so I backed and went down the creek some distance till I came to a hollow, and then took up that, till I come to a place where I could climb up the hill. It was mighty dark, and was difficult to see my way or any thing else. When I got up the hill, I found I had passed the dogs; and so I turned and went to them. I found, when I got there, they had treed the bear in a large forked poplar, and it was setting in the fork.

I could see the lump, but not plain enough to shoot with any certainty, as there was no moonlight; and so I set in to hunting for some dry brush to make me a light; but I could find none, though I could find that the ground was torn mightily to pieces by the cracks.

At last I thought I could shoot by guess, and kill him; so I pointed as near the lump as I could, and fired away. But the bear didn't come; he only clomb up higher, and got out on a limb, which helped me to see him better. I now loaded up again and fired, but this time he didn't move at all. I commenced loading for a third fire, but the first thing I knowed the bear was down among my dogs and they were fighting all around me. I had my big butcher in my belt, and I had a pair of dressed buckskin breeches on. So I took out my knife, and stood, determined, if he should get hold of me, to defend myself in the best way I could. I stood there for some time, and could now and then see a white dog I had, but the rest of them, and the bear, which were very dark coloured, I couldn't see at all, it was so miserable dark. They still fought around me, and sometimes within three feet of me; but at last, the bear got down into one of the cracks, that the earthquake had made in the ground, about four feet deep, and I could tell the biting end of him by the hollering of my dogs. So I took my gun and pushed the muzzle of it about, till I thought I had it against the main part of his body, and fired; but it happened to be only the fleshy part of his foreleg. With this, he jumped out of the crack, and he and the dogs had another hard fight around me, as before. At last, however, they forced him back into the crack again, as he was when I had shot.

I had laid down my gun in the dark, and I now began to hunt for it; and, while hunting, I got hold of a pole, and I concluded I would punch him awhile with that. I did so, and when I would punch him, the dogs would jump in on him, when he would bite them badly, and they would jump out again. I concluded, as he would take punching so patiently, it might be that he would lie still enough for me to get down in the crack, and feel slowly along till I would find the right place to give him a dig with my butcher. So I got down, and my dogs got in before him and kept his head toward them, till I got along easily up to him; and placing my hand on his rump, felt for his shoulder, just behind which I intended to stick him. I made a lounge with my long knife, and fortunately stuck him right through the heart; at which he just sank down, and I crawled out in a hurry. In a little time my dogs all come out too, and seemed satisfied, which was the way they always had of telling me that they had finished him.

I suffered very much that night with cold, as my leather breeches, and everything else I had on, was wet and frozen. But I managed to get my bear out of this crack after several hard trials, and so I butchered him, and laid down to try to sleep. But my fire was very bad, and I couldn't find anything that would burn well to make it any better; and I concluded I should freeze, if I didn't warm myself in some way by exercise. So I got up, and hollered a while, and then I would just jump up and down with all my might, and throw myself into all sorts of motions. But all this wouldn't do; for my blood was now getting cold, and the chills coming all over me. I was so tired, too, that I could hardly walk; but I thought I would do the best I could to save my life, and then, if I died, nobody would be to blame. So I went to a tree about two feet through, and not a limb on it for thirty feet, and I would climb up it to the limbs, and then lock my arms together around it, and slide down to the bottom again. This would make the insides of my legs and arms feel mighty warm and good. I continued this till daylight in the morning, and how often I clomb up my tree and slid down I don't know, but I reckon at least a hundred times.

Mike Fink Meets David Crockett

Mike Fink gained fame as a keelboatman on the Mississippi River. He was known for his great strength and also for his outrageous behavior and speech. Whether or not there ever was such a meeting between the two legendary figures is anyone's guess.

"I expect, stranger," said Davy, "you think old Davy Crockett war never beat at the long rifle; but he war, though. I expect that there's no man so strong but what he will find some one stronger.

"If you haven't heerd tell of one Mike Fink, I'll tell you something about him, for he war a helliferocious fellow, and made an almighty fine shot. Mike was a boatman on the Mississip', but he had a little cabin on the head of the Cumberland, and a horrid handsome wife, that loved him the wickedest that ever you see.

"Mike only worked enough to find his wife in rags, and himself in powder and lead and whiskey, and the rest of the time he spent in knocking over b'ar and turkeys, and bouncing deer, and sometimes drawing a lead on an Injun. So one night I fell in with him in the woods, where him and his wife shook down a blanket for me in his wigwam.

"In the morning says Mike to me, 'I've got the handsomest wife, and the fastest horse, and the sharpest shooting iron in all Kentuck, and if any man dare doubt it, I'll be in his hair quicker than hell could scorch a feather.'

"This put my dander up, and sez I, 'I've nothing to say agin your wife, Mike, for it can't be denied she's a shocking handsome woman, and Mrs. Crockett's in Tennessee, and I've got no horses. Mike, I don't exactly like to tell you you lie about what you say about your rifle, but I'm damned if you speak the truth, and I'll prove it. Do you see that are cat sitting on the top rail of your potato patch, about a hundred fifty yards off? If she hears agin, I'll be shot if it shan't be without ears!'

"So I blazed away, and I'll bet you a horse, the ball cut off both the old tom cat's ears close to his head, and shaved the hair clean off the skull, as slick as if'd done it with a razor, and the critter never stirred, nor knew he'd lost his ears till he tried to scratch 'em.

" 'Talk about your rifle after that, Mike!' sez I.

" 'Do you see that are sow off furder than the end of the world,' set Mike, 'with a litter of pigs around her?' And he lets fly.

"The old sow gave a grunt, but never stirred in her tracks, and Mike falls to loading and firing for dear life, till he hadn't left one of them are pigs enough tail to make a toothpick on.

" 'Now' sez he, 'Colonel Crockett, I'll be pretticulary obleedged to you if you'll put them are pigs' tails on again,' set he.

" 'That's onpossible, Mike,' sez I, 'but you've left one of 'em about an inch to steer by, and if that had a-been my work, I wouldn't have done it so wasteful. I'll mend your shot.' And I lets fly, and cuts off the apology he's left the poor cre-tur for decency. I wish I may drink the whole Mississip', without a drop of the rale stuff in it, if you wouldn't have thort the tail had been drove in with a hammer.

"That made Mike kinder sorter wrothy, and he sends a ball after his wife as she was going to the spring after a gourd full of water, and knocked half her comb out of her head, without stirring a hair, and calls out to her to stop for me to take a blizzard at what was left on it. The angeliferous critter stood still as a scarecrow in a cornfield, for she'd got used to Mike's tricks by long practice.

" 'No, no, Mike,' sez I. 'Davy Crockett's hand would be sure to shake, if his iron war pointed within a hundred mile of a shemale, and I give up beat, Mike.' "

The Ballad of Casey Jones

An article in The Erie Railroad *magazine in 1928 describes Casey Jones as "6 feet 4 1/2 inches tall, dark-haired and gray-eyed," and it was said of him that "he always had a smile or a broad grin. The faster he could get his engine to roll, the happier he was. He would lean out of the cab window . . . and when he got her going so fast that the side rods looked solid, he would look at you and grin all over, happy as a boy with his first pair of red boots." Songs about Casey Jones have been found among railroad men all over the world, with French, German, and even South African versions. The following stanzas represent the traditional ballad that began circulating soon after Casey's death.*

Come all you rounders for I want you to hear
The story told of a brave engineer;
Casey Jones was the rounder's name
On a heavy six-eight wheeler he rode to fame.

Caller called Jones about half-past four,
Jones kissed his wife at the station door,
Climbed into the cab with the orders in his hand,
Says, "This is my trip to the promised land."

Through South Memphis yards on the fly,
He heard the fireman say, "You've got a white-eye,"
All the switchmen knew by the engine's moans,
That the man at the throttle was Casey Jones.

It had been raining for more than a week,
The railroad track was like the bed of a creek.
They rated him down to a thirty mile gait,
Threw the south-bound mail about eight hours late.

Fireman says, "Casey, you're runnin' too fast,
You run the block signal the last station you passed."
Jones says, "Yes, I think we can make it though,
For she steams much better than ever I know."

Jones says, "Fireman, don't you fret,
Keep knockin' at the firedoor, don't give up yet;
I'm goin' to run her till she leaves the rail
Or make it on time with the south-bound mail."

Around the curve and a-down the dump
Two locomotives were a-bound to bump.
Fireman hollered, "Jones, it's just ahead,
We might jump and make it but we'll all be dead."

'Twas around this curve he saw a passenger train;
Something happened in Casey's brain;
Fireman jumped off, but Casey stayed on,
He's a good engineer but he's dead and gone—

Poor Casey was always all right,
He stuck to his post both day and night;
They loved to hear the whistle of old Number Three
As he came into Memphis on the old K.C.

Headaches and heartaches and all kinds of pain
Are not apart from a railroad train;
Tales that are earnest, noble and gran'
Belong to the life of a railroad man.

Johnny Appleseed

Americans have always valued eccentricity and the freedom it brings. As a folk hero, Johnny Appleseed is as famous for being odd as for planting trees. It is rumored that Johnny graduated from Harvard and was soon after either kicked by a horse, jilted by a girl, or suffered from malaria, any or all of which events caused him to start wandering. The life of John Chapman spawned innumerable tales. Many, like the first presented here, romanticize his mission in life. Others attest to the possibility that he might have been a little bit beyond the bend.

John Chapman was born in the year 1775, at or near Springfield, Mass. In the latter years of the last century, or beginning of the present, he, with his half-brother, Nathaniel Chapman, came to Ohio, and stayed a year or two, and then returned to Springfield, and moved their father's family to Marietta, Ohio. Soon after that, Johnny located in Pennsylvania, near Pittsburgh, and began the nursery business, and continued it on westward.

He was an earnest disciple of the faith taught by Emanuel Swedenborg, and claimed that he had conversation with spirits and angels. In the bosom of his shirt he always carried a Testament and one or two old volumes of Swedenborg's works. These he read daily. He was a man rather above middle stature, wore his hair and beard long and dressed oddly. He generally wore old clothes that he had taken in exchange for the one commodity in which he dealt—apple trees. Dr. Hill says in 1801, an old uncle of ours, a pioneer in Jefferson County, Ohio, said the first time he ever saw him (Johnny) he was going down the river with two canoes lashed together and well laden with apple seeds which he obtained at the cider presses of western Pennsylvania. Sometimes he carried a bag or two of seeds on an old horse, but more frequently he bore them on his back, going from place to place on the wild frontier, clearing a little patch, surrounding it with a rude enclosure and planting seeds therein. He had little nurseries all through Ohio, Pennsylvania and Indiana. If a man wanted trees and was not able to pay for them,

Johnny took his note, and if the man ever got able and was willing to pay the debt, he took the money thankfully; but if not,
it was well.

He was such a good, kind, generous man, that he
thought it wrong to expend money on clothes to be worn just for
their fine appearance. He thought if he was comfortably clad, and in
attire that suited the weather, it was sufficient. His head covering was often a
pasteboard hat of his own making, with one broad side to it, that he wore next the
sunshine to protect his face. It was a very unsightly object to be sure, and yet never
one of us children ventured to laugh. We held Johnny in tender regard. His pan-
taloons were old and scant and short, with some sort of a substitute for "gallows"
or suspenders. He never wore a coat unless it was in the wintertime, and his feet
were knobby and horny and frequently bare. Sometimes he wore sandals
instead—rude soles with thong fastenings. The bosom of his shirt was always
pulled out loosely so as to make a kind of pocket or pouch in which he carried his
books. We have seen Johnny frequently wearing an old coffee sack for a coat, with
holes cut in it for his arms.

All the orchards in the white settlements came from the nurseries of
Johnny's planting. Even now after all these years, and though this region is densely populated, I can count from my window no less than five orchards or remains
of orchards that were once trees taken from his nurseries. Long ago if he was
going a great distance and carrying a sack of seeds on his back he had to provide
himself with a leather sack, for the dense underbrush, brambles and thorny thickets would have made it unsafe for a coffee sack. I remember distinctly of falling
over one of Johnny's well filled sacks early one morning immediately after rising.
It was not light in the room, at the head of the stairs, and it was not there when
I went to bed the night before. It seems that he arrived at night, and for safe-
keeping the sack was put upstairs, while he lay beside the kitchen fire. I never saw
him sleep in a bed. He preferred to lie on the floor with his poor old horny feet
to the fire. . . .

In 1806 he planted sixteen bushels of seed on an old farm on the

Walhonding River, and he planted in Licking County, Ohio, and Richland County, and had other nurseries further west. One of his nurseries is near us, and I often go to the secluded spot on the quiet banks of the creek shut in by sycamore trees, with the sod never broken since the poor man did it. And when I look up and see the wide out-stretched branches over the place like out-spread arms in loving benediction, I say in a reverent whisper, "Oh the angels did commune with the good old man, whose loving heart prompted him to go about doing good. . . ."

On the subject of apples he was very charmingly enthusiastic. One would be astonished at his beautiful description of excellent fruit. I saw him once at the table when I was very small, telling about some apples that were new to us. His description was poetical, the language remarkably well chosen. It could have been no finer had the whole of Webster's Unabridged, with all its royal vocabulary been fresh upon his ready tongue. I stood back of mother's chair, amazed, delighted, bewildered, and vaguely realizing the wonderful powers of true oratory. I felt more than I understood.

He was scrupulously honest. I recall the last time we ever saw his sister, a very ordinary woman, the wife of an easy old gentleman and the mother of a family of handsome girls. They had started to move west in the winter season, but could move no farther after they reached our house. To help them along and to get rid of them, my father made a queer, little one-horse vehicle on runners, hitched their poor caricature of a beast to it, helped them pack and stow therein their bedding and a few movables, gave them a stock of provisions and five dollars, and sent the whole kit on their way rejoicing. And that was the last we ever saw of our poor neighbors.

The next time Johnny came to our house he very promptly laid a five dollar bill on my father's knee and shook his head very decidedly when it was handed back. Neither could he be prevailed upon to take it back again.

He was never known to hunt any animal or to give any living thing pain; not even a snake. One time when overtaken by night while traveling he crawled into a hollow log and slept till morning. In the other end of the log was a bear and her cubs. Johnny said he knew the bear would not hurt him, and that there was room enough for all.

The Indians all liked and treated him very kindly. They regarded him from his habits as a man above his fellows. He could endure pain like an Indian warrior; could thrust pins into his flesh without tremor. Indeed so insensible was he to acute pain that treatment of a wound or sore was to sear it with a hot iron and then treat it as a burn. He ascribed great medical virtues to the fennel, which he found probably in Pennsylvania. The overwhelming desire to do good and benefit and bless others induced him to gather a quantity of the seed, which he carried in his pockets, and occasionally scattered along his path in his journeys, especially at the waysides, near dwellings. Poor old man! He inflicted on the farming population a positive evil, when he sought to do good, for the rank fennel with its pretty, but pungent blossom, lines our roadsides and borders our lanes, and steals into our door-yard, and is a pest second to the daisy.

The last time we saw Johnny was one summer day when we were quilting upstairs. A door opened out upon the ground, and he stood his little bundle on the sill and lay down upon the floor, resting his head on the parcel. Then he drew out of his bosom one of his dingy books and read aloud to us.

In 1838 he resolved to go further on. Civilization was making the wilderness to blossom like the rose. Villages were springing up, stagecoaches laden with travelers were common, schools were everywhere, mail facilities were very good, frame and brick houses were taking the places of the humble cabins; and so Johnny went around among all his friends and bade them farewell. The little girls he had dandled upon his knees, and presented with beads and gay ribbons, were now mothers and the heads of families. This must have been a sad task for the old man, who was then well stricken in years, and one would have thought that he would have preferred to die among his friends. He came back two or three times to see us all in the intervening years that he lived; the last time was in the year he died, 1845. In the Spring of that year, one day after traveling twenty miles, he entered the house of an acquaintance in Allen County, Indiana, and was as usual, cordially received. He declined to eat anything except some bread and milk, which he ate, sitting on the doorstep occasionally looking out towards the setting sun.

Before bedtime he read from his little books "fresh news right from heaven," and at the usual hour for retiring he lay down upon the floor, as was his invariable custom. In the morning the beautiful sight supernal was upon his countenance, the death angel had touched him in the silence and the darkness, and though the dear old man essayed to speak, he was so near dead that his tongue refused its office. The physician came and pronounced him dying, but remarked that he never saw a man so perfectly calm and placid, and he inquired particularly concerning Johnny's religion. His bruised and bleeding feet, worn, walk the gold paved streets of the New Jerusalem, while we so brokenly and crudely narrate the sketch of his life. A life full of labor and pain and unselfishness, humble unto self-abnegation, his memory glowing in our hearts, while his deeds live anew every springtime in the fragrance of the apple-blossoms he loved so well.

A FOLKTALE OF JOHNNY APPLESEED

In Paris, France, two young men were condemned to death during the French Revolution. Disguised as laborers they escaped to London and subsequently came to America, landing at New Orleans. There they gathered together a few of their countrymen, secured a boat, and made their way up the Mississippi River to a point now known as Louisiana, Missouri. Finding the mouth of Salt River they followed the stream to where New London now stands. There one of these leaders, Dr. Antoine Saugrain, separated from his companions and, going into the Saverton Hills, built a fort, and spent the winter trapping. Afterward he joined the Lewis and Clark expedition.

The other young Frenchman, Mathuran Bouvet, and others of the company, went further up the Salt River and built a fort at what is now known as Spalding Springs. The Indians called this stream "Ohaha." The Spanish called it

"Rio de Salle," on account of the many salt springs along its course.

On a night shortly after building his fort, Bouvet was sitting in his cabin looking over some maps he had made of the country traversed, when he heard a noise at the door. When he ascertained that one man only was without he ordered the door opened. In walked a gaunt, peculiar looking character, singing:

I sow while others reap,

Be sure my warning keep,

Indians will come by break of day,

Indians hunting scalps, I say,

and he walked out. The Indians came "by break of day" and fought with burning arrows trying to fire the fort, but failed and were repulsed by the French. Bouvet then established salt works and began the manufacture of salt by boiling the water from these salt springs, and as fast as he made a load a boat took it to St. Louis. Returning from one of these trips he found the works had been destroyed by the Indians. He rebuilt them, but in a second attack by the Indians, so many of the whites were killed that those who survived abandoned the fort and made their escape to other settlements.

The man who gave this fort warning was "Johnny Appleseed," whose real name was John Chapman.

Johnny Appleseed when a young man living in Owensboro, Kentucky, was engaged to marry Sarah Crawford, a very beautiful young girl. The night before the day of their wedding she died. Johnny's grief unbalanced his mind, and in his delirium he thought he was called by the Lord as a harbinger of peace to the west and that his special mission was to plant appleseed along the way, that those who followed might reap the benefit of his sowing. So he went to the orchards where cider was being made and gathered a bag of seed and in the spring started on his mission.

Because of his mental condition and of a superstition among the Indians regarding the insane, he was allowed to go and come unmolested, even among the most savage tribes. He lived among them, learned their language, adopted their dress and habits, but never lost his loyalty to the white man and often gave them warning when the Indians were on the war path. Thus he passed through the wilderness, along the water courses and by the clearings singing, "I sow while others reap."

Johnny Appleseed married an Indian girl and lived with her in a tepee on Turkey Creek, in this (Ralls) county, Missouri. One morning he walked into his tepee, gazed longingly at his baby and walked away. He was never heard of again.

The Cherry Tree Legend

Few legends are so ingrained in the national consciousness of the United States as that of George Washington and the cherry tree he allegedly chopped down. Here is perhaps the earliest version of the story, from a book written shortly after Washington's death. (The first edition of the book appeared in 1800, but the cherry tree story wasn't added until the fifth edition, in 1806.)

Never did the wise Ulysses take more pains with his beloved Telemachus, than did Mr. Washington with George, to inspire him with an *early love of truth.* "Truth, George," said he, "is the loveliest quality of youth. I would ride fifty miles, my son, to see the little boy whose heart is so *honest,* and his lips so *pure,* that we may depend on every word he says. O how lovely does such a child appear in the eyes of everybody; his parents dote on him. His relations glory in him. They are constantly praising him to their children, whom they beg to imitate him. They are often sending for him to visit them; and receive him, when he comes, with as much joy as if her were a little angel, come to set pretty examples to their children.

"But, O! how different, George, is the case with the boy who is given to lying, that nobody can believe a word he says! He is looked at with aversion wherever he goes, and parents dread to see him come among their children. O, George! my son! rather than see you come to this pass, dear as you are to my heart, gladly would I assist to nail you up in your little coffin, and follow you to your grave. Hard, indeed, would it be to me to give up my son, whose little feet are always so ready to run about with me, and whose fondly looking eyes, and sweet prattle make so large a part of my happiness. But still I would give him up, rather than see him a common liar."

"Pa," said George very seriously, "do I ever tell lies?"

"No, George, I *thank* God you do not, my son; and I rejoice in the hope you never will. At least, you shall never, from me, have cause to be guilty of so shameful a thing. Many parents, indeed, even compel their children to this vile practice, by barbarously beating them for every little fault: hence, on the next offence, the little terrified creature slips out a *lie!* just to escape the rod. But as to yourself George, you know I have *always* told you, and now tell you again, that, whenever by accident, you do anything wrong, which must often be the case, as you are but a poor little boy yet, without *experience or knowledge*, you must never tell a falsehood to conceal it; but come *bravely* up, my son, like a *little* man, and tell me of it: and instead of beating you, George, I will but the more honor and love you for it, my dear."

This, you'll say, was sowing good seed!—Yes, it was: and the crop, thank God, was, as I believe it ever will be, where a man acts the true parent, that is, the *Guardian Angel*, by his child.

The following anecdote is a *case in point*. It is too valuable to be lost, and too true to be doubted; for it was communicated to me by an excellent lady.

"When George," said she, "was about six years old, he was made the wealthy master of a *hatchet!* of which, like most little boys, he was immoderately fond, and was constantly going about chopping every thing that came in his way. One day, in the garden, where he often amused himself hacking his mother's pea-sticks, he unluckily tried the edge of his hatchet on the body of a beautiful young English cherry-tree, which he barked so terribly, that I don't believe the tree ever got the better of it. The next morning the old gentleman, finding out what had befallen his tree, which, by the by, was a great favorite, came into the house; and with much warmth asked for the mischievous author, declaring at the same time, that he would not have taken five guineas for his tree. Nobody could tell him anything about it. Presently George and his hatchet made their appearance. 'George,' said his father, 'do you know who killed that beautiful little cherry tree yonder in the garden?' This was a *tough question*; and George staggered under it for a moment; but quickly recovered himself, and looking at his father, with the sweet face of youth brightened with the inexpressible charm of all-conquering truth, he bravely cried out, 'I can't tell a lie, Pa; you know I can't tell a lie. I did cut it with my hatchet.'

'Run to my arms, you dearest boy,' cried his father in transports. 'Run to my arms; glad am I, George, that you killed my tree; for you have paid me for it a thousand fold. Such an act of heroism in my son is worth more than a thousand trees, though blossomed with silver, and their fruits of purest gold.'"

It was in this way by interesting at once both his *heart* and *head*, that Mr. Washington conducted George with great ease and pleasure along the happy paths of virtue.

Belle Starr

———•+•———

Not all North American folk heroes are famous for their goodness or skill. Belle Starr was known as the Cleopatra of the Plains, though she was neither beautiful nor did she have access to powerful people other than outlaws. She was also known as the Bandit Queen of Dallas, which is more descriptive of her exploits. She had ties to the James brothers, and operated a safe haven for thieves on the Canadian River in Oklahoma's Indian Territory. She died a violent death in 1889, shot by an unknown bushwhacker. For all that, though, she has been lionized in books and films and remains heroic as one of the few women among the outlaws of the frontier.

———

BELLE'S ARREST

Belle was arrested twice with her husband, Sam Starr. The first time she was sentenced to one year in the Detroit penitentiary. The second time she was not sentenced, and enjoyed a week of sight-seeing in Fort Smith, Texas, while awaiting trial. The following newspaper account reveals just how seriously Belle took the charges against her.

For the past week the noted Belle Starr has been quite an attraction on the streets of this city. She came to answer two indictments in the Federal Court . . . first for being implicated in the stealing of a fine mare, the one ridden by the notorious John Middleton when he was drowned in the Poteau River, twenty-five miles above this city, in May, 1885; and second, on a charge of robbery, in which it is claimed that Belle, dressed in male attire, led a party of three men who robbed an old man named Ferrell and his three sons. . . .

Monday night Belle swung her Winchester to her saddle, buckled her revolver around her, and mounting her horses, set out for her home on the Canadian. Before leaving, she purchased a fine pair of 45-calibre revolvers . . . Belle says she anticipates no trouble in establishing her innocence in the cases against her, but thinks it terribly annoying to have to spend her time and money coming down here to court five and six times a year.

Belle attracts considerable attention wherever she goes, being a dashing horsewoman, and exceedingly graceful in the saddle. She dresses plainly, and wears a broad-brimmed white man's hat, surmounted by a wide black plush band, with feathers and ornaments, which is very becoming to her. She is of medium size, well formed, a dark brunette, with bright and intelligent black eyes. . . .

Belle is a crack shot, and handles her pistols with as much dexterity as any frontiersman. No man enters Younger's Bend without first giving a thorough account of himself before he gets out.

Belle related many incidents of her life that would be of interest, and says she has been offered big money by publishers for a complete history of it, but she does not desire to have it published yet. She has a complete manuscript record, and when she dies she will give it to the public. She spends most of her time writing when at home.

"You can just say that I am a friend to any brave and gallant outlaw, but have no use for that sneaking coward class of thieves who can be found in every locality, and who would betray a friend or comrade for the sake of their own gain. . . ."

BELLE STARR'S HORSE RACE

Stories like this one, which show Belle's trickster qualities, are popular in the Ozark region of Missouri where she was born.

———

John Hargrove, a pioneer businessman and one of the founders of this community on the Arkansas–Indian Territory border, raised the finest thoroughbred horses in the region. His black stallion had never been beaten in a race, and Hargrove's financial holdings increased greatly as his stallion outran all challengers year after year.

Belle Starr, also a lover of fine horses, acquired a spirited sorrel from a Kansas breeder. Returning with her new horse to her Youngers Bend home, she stopped in Siloam Springs and challenged Hargrove to a race. Belle and Hargrove agreed to bet $500 on the contest. Word of Belle Starr's challenging Hargrove's unbeaten stallion spread throughout the region and large crowds gathered to see the race and to wager among themselves. Belle hired a young Indian boy as a jockey, and, knowing her animal could easily beat Hargrove's stallion, she instructed her jockey to hold the sorrel back and let Hargrove's horse win by at least one length.

Belle paid Hargrove the $500 and reluctantly admitted he had the better horse. The next day she approached Hargrove again and told him she would like a rematch, but that she wanted the stakes to be raised to $5,000. Convinced his stallion had won easily over Belle's challenger, Hargrove accepted the offer wholeheartedly, and the race was scheduled for two days later. As race time approached the crowds grew even larger than before. People came from miles around to see the contest between the notorious Belle Starr and Siloam's leading citizen. This time Belle told her jockey to let the horse run with all he had. As she expected, her horse outran Hargrove's stallion by several lengths. Belle left $5,000 richer with a sorrel that was now worth a great deal as a result of its being the only horse ever to beat Hargrove's champion stallion. Hargrove was embarrassed by the trick Belle had played on him, and poorer by $4,500.

Judge Roy Bean's Necktie Justice

Judge Roy Bean lived on the Texas frontier during the latter part of the nineteenth century. He became known as the one and only representative of the "Law West of the Pecos." After living a life of questionable legality himself, Roy Bean settled in Langtry, Texas, in 1882, and was appointed Justice of the Peace. From then until 1903, he conducted court in the Jersey Lily Saloon from whence hilarious stories of his flamboyance traveled fast along the fledgling railroad lines leading back to civilization.

"Hear ye! Hear ye! This honorable court's now in session; and if any galoot wants a snort afore we start, let him step up to the bar and name his pizen. Oscar, serve the gentlemen." Thus did Judge Bean open court to try one Carlos Robles, an opening typical of his original procedure.

"Carlos Robles," he said solemnly after witnesses and hangers-on had downed their liquor, "it is the findin' of this court that you are charged with a grave offense against the peace and dignity of the law West of the Pecos and the State of Texas, to wit: cattle rustlin'. Guilty or not guilty?"

Not being able to speak or comprehend English, Robles merely grunted.

"Court accepts yore plea of guilt. The jury will now deliberate; and if it brings a verdict short of hangin' it'll be declared in contempt. Gentlemen, is yore verdict ready?"

The twelve nondescript citizens cleared their throats in unison. "It is, your honor," several spoke.

"Thank you, gentlemen. Stand up, Carlos Robles, and receive your sentence. You got anything to say why judgement shouldn't be passed on you in this court?"

Of course Carlos had not, in view of the fact that he had only the vaguest idea of what was transpiring.

"Carlos Robles," Judge Roy continued, his voice almost quaking with the solemnity of the occasion, "you been tried by twelve true and good men . . . and they've said you're guilty of rustlin' cattle.

"Time will pass and seasons will come and go; Spring with its wavin' green grass and heaps of sweet-smellin' flowers on every hill and in every dale. Then will come sultry Summer, with her shimmerin' heat-waves on the baked horizon; and Fall, with her yeller harvest-moon and the hills growin' brown and golden under a sinkin' sun; and finally Winter, with its bitin', whinin' wind, and all the land will be mantled with snow. But you won't be here to see any of 'em, Carlos Robles; not by a dam' sight, because it is the order of this court that you be took to the nearest tree and hanged by the neck till you're dead, dead, dead, you . . . son-of-a-billy goat!"

The Law West of the Pecos could be cruel in administering his brand of justice; but he was cruel only when he deemed the accused and the crime fully warranting such cruelty. He more frequently tempered justice with his own peculiar brand of mercy, especially if there was any means by which he could profit by that mercy.

One afternoon several ranchmen brought in a twenty-year-old boy accused of horse-stealing. They demanded that he be tried and dealt with according to the enormity of the crime.

Judge Bean duly opened court. He appointed six men as jurors, the actual number meaning nothing to him and depending entirely upon men available. He would not appoint just any citizens to jury duty. They must be good customers of the liquor bar at the other end of the shack during intermissions, or their services as jurors no longer were desirable or acceptable. Every transaction must be made to return the utmost in profit, and non-drinking jurors were strictly dead timber.

"Hear ye! This honorable court is again in session. Anyone wishin' a snort, have it now. This here prisoner is charged with the grave offense of stealin' a horse and Oscar, where are the witnesses?" the Law West of the Pecos opened. He appreciated his own sense of humor in varying his court openings to relieve the monotony; but he seldom varied to the extent of omitting the invitation to participate in a snort at the other bar.

"We caught him in the act of stealin' the animal," the ranchman testified. "He admitted his intentions."

"That right, young feller? You was stealin' the cayuse?"

The young prisoner dropped his head, unruly red hair tumbling down over his high forehead. "Yes, your honor," he mumbled.

"Gentlemen of the jury," His Honor instructed, "the accused pleads guilty to horse theft. You know as well as I do the penalty. I'm ready for yore verdict." And it was promptly forthcoming.

Gravely the judge passed sentence. "If there's any last word, or anything, I'll give you a few minutes," he told the pale Easterner, thus extending an infrequent favor.

"I would like to write a note—to my mother back in Pennsylvania," the doomed prisoner mumbled with obvious emotion. "Thank you."

"Oscar, fetch the prisoner a piece of wrappin' paper and a pencil. I think we got a pencil back there behind that row of bottles." Bean gently handed the convicted thief these writing facilities, got up and tendered him the beer barrel and rickety table from which sentence had just been passed. Then he took a position directly behind the boy so that he could watch over his shoulder at what he wrote.

The victim wrote at length in apology for the grief and trouble he had caused his mother and earnestly sought her forgiveness. "In small part perhaps I can repay you for the money I have cost you in keeping me out of trouble. Enclosed is $400, which I've saved. I want you— "

Judge Bean started, cleared his throat, cut in at this point. "By gobs!" he exclaimed, "gentlemen, I got a feelin' there's been a miscarriage of justice, in this case. I hereby declare it re-opened. Face the bar, young man."

The prisoner removed himself from the beer keg and stood erect in front of the judicial bench, befuddled at this sudden turn.

"After all, that wasn't much of a cayuse the lad tried to steal and he didn't actually steal him. So I rule it's a finable case. I hereby fine the accused three hundred dollars and get to hell outer this country afore I change my mind. . . . Court's adjourned and what'll it be for you down there, Slim?"

Wild Bill Hickock's Duel with Dave Tutt

What makes Wild Bill Hickock such a fascinating folk legend is the fact that, though he reportedly killed dozens of opponents in flamboyant gun battles, he is often depicted as a reluctant killer. There is a melancholy about him because it seems that trouble came to him unbidden. His appeal also lies in his unwavering self-confidence as a skilled marksman. This account, taken down by a literate man from someone who supposedly knew Wild Bill firsthand, demonstrates how oral reports were exaggerated and propelled prominent, real-life heroes into the realm of legend.

Bill was born of Northern parents in the State of Illinois. He ran away from home when a boy, and wandered out upon the plains and into the mountains. For fifteen years he lived with the trappers, hunting and fishing. When the war broke out he returned to the States and entered the Union service. No man probably was ever better fitted for scouting than he. Joined to his tremendous strength he was an unequaled horseman; he was a perfect marksman; he had a keen sight, and a constitution which had no limit of endurance. He was cool to audacity, brave to rashness, always possessed of himself under the most critical circumstances; and, above all, was such a master in the knowledge of woodcraft that it might have been termed a science with him—a knowledge which, with the soldier, is priceless beyond description.

The main features of the story of the duel was [*sic*] told me by Captain Honesty, who was unprejudiced, if it is possible to find an unbiased mind in a town of 3000 people after a fight has taken place. I will give the story in his words:

"They say Bill's wild. Now he isn't any sich thing. I've known him goin on ter ten year, and he's as civil a disposed person as you'll find he-e-arabouts. But he won't be put upon.

"I'll tell yer how it happened. But come inter the office; thar's a good many round hy'ar as sides with Tutt—the man that's shot. But I tell yer 'twas a far fight. Take some whisky? No! Well, I will, if yer'l excuse me.

"You see," continued the Captain, setting the empty glass on the table in an emphatic way, "Bill was up in his room a-playin seven-up, or four-hand, or some of them pesky games. Bill refused ter play with Tutt, who was a professional gambler. Yer see, Bill was a scout on our side durin the war, and Tutt was a reb scout. Bill had killed Dave Tutt's mate, and, atween one thing and another, there war an onusual hard feelin atwixt 'em.

"Ever sin Dave come back he had tried to pick a row with Bill; so Bill wouldn't play cards with him any more. But Dave stood over the man who was gambling with Bill and lent the feller money. Bill won about two hundred dollars, which made Tutt spiteful mad. Bime-by, he says to Bill:

"'Bill, you've got plenty of money—pay me that forty dollars yer owe me in that horse trade.'

"And Bill paid him. Then he said:

"'Yer owe me thirty-five dollars more; yer lost it playing with me t'other night.'

"Dave's style was right provoking; but Bill answered him perfectly gentlemanly:

"'I think yer wrong, Dave. It's only twenty-five dollars. I have a memorandum of it in my pocket down stairs. Ef it's thirty-five dollars I'll give it yer.'

"Now Bill's watch was lying on the table. Dave took up the watch, put it in his pocket, and said: 'I'll keep this yere watch till yer pay me that thirty-five dollars.'

"This made Bill shooting mad; fur, don't yer see, Colonel, it was a-doubting his honor like, so he got up and looked Dave in the eyes, and said to him: 'I don't want ter make a row in this house. It's a decent house, and I don't want ter injure the keeper. You'd better put that watch back on the table.'

"But Dave grinned at Bill mighty ugly, and walked off with the watch, and kept it several days. All this time Dave's friends were spurring Bill on ter fight; there was no end ter the talk. They blackguarded him in an underhand sort of a way, and tried ter get up a scrimmage, and then they thought they could lay him out. Yer see Bill has enemies all about. He's settled the accounts of a heap of men who lived round here. This is about the only place in Missouri whar a reb can come back and live, and ter tell yer the truth, Colonel—" and the Captain, with an involuntary movement, hitched up his revolver-belt, as he said, with expressive significance, "they don't stay long round here!

"Well, as I was saying, these rebs don't like ter see a man walking round town who they knew in the reb army as one of their men, who they now know was on our side, all the time he was sending us information, sometimes from Pap Price's own head-quarters. But they couldn't provoke Bill inter a row, for he's afeard of hisself when he gits *awful* mad; and he allers left his shootin irons in his room when he went out. One day these cusses drew their pistols on him and dared him to fight, and then they told him that Tutt was a-goin ter pack that watch across the squar next day at noon.

"I heard of this, for every body was talking about it on the street, and so I went after Bill, and found him in his room, cleaning and greasing and loading his revolvers.

"'Now, Bill,' says I, 'you're goin ter git inter a fight.'

"'Don't you bother yerself, Captain,' says he. 'It's not the first time I have been in a fight; and these d—d hounds have put on me long enough. You don't want me ter give up my honor, do yer?'

"'No, Bill,' says I, 'yer must keep yer honor.'

"Next day, about noon, Bill went down to the squar. He had said that Dave Tutt shouldn't pack that watch across the squar unless dead men could walk.

"When Bill got onter the squar he found a crowd standin in the corner of the street by which he entered the squar, which is from the south, yer know. In this crowd he saw a lot of Tutt's friends; some were cousins of his'n, just back from the reb army; and they jeered him, and boasted that Dave was a-goin to pack that watch across the squar as he promised.

"Then Bill saw Tutt standin near the courthouse, which yer remember is on the west side, so that the crowd war behind Bill.

"Just then Tutt, who war alone, started from the courthouse and walked out into the squar, and Bill moved away from the crowd toward the west side of the squar. Bout fifteen paces brought them opposite to each other, and about fifty yards apart. Tutt then showed his pistol. Bill had kept a sharp eye on him, and before Tutt could pint it Bill had his'n out.

"At that moment you could have heard a pin drop in that squar. Both Tutt and Bill fired, but one discharge followed the other so quick that it's hard to say which went off first. Tutt was a famous shot, but he missed this time; the ball from his pistol went over Bill's head. The instant Bill fired, without waitin ter see ef he had hit Tutt, he wheeled on his heels and pointed his pistol at Tutt's friends, who had already drawn their weepons.

"'Aren't yer satisfied, gentlemen?' cried Bill, as cool as an alligator. 'Put up your shootin-irons, or there'll be more dead men here.' And they put 'em up, and said it war a far fight."

"What became of Tutt?" I asked of the Captain, who had stopped at this point of his story, and was very deliberately engaged in refilling his empty glass.

"Oh! Dave? He was as plucky a feller as ever drew trigger; but, Lord bless yer! it was no use. Bill never shoots twice at the same man, and his ball went through Dave's heart. He stood stock-still for a second or two, then raised his arm as if ter fire again, then he swayed a little, staggered three or four steps and then fell dead.

"Bill and his friends wanted ter have the thing done regular, so we went up ter the Justice, and Bill delivered himself up. A jury was drawn; Bill was tried and cleared the next day. It was proved that it was a case of self-defense. Don't yer see, Colonel?"

I answered that I was afraid that I did not see that point very clearly.

"Well, well!" he replied, with an air of compassion. "You haven't drunk any whisky, that's what's the matter with yer." And then, putting his hand on my shoulder with a half-mysterious, half-conscious look in his face, he muttered, in a whisper:

"The fact is, thar was an undercurrent of a woman in that fight!"

I had a curiosity, which was not an idle one, to hear what this man [Bill] had to say about his duel with Tutt, and I asked him:

"Do you not regret killing Tutt? You surely do not like to kill men?"

"As ter killing men," he replied, "I never thought much about it. The most of the men I have killed it was one or t'other of us, and at sich times you don't stop to think, and what's the use after it's all over? As for Tutt, I had rather not have killed him, for I want ter settle down quiet here now. But thar's been hard feeling between us a long while. I wanted ter keep out of that fight; but he tried to degrade me, and I couldn't stand that, you know, for I am a fighting man, you know."

A cloud passed over the speaker's face for a moment as he continued:

"And there was a cause of quarrel between us which people round here don't know about. One of us had to die; and the secret died with him."

"Why did you not wait to see if your ball had hit him? Why did you turn round so quickly?"

The scout fixed his gray eyes on mine, striking his leg with his riding-whip, as he answered.

"I *knew* he was a dead man. I never miss a shot. I turned on the crowd because I was sure they would shoot me if they saw him fall."

"The people about here tell me you are a quiet, civil man. How is it you get into these fights?"

"D—d if I can tell," he replied, with a puzzled look which at once gave place to a proud, defiant expression as he continued—"but you know a man must defend his honor."

"Yes," I admitted, with some hesitation, remembering that I was not in Boston but on the border, and that the code of honor and mode of redress differ slightly in the one place from those of the other.

Stackalee

———◆•◆———

Just as white American tradition makes heroes out of outlaws, so African American culture confers hero status on its most famous scoundrels. Stackalee—sometimes called Stagolee—reigns supreme as the most notorious bad man of all. Numerous tales have been published and countless ballads made to detail his exploits. The ballads are almost always in a rhyme scheme and rhythm that belong to the African American tradition known as the toast, a style of speech that has more recently evolved into rap.

THE LEGEND OF STACKALEE

Stackalee was a big Negro bad man born on Market Street in St. Louis in 1861. He was born double-jointed and with a full set of teeth and red eyes. "A gipsy told his mother, Told her like a friend, Your double-jointed baby, Won't come to no good end." So says one of the legends which celebrate his name.

Stackalee was named for the famous boat he worked on. He was a stoker or roustabout on the Mississippi-Ohio River packet *Stacker Lee*, which plied between Memphis, Cincinnati, St. Louis, and Vicksburg. People spell his name Stagolee sometimes, but mostly they call him Stack.

Stack was a fine musician. He could play the guitar and the piano, and he was always moaning the blues or beating out some rag. Women loved him. When he hugged the girls he squeezed the breath out of them, and they liked that.

Stack's own girl was born on Market Street in St. Louis in 1861, just like Stack himself. Her name was Stack o' Dollars. They called her that because she not only *had* a stack of dollars but always bet them all in a gambling game. She was a big fat girl with diamond teeth and *some smile*. She smoked cigars and could lick any man in town in a fist fight. Stack did like a spirited woman. She wore a Stetson hat, too—a bigger one than Stack's.

Stack always wore a Stetson hat, the five-gallon size. He dearly loved a Stetson, and had a whole row of them, all different colors, hanging on pegs in the house on Market Street. Everybody says he sold his soul to the Devil in return for a magic spell on his favorite Stetson. He could get away with anything as long as he wore that hat. And he was never caught as long as he had it.

Stackalee was a gambler, a gunman, and a killer. Nobody knows how many notches he had on his gun for the men he had killed. He feared no one. He even challenged Jesse James once, but that was a mistake. Nobody was a match for Jesse James in *any* kind of fight, and the minute Jesse let go of him Stack beat it for the mountains.

Once in the mountains he met up with two deputies who were out looking for him in order to collect the $5,000 reward on his head. So he sat down to chat with them and pass the time of day. Stack learned their names and then shot their initials in their hats before they discovered who he was. He nearly split his sides laughing to see how fast they left the neighborhood.

But every bad man gets caught up with, one way or another, it seems, and the Devil was getting tired of Stack's devilment. He was tired of waiting to snatch Stack's soul to hell, too.

Stack was in a gambling game one night in St. Louis. He was winning, seemed as if he couldn't lose, and he was so busy scraping in the money that he forgot about his hat which he had hung on the back of his chair. This was the Devil's chance. In the guise of a nice young man named Billy Lyons he took the hat and headed for a barrel house down the street, where he knew Billy Lyons to be. With a yell in his throat and a gun in each hand Stack tore after him. When he got there, there was Billy Lyons all right, smoking a cigarette, easylike, expecting nothing; but the Stetson hat was not in sight.

Stack shot him on sight and killed him dead for stealing the magic Stetson that had always saved him from the law. Onlookers said Billy had not left the barrel house all evening, but Stack did not believe that.

The police wagon came and hauled Stackalee off to jail. But the Devil got cheated out of Stack's soul, after all, for they did not hang him. The judge sentenced him to a stretch of seventy-five years in Jefferson penitentiary, and there he is. He has served thirty-four years and has forty-one still to go. So the Devil is still waiting.

THE BALLAD OF STACKALEE

It was in the year of eighteen hundred and sixty-one
In St. Louis on Market Street where Stackalee was born.
Everybody's talkin 'bout Stackalee.

It was on one cold and frosty night
When Stackalee and Billy Lyons had one awful fight,
All about an old Stetson hat.

Stackalee got his gun. Boy, he got it fast!
He shot poor Billy through and through; the bullet broke a lookin glass.
Oh, oh, Lord, Lord, Lord.

Stackalee shot Billy once; his body fell to the floor.
He cried out, "Oh, please, Stack, please don't shoot me no more."

The White Elephant Barrel House was wrecked that night;
Gutters full of beer and whisky; it was an awful sight.

Jewelry and rings of the purest solid gold
Scattered over the dance and gamblin hall.

The can can dancers they rushed for the door
When Billy cried, "Oh, please, Stack, don't shoot me no more."

"Have mercy," Billy groaned. "Oh, please spare my life;
I've got two little babies and an innocent wife."

Stack says, "God bless your children, damn your wife!
You stole my magic Stetson; I'm gonna steal your life."

"But," says Billy, "I always treated you like a man.
'Tain't nothin to that old Stetson but the greasy band."

He shot poor Billy once, he shot him twice,
And the third time Billy pleaded, "Please go tell my wife."

Yes, Stackalee, the gambler, everybody knowed his name;
Made his livin hollerin high, low, jack and the game.

Meantime the sergeant strapped on his big forty-five,
Says, "Now we'll bring in this bad man, dead or alive."

And brass-buttoned policemen all dressed in blue
Came down the sidewalk marchin two by two.

Sent for the wagon and it hurried and come
Loaded with pistols and a big Gatling gun.

At midnight on that stormy night there came an awful wail—
Billy Lyons and a graveyard ghost outside the city jail.

"Jailer, jailer," says Stack, "I can't sleep.
For around my bedside poor Billy Lyons still creeps.

"He comes in shape of a lion with a blue steel in his hand,
For he knows I'll stand and fight if he comes in shape of man."

Stackalee went to sleep that night by the city clock bell,
Dreaming the devil had come all the way up from hell.

Red devil was sayin, "You better hunt your hole;
I've hurried here from hell just to get your soul."

Stackalee told him, "Yes, maybe you're right,
But I'll give even you one hell of a fight."

When they got into the scuffle, I heard the devil shout,
"Come and get this bad man before he puts my fire out."

The next time I seed the devil he was scramblin up the wall,
Yellin, "Come an get this bad man fore he mops up with us all."

Then here come Stack's woman runnin, says, "Daddy, I love you true;
See what beer, whisky, and smokin hop has brought you to.

"But before I'll let you lay in there, I'll put my life in pawn."
She hurried and got Stackalee out on a five thousand dollar bond.

Stackalee said, "Ain't but one thing that grieves my mind.
When they take me away, babe, I leave you behind."

But the woman he really loved was a voodoo queen
From Creole French market, way down in New Orleans.

He laid down at home that night, took a good night's rest,
Arrived in court at nine o'clock to hear the coroner's inquest.

Crowds jammed the sidewalk, far as you could see,
Tryin to get a good look at tough Stackalee.

Over the cold, dead body Stackalee he did bend,
Then he turned and faced those twelve jury men.

The judge says, "Stackalee, I would spare your life,
But I know you're a bad man; I can see it in your red eyes."

The jury heard the witnesses, and they didn't say no more;
They crowded into the jury room, and the messenger closed the door.

The jury came to agreement, the clerk he wrote it down,
And everybody was whisperin, "He's penitentiary bound."

When the jury walked out, Stackalee didn't budge.
They wrapped the verdict and passed it to the judge.

Judge looked over his glasses, says, "Mr. Bad Man Stackalee,
The jury finds you guilty of murder in the first degree."

Now the trial's come to an end, how the folks gave cheers;
Bad Stackalee was sent down to Jefferson pen for seventy-five years

Now late at night you can hear him in his cell,
Arguin with the devil to keep from goin to hell.

And the other convicts whisper, "Whatcha know about that?
Gonna burn in hell forever over an old Stetson hat!"
Everybody's talkin 'bout Stackalee.

4

Larger Than Life

~

Every traditional group in history has had its culture heroes—godlike people with extraordinary powers who created the physical landscape and, more importantly, symbolized the moral character of the entire group. Native Americans, for example, have a centuries-old pantheon of culture heroes, some of whose stories appear in Chapter 1. Although pioneer America had its share of flesh-and-blood heroes, by the middle of the nineteenth century the unique culture that had grown out of the frontier experience still lacked mythic heroes. And so Americans did what they always do when something is not readily available. They invented for themselves a multitude of demigods to take the place of the real heroes whose heyday was nearly over.

It stands to reason that the culture heroes of the United States would be primarily comic figures. Though their ultimate purpose was serious—to symbolize the spirit of the nation—Paul Bunyan, Pecos Bill, and all their kin were born when the tall tale was enjoying enormous popularity. The characters attracted whoppers, lies, and brags like magnets, and stories about them breathed new life into many a familiar tall tale. Not every mythical hero in American lore is meant to be funny, but the tall-tale humor in the majority of the tales reflects an important aspect of the American character of the period. What the heroes did for a living also reveals a great deal about what was happening in American society. As river workers, seamen, loggers, railroad men, plainsmen, and cowboys, they represented the national preoccupation with strength, expansion, and commerce.

Many folklorists believe that Pecos Bill, Paul Bunyan, and other American demigods began life on the printed page, the products of professional writers' imaginations. Others think it possible that the culture heroes in this chapter began as stories generated among the workers, which found their way into print only after the tales had become popular. It is, in fact, impossible to separate the stories that originated in oral tradition and those that were penned by professional writers, so the debate will probably never be resolved. One thing is certain, however: These characters are firmly entrenched in the minds of most Americans as part of our traditional lore, how ever they came into being.

The Birth of Paul Bunyan

Stories about Paul Bunyan began to circulate in the early part of the twentieth century, providing those Americans inclined to tell tall tales with a perfect vehicle for their lies. There is known to have been a Canadian logger named Paul Bunyon who, some people think, may have been a model for the stories. But the first printed mention of the hero was, of all places, in the advertising literature for a lumber company, and some suspect that the character was invented for that purpose. Of all North American folktales, those about Paul Bunyan were the quickest to be turned into literature, as frontier newspaper writers filled their pages with stories that were eventually collected in books. With so many people at work on his image, he gathered around him a bizarre array of men and beasts the like of which has seldom been surpassed in North American lore or literature.

If what they say is true, Paul Bunyan was born down in Maine. And he must have been a pretty husky baby, too, just like you'd expect him to be, from knowin' him afterwards.

When he was only three weeks old he rolled around so much in his sleep that he knocked down four square miles of standin' timber and the government got after his folks and told 'em they'd have to move him away.

So then they got some timbers together and made a floatin' cradle for Paul and anchored it off Eastport. But every time Paul rocked in his cradle, if he rocked shoreward, it made such a swell it came near drownin' out all the villages on the coast of Maine. The waves was so high Nova Scotia came pretty near becomin' an island instead of a peninsula.

That wouldn't do, of course, and the government got after 'em again and told 'em they'd have to do somethin' about it. They'd have to move him out of there and put him somewheres else, they was told. So they figured they'd better take him home again and keep him in the house for a spell.

But it happened Paul was asleep in his cradle when they went to get him. They had to send for the British Navy, and it took seven hours of bombardin' to wake him up. Then, when Paul stepped out of his cradle, it made such a swell it caused a seventy-five-foot tide in the Bay of Fundy. Several villages were swept away, and seven of the invincible English warships were sunk to the bottom of the sea.

Well, Paul got out of his cradle then, and that saved Nova Scotia from becomin' an island, but the tides in the Bay of Fundy are just as high as they ever were.

So I guess the old folks must have had their hands full with him, all right. And I ought to say, the King of England sent over and confiscated the timbers in Paul's cradle and built seven new warships to take the place of the ones he'd lost.

When Paul was only seven months old, he sawed off the legs from under his dad's bed one night. The old man noticed when he woke up in the mornin' that his bed seemed considerable lower than it used to be, so he got up and investigated. Sure enough, there were the legs all sawed off from under it and the pieces layin' out on the floor.

Then he remembered he'd felt somethin' the night before, but he'd thought he must be dreamin'—the way you dream that you're fallin' down sometimes when you first go off to sleep. He looked around to see who could have done it and there was Paul layin' there sound asleep with his dad's cross-cut saw still held tight in his fist and smilin' in his sleep as pretty as anythin'.

He called his wife, and when she came in he said to her, "Did you feel anythin' in the night?"

"No," she said. "Is anythin' wrong?"

"Well, just look here," he said. And he showed her the four-by-eights layin' there on the floor and the saw in their kid's hand.

"I didn't light the lamp when I went to get up this mornin'," she said, "and I guess I didn't notice it."

"Well, he's done it, anyway," said the old man. "I'll bet that boy of ours is goin' to be a great logger someday. If he lives to grow up, he's goin' to do some great loggin' by and by, you just see—a whole lot bigger than any of the men around here have ever done."

And they was right, all right. There ain't never been loggin' before nor since like Paul Bunyan done.

Babe the Blue Ox

It is the rare person in America who does not have the image of a big blue ox firmly lodged in his or her imagination. There are conflicting stories of how the friendship between Paul Bunyan and his faithful companion came to pass. The following tale is the most commonly accepted account.

One day when Paul was working in his father's logging camp in the Maine woods it started to snow. Day after day the soft fluffy snowflakes fell until the entire camp was covered with a blanket of snow. Log cabins disappeared from sight, and all but the tallest trees were buried under the great snowdrifts.

And the strangest thing of all was that the snow, instead of being white, was a bright sapphire blue! For miles and miles as far as one could see the forest was covered with beautiful blue snow. Loggers even today remember that year and call it the Winter of the Blue Snow.

When the snow had stopped falling, Paul put on his snowshoes and went out to find wood for his fireplace. As he was returning, he noticed two little ears sticking up through a snowdrift.

"It must be some poor animal lost and freezing to death," thought Paul. He reached down with one of his great hands and scooped the little thing out of the snow. It was a baby ox calf with thin wobbly legs. Paul put the little calf inside one of his large pockets and took him home. Soon he was curled up in front of the fireplace and as happy and warm as could be.

"Poor little baby!" said Paul as the little calf drank some warm milk and gratefully caressed Paul's hand with his tongue. Paul decided to call the little calf "Babe" and keep him for a pet.

The strangest thing about Babe was that, even after he became thawed out, his coat remained a soft glossy blue. Paul nursed his new pet back to health, but his color never changed. The Winter of the Blue Snow had colored him blue, and blue he remained forever after.

Babe followed Paul wherever he went and grew larger each day. Every time Paul looked around the little calf seemed to have grown a foot taller.

In the spring, Paul built a little barn for Babe and put the calf inside for the night. The next morning, the barn was gone and so was the little blue calf. Paul searched high and low. Finally he found Babe calmly eating grass in a neighboring valley—with the barn perched right up on his back! He had outgrown it in a single night!

Paul became very fond of Babe and took him on all his adventures in the woods. He grew by leaps and bounds and soon was almost as large as Paul himself. Woodsmen tell us that when Babe was full grown he measured forty-two axe-handles between the eyes.

His appetite was tremendous. Every evening he ate a ton and a half of hay. Even then he wouldn't be satisfied to go to bed unless he had three wagonloads of turnips for dessert.

Paul taught him to help with the logging in the woods, and would give him an eighty-pound lump of sugar if he had been a good ox during the day. Babe was always full of mischief, however. He liked to roar and stamp his feet at night so the men would run out of the bunkhouses where they slept, thinking it was an earthquake! When Paul scolded him for it, Babe only chuckled to himself and pretended he was asleep.

Once when Babe was standing beside the cookhouse he winked at Paul and put his head in the cookhouse window. Babe gave a great sneeze and blew a whole barrel of flour over Hot Biscuit Slim, the cook, and his helper, Cream Puff Fatty!

Babe was very useful in many ways. For instance, Paul had a lot of trouble with the crooked, twisting road that wound in and out through the forest. He finally tied one end of the road to a large stump and hitched Babe to the other end with a large logging chain. Babe dug his great hoofs in the ground and strained and tugged until he had pulled the entire road out straight. It was a mighty feat of strength. In doing it, he stretched the heavy iron links of the logging chain until it was a single iron bar!

During his first summer, Babe became fat and lazy and one day refused to pull the logs down the road to the river. He wanted to wait until winter when the snow was on the ground and logs would slide easier. Paul didn't say a word, but that night he had the men secretly whitewash the road. The next morning, Babe thought it was snow and pulled the logs without further trouble.

When winter finally came again and covered the Maine woods with beautiful white snow, Babe was the happiest ox in the world. He loved to roam through the woods on the new snowshoes that Paul had given him for his first birthday. The greatest trouble Paul had that winter was finding enough food for Babe, who was getting thin. One day he thought of a great idea and called Ole the big Swede. Ole was the camp blacksmith, and next to Paul, the largest man in camp.

"Ole," he said, "I want you to make the largest pair of green eyeglasses in the world." When Ole finished, Paul put the glasses on Babe, strapping them over his nose. He then turned Babe out in the snow again. To Babe, with his new green glasses, all the snow looked like nice green grass! He ate and ate and grew fat and healthy again in no time at all.

In all the woods, there was no one so kindly toward Babe as Paul Bunyan, and no ox was ever as faithful to its master as Babe, the famous Blue Ox.

Pipeline Days

It is a little known fact that, besides working as a logger, Paul Bunyan also made a name for himself drilling for oil in the American South. The following story is written as a conversation among Paul's acquaintances that evolves into a bragging contest.

. . . "Say," said Fat, "did any of you guys ever see Paul Bunyan in a poker game. The cards he used were so big that it took a man five hours to walk around one of them. Paul used to play a lot of poker that time we was digging Lake Michigan to mix concrete in when he was building the Rocky Mountains. A little while after that we dug Lake Superior for a slush pit for one of them big wells we was drilling. Any of you birds want to play some poker?"

"You know so much about Paul Bunyan," said [the Contender]. "Did you ever hear about that big steer that he had? He called her Babe and she just measured forty-two pick-handles lengths and the width of a size seven derby hat between the eyes. And strong! Why that steer could pull anything!

"I remember one time when we was drilling a well down Breckenridge way. Wasn't much of a hole, just sixteen inches. Well, we drilled and drilled and didn't ever strike nothing—except dust, and a God's plenty of that; so finally Paul he said we might as well give it up as a dry hole and let it go at that.

"But Paul was mad! He swore around for two or three days and smashed the derrick into kindling wood and was about to quit drilling when he saw a advertisement in the paper by some bird out on the plains that wanted to buy some post-holes. Ten thousand post-holes it was he wanted. Ten thousand holes three feet long.

"Well, Paul he hitched a chain around this duster [dry well] hole and hooked up Babe and pulled fifteen thousand feet of it out of the ground. He got mad again because the hole broke off and left over half of it in the ground. But directly he said that they wasn't no use of a post-hole being sixteen inches across;

so he just quartered the hole and then sawed it up into the right lengths. . . ."

"I worked for Paul on one of them deep wells once," said Fat. "It was out in Arkansas. Jimmy Blue was running the rig and we was drilling with standard tools. We got down thirty thousand feet and struck a rock formation that a bit wouldn't touch. And we was using a pretty good sized bit too, drilling a fifty-inch hole.

"Well, we worked on this formation for three weeks without doing any good and then we called up Paul. Paul he come out there and took charge of the rig himself and worked for three more weeks, day and night, without doing anything except ruin a lot of bits. And finally he got so mad that he jumped down on the derrick floor and pulled up the bit with his hands. Then he threw it down into the hole as hard as he could throw it. Well, we busted the rock that time. The bit just kept on going and when the line run out it pulled derrick, rig, and all into the hole after it.

"We got a gusher that time. But when Paul seen that the rig had pulled Jimmy into the hole with it he was just about to plug off the hole and abandon it. But in a few days we got a telegram from Jimmy in China saying that he had a 100,000 barrel gusher and was spudding in on another location."

"Did any of you guys work for Paul on that big line he laid?" asked the Contender. "Well, I worked for him on that 100-inch aluminum line that he laid from Pennsylvania to California. We laid it to pipe buttermilk out to his camp out there. Paul liked buttermilk so well himself that he had a twenty-four-inch petcock running wide open all the time to catch enough for him to drink."

"Yeh," said Fat, "I know all about that. I helped Paul drill the buttermilk well that furnished that line. We drilled down thirty-two thousand feet and then struck a formation of cornbread. We drilled for five hundred feet through the cornbread and then for twelve hundred feet through solid turnip greens—except that every few feet would be a layer of fried sow-belly. That's where the old song started: 'Cornbread, Buttermilk, and Good Old Turnip Greens.'"

. . . The Contender put in, "Did you ever hear about the cattle line that Paul Bunyan laid from his ranch to Chicago?

"Well, Paul he got tired of paying such high freight to get his stock to market; so he just laid a pipeline all the way to the stockyards in Chicago and pumped them through it. Everything went all right except that the pipe was so big that the calves and half-grown yearlin's would get lost in the threads and starve to death before they could get to the outside. And one time the line sprung a leak and Paul lost thirty-five carloads of cattle before he could get it corked [caulked]. But he sure did do a good job of corking when he did get to it."

"How the devil did he cork a hole that big?" asked Fat after a minute or two of silence.

"Why with B.S., you big windbag, same as that that you have been spouting off."

Paul's Popcorn

This favorite tale displays Paul Bunyan's ingenuity and makes clear why he became a symbol for the "can-do" spirit of America.

Having got the water meandering around to make the soil moist, Paul figured he'd test the land out with popcorn. So he picked up a good healthy looking kernel, walked out to a likely looking place that had been irrigated lately, and dug a hole about a foot deep with his middle finger. He couldn't use his forefinger or thumb, naturally, because he was holding the corn between them.

Well, Paul had no more than started back to camp to get Ole to act as a witness, than there was a sort of sputtering up of brown dirt, and a cornstalk came skyhooting through. In no time at all, the corn was up to Paul's knee. And by the time he got back with Ole, the cornstalk had grown so much that the top was buried in a cloud.

"Ole!" says Paul. "Climb up to the top of that baby and chop the top off so she won't grow any more!"

Ole started shinning up the stalk at a great rate. But the thing kept shooting up, and in a minute or so Ole, too, was out of sight in that cloud. It was a handsome cloud with cottony bumps and scallopy edges, but Ole said afterwards that being inside of it wasn't different from being inside any old cloud. "Nothing but fog inside it," he said.

"When you chop the top off, throw her down," Paul yelled.

Ole's voice came booming down. "The top's above me," he said. "I can't get *to* the thing." Ole's big voice had something like the effect of thunder, and the cloud rained away from around him. But this new moisture made the stalk grow even faster.

"This won't do!" Paul yelled. "Come down, and we'll handle her some other way!"

"Can't come down, either," Ole yelled in a minute. "Every time I go down one yard, this thing shoots up three, and I'm losing ground. I'm getting hungry, too."

Paul yelled for Babe, right then. And while he was waiting for Babe to come along, he used his shotgun to shoot up a few crullers which he hoped—for the time being, at any rate—would keep Ole from starving to death.

When Babe came along, Paul hurried with the beast over to Jim Hill's railroad, the Great Northern, which (by good luck) wasn't far away. Paul loaded Babe up with a pile of steel rails, then hurried back to the cornstalk with them.

"I'll see if I can't choke off the moisture in this cornstalk," Paul said. And with that he started tying those rails together and then knotting them around the cornstalk.

It worked, too.

Soon the ears of corn away up near the top stopped getting moisture and started to dry out. Then the hot sun hit them hard, and shortly the corn began to pop, making considerable noise, too.

After a while, this popped corn came drifting down like so many snowballs. Babe, who'd lived through so much fierce weather, didn't do any more than shiver a little. But a big herd of cattle grazing near by decided they were in a world-beating blizzard and promptly froze to death.

Meanwhile, growing in spite of those knotted steel rails the way it had, the cornstalk had been bitten into by the things, and had cut itself off of itself. Now it started to tumble, slow but sure. Ole rode it down to the ground, just like a logger standing on a log in white water, then at the right time he jumped off lightly and headed back for Paul, following along the cornstalk.

When Ole got there, the owner of the cattle herd, who'd hurried over, was talking up right sassy to Paul. "Look what you did to my cattle, just when they were fat for market!" he yelled. "You'll have to pay for them."

"Course I will," Paul said. And he settled for the cattle, right on the spot, for Paul was always fair and square, regardless of cost.

"Hello, Ole," says Paul. "Glad to see you back. Just bought me a herd of frozen cattle."

"Goodness gracious!" Ole said. "And with our camp so far from where the cattle are, if we ship them they're likely to spoil."

"That won't do," Paul said. "We'll have to figure a way to use the critters. Teddy Roosevelt wouldn't like it if we wasted all those natural resources. Let me think."

After thinking a while, Paul snapped his fingers. "I've got it!" he said. "If the popcorn froze them, the popcorn can keep them frozen."

With that, he strolled over to the railroad and called on the head man, Jim Hill. Jim rented him a raft of box cars. Then, with the help of Babe, Paul stuffed those box cars with animals *and* popcorn. And that way, the meat kept fine until it had been delivered at Paul's camp.

So, without knowing it at the time, Paul had gone and invented refrigerator cars.

Paul Bunyan Takes Care of Mosquitoes

With mosquitoes being something of a national bird among tall-tale tellers, it is only natural that Paul Bunyan encountered some, and he knew just what to do.

Boys, did I ever tell you about the time I drove the Naubinway over to Paul Bunyan's camp on Big Mantisque Lake? Boys, I want to tell you there's some dandy mosquitoes over in that swamp even now, but the modern mosquitoes are nothing like their ancestors.

Well, just as I was pulling into Paul Bunyan's camp that day I heard some terrible droning noise like one of these modern airplanes. Even Paul, big as he was, seemed excited and yelled to me to hurry into his office. So I knew something was wrong.

Then Paul told me that some of the big mosquitoes was loose. He had trapped them several years ago, because they was bothering his cattle. Paul told me that two mosquitoes was trying to kill his prize heifer. They had the critter down and was trying to drag it off, he said, when along came a really big mosquito. The big mosquito simply killed off the other two, picked up the cow, and flew away. So Paul decided then and there to put on a campaign against them. He and his men trapped several of them in live traps, he said, and the rest got scared and flew away.

But this day, when I come to visit Paul, some of the mosquitoes had broken loose. We had barred the doors when we heard the mosquitoes droning overhead. They were landing on the roof. I shook like a leaf, but Paul wasn't scared. Overhead I heard a terrible cracking and looked to see swordlike weapons piercing the roof. Paul said they were mosquito stingers. So he grabbed his sledge and clinched those stingers like a carpenter clinches a nail. Next day he put twelve of his star lumberjacks to executing mosquitoes on that roof. He said he was through showing kindness to the mosquitoes. It didn't pay. They'd stab you in the back.

Cal Bunyan's Ireland, Jerusalem, Australia & Southern Indiana Railroad

Who would have thought that Paul Bunyan had a brother, and that he was a railroad man of extraordinary vision who was responsible for the longest, biggest, and fastest railroad in America?

I first heard about Cal from "Springheels" Conley, an old boomer who, in talking about some of the railroads where he had worked, mentioned the IJA&SI.

"What?" demanded Conley, when I told him I couldn't remember any railroad with those initials. "Do you mean that you've never heard of the Ireland, Jerusalem, Australia & Southern Indiana Railroad?"

I confessed that I never had, and "Springheels," after pouring himself another malted milk from the shaker the soda fountain clerk had set on the counter in front of us, told me all about Cal Bunyan and his railroad.

"You see, it was this way," said "Springheels," as he helped himself to my cigarettes. "Cal got the idea about starting the IJA&SI after Jim Hill finished building the Great Northern. I guess Cal was a little jealous of all the nice things the newspapers were saying about Hill. Anyway, Cal decided to build a road bigger than any that Jim Hill or any of those other guys could build.

"So he started laying the track of the IJA&SI. Ordinary ballast, such as cinders and gravel, wouldn't do for the tracks, so Cal used boulders which he brought from the Rocky Mountains. Each boulder weighed six tons and Cal used millions of them.

"Present-day section men think that big rails are now being used. They should have seen the kind on the IJA&SI. It took the largest steel mill in the United States, operating on a thirty-six-hour-day and nine-day-week schedule, two years to produce one rail for Cal.

"Each tie was made from an entire giant redwood tree. And the section men had to use pile-drivers to spike down the rails. One day a section foreman slipped and fell to the ground from the top of a rail. It was a 500-foot sheer drop and he was killed instantly.

"After the track was built, the next job was to get an engine and cars. They had to be made to order and it was a hard task finding machinery large enough to turn out the parts. Cal finally solved the problem by taking the two largest Ferris wheels he could find and setting them in line about a block apart to use for lathes in which to turn the axles for the new locomotive. He bought a merry-go-round and used it for a journal box boring mill. The Eiffel Tower in Paris was rigged up for a drill press.

"The rivets and staybolts used for the engine's boiler and firebox were 24 feet in diameter. A volcano was used to heat the rivets, and then the boilermakers drove them in place by firing cannon balls at them.

"Building the coaches was some job, too. Each nail was driven by two husky carmen wielding fence post mauls. Long-stroke air hammers were used for tacking the upholstery on coach seats.

"Finally, an engine and 700 cars were ready for the first train. Before the engine was fired up, however, the 3,600 members of the road's board of directors held a banquet in the locomotive's firebox.

"There was only one tragedy to mark the day of the train's first run. When the engineer started the air pump, the first stroke sucked all of the air out of four neighboring states and hundreds of people suffocated to death.

"A roll of paper, like is used on newspaper printing presses, was used to write out orders for the engineer and conductor. The telegraphers who sent these orders were all clog dancers. They pounded out the dots and dashes by dancing jigs on the keys of their instruments.

"All of the clerks on the IJA&SI used fountain pens which, like Johnny Inkslinger's, took a barrel of ink at each filling.

"The engineer and fireman had to use a balloon to get up to the engine cab. If they had tried to climb up the gangway the 16-hour law would have caught them long before they got near the top.

"No man was strong enough to pull the throttle on this locomotive, so a stationary engine was installed on the right side to do the job.

"Mules and mine cars were used to haul coal from the tender and dump it on the deck in front of the firebox door. The fireman's scoop shovel held two tons.

"The train was so long that the conductor rode on a motorcycle to take up the tickets. He punched each ticket by shooting holes through it with a .45-caliber automatic pistol.

"On the dining car, a whole beef was used for each steak. Two cement mixers were required to stir the gravy, and potatoes were lifted out of the frying pans by steam shovels. A tank car was coupled in the front of each diner to carry the cream for the passengers' coffee.

"Just as the train started out, the engineer blew the whistle. When the steam condensed, it made a cloudburst which flooded the whole country.

"The train started to pick up speed and the engineer had to put on a pair of goggles that had lenses 18 inches thick. By and by he got going so fast that the suction from the train picked all of the leaves off the trees and pulled the farmers' corn out of the ground for eight miles each side of the right-of-way.

"No train ever went at the speed this one did. It went so fast that after it was brought to a dead stop it was still making 65 miles an hour. Two months later the schedule was speeded up so that the train arrived at its destination an hour before it left its starting point.

"At first there was a lot of trouble on the night runs—over the headlight. It was so powerful that it lighted up an area of 50,000 acres on each side of the track and kept it lighted for twelve hours after the train had passed. The farmers raised an awful rumpus about this—all of their chickens were dying from the loss of sleep. Also, the heat from the headlight was burning up wheat fields and drying up rivers. So the engineer tried to cover the headlight with a shield of six-inch armor plate, but the light shone through just the same. Finally, he took out the reflector, cut all the wires, and smashed the dynamo with a sledge hammer. This cut down the range of the light to a mile and a half, and half of the farmers stopped kicking.

"After that everything went along fine until one day when it was decided to double the speed of the train. It was no trick to do this, because at no time had the engineer ever had the throttle open more than three notches.

" 'Give her all she's got,' Cal Bunyan told the engineer when they started out on the new test run.

"The engineer opened her wide up. And did she make speed! But that was the end of the IJA&SI. The train went so fast that the friction melted all the rails and burned all the ties to ashes. And on the last half mile of the line, where the track went up a steep grade, the train was going at such a speed that when it reached the top the engine took off like an airplane and carried itself and its 700 cars so far into the stratosphere that the law of gravitation quit working. That was years ago, but the train is still rushing through space up there."

That was all of the story. "Springheels" tried to add a few more words, but his voice broke and he began sobbing. I got up quietly and slipped out a side door. The next day when I passed there, I glanced in. "Springheels" was still standing at the soda counter, crying into his malted milk over the sad fate of the IJA&SI.

The Birth of John Henry

The existence of a living railroad man named John Henry has never been proven, although many people claimed to have known him. He was embraced, especially among African Americans, as the ultimate strong man. The folklorist B. A. Botkin notes that, compared to Paul Bunyan, there has been "a surprisingly small amount of exaggeration in the stories about John Henry." In the following story, however, it is clear that the folk process has been at work.

Now John Henry was a man, but he's long dead.

The night John Henry was born the moon was copper-colored and the sky was black. The stars wouldn't shine and the rain fell hard. Forked lightning cleaved the air and the earth trembled like a leaf. The panthers squalled in the brake like a baby and the Mississippi River ran upstream a thousand miles. John Henry weighed forty-four pounds.

John Henry was born on the banks of the Black River, where all good rousterbouts come from. He came into the world with a cotton-hook for a right hand and a river song on his tongue:

> "Looked up and down de river,
>> Twice as far as I could see.
> Seed befo' I gits to be twenty-one,
>> De Anchor Line gonter b'long to me, Lawd, Lawd,
>> Anchor Line gonter b'long to me."

They didn't know what to make of John Henry when he was born. They looked at him and then went and looked at the river.

"He got a bass voice like a preacher," his mamma said.

"He got shoulders like a cotton-rollin' rousterbout," his papa said.

"He got blue gums like a conjure man," the nurse woman said.

"I might preach some," said John Henry, "but I ain't gonter be no preach-er. I might roll cotton on de boats, but I ain't gonter be no cottonrollin' rouster-bout. I might got blue gums like a conjure man, but I ain't gonter git familiar wid de sperits. 'Cause my name is John Henry, and when fo'ks call me by my name, dey'll know I'm a natchal man."

"His name is John Henry," said his mamma. "Hit's a fack."

"And when you calls him by his name," said his papa, "he's a natchal man."

So about that time John Henry raised up and stretched. "Well," he said, "ain't hit about supper-time?"

"Sho hit's about supper-time," said his mamma.

"And after," said his papa.

"And long after," said the nurse woman.

"Well," said John Henry, "did de dogs had they supper?"

"They did," said his mamma.

"All de dogs," said his papa.

"Long since," said the nurse woman.

"Well, den," said John Henry, "ain't I as good as de dogs?"

And when John Henry said that he got mad. He reared back in his bed and broke out the slats. He opened his mouth and yowled, and it put out the lamp. He cleaved his tongue and spat, and it put out the fire. "Don't make me mad!" said John Henry, and the thunder rumbled and rolled. "Don't let me git mad on de day I'm bawn, 'cause I'm skeered of my ownse'f when I gits mad."

And John Henry stood up in the middle of the floor and he told them what he wanted to eat. "Bring me four ham bones and a pot full of cabbages," he said. "Bring me a bait of turnip greens tree-top tall, and season hit down wid a side er middlin'. Bring me a pone er cold cawn bread and some hot potlicker to wash hit down. Bring me two hog jowls and a kittleful er whippowill peas. Bring me a skittletful er red-hot biscuits and a big jugful er cane molasses. 'Cause my name is John Henry, and I'll see you soon."

So John Henry walked out of the house and away from the Black River Country where all good rousterbouts are born.

The Ballad of John Henry

John Henry is most famous for the stance he took against the coming of the machine age, which symbolized the oppression of individual workers. Among the best known and most often sung of the American ballads, "The Ballad of John Henry" recounts the famous story of the contest between John and the steam drill, which earned him his place as hero of the workingman.

John Henry was a li'l baby, uh-huh,
Sittin' on his mama's knee, oh, yeah,
Said: "De Big Bend Tunnel on de C. & O. road
Gonna cause de death of me,
Lawd, Lawd, gonna cause de death of me."

John Henry, he had a woman,
Her name was Mary Magdalene,
She would go to de tunnel and sing for John,
Jes' to hear John Henry's hammer ring,
Lawd, Lawd, jes' to hear John Henry's hammer ring.

John Henry had a lil woman,
Her name was Lucy Ann,
John Henry took sick an' had to go to bed,
Lucy Ann drove steel like a man,
Lawd, Lawd, Lucy Ann drove steel like a man.

Cap'n says to John Henry,
"Gonna bring me a steam drill 'round,
Gonna take dat steam drill out on de job,
Gonna whop dat steel on down,
Lawd, Lawd, gonna whop dat steel on down."

John Henry tol' his cap'n,
Lightnin' was in his eye:
"Cap'n, bet yo' las' red cent on me,
Fo' I'll beat it to de bottom or I'll die,
Lawd, Lawd, I'll beat it to de bottom or I'll die."

Sun shine hot an' burnin',
Wer'n't no breeze a-tall,
Sweat ran down like water down a hill,
Dat day John Henry let his hammer fall,
Lawd, Lawd, dat day John Henry let his hammer fall.

John Henry went to de tunnel,
An' dey put him in de lead to drive;
De rock so tall an' John Henry so small,
Dat he lied down his hammer an' he cried,
Lawd, Lawd, dat he lied down his hammer an' he cried.

John Henry started on de right hand,
De steam drill started on de lef'—
"Before I'd let dis steam drill beat me down,
I'd hammer my fool self to death,
Lawd, Lawd, I'd hammer my fool self to death."

White man tol' John Henry,
"Nigger, damn yo' soul,
You might beat dis steam an' drill of mine,
When de rocks in dis mountain turn to gol',
Lawd, Lawd, when de rocks in dis mountain turn to gol'."

John Henry said to his shaker,
"Nigger, why don' you sing?
I'm throwin' twelve poun's from my hips on down,
Jes' listen to de col' steel ring,
Lawd, Lawd, jes' listen to de col' steel ring."

Oh, de captain said to John Henry,
"I b'lieve this mountain's sinkin' in."
John Henry said to his captain, oh my!
"Ain' nothin' but my hammer suckin' win',
Lawd, Lawd, ain' nothin' but my hammer suckin' win'."

John Henry tol' his shaker,
"Shaker, you better pray,
For, if I miss dis six-foot steel,
Tomorrow'll be yo' buryin' day,
Lawd, Lawd, tomorrow'll be yo' buryin' day."

John Henry tol' his captain,
"Looka yonder what I see—
Yo' drill's done broke an' yo' hole's done choke,
An' you cain' drive steel like me,
Lawd, Lawd, an' you cain' drive steel like me."

De man dat invented de steam drill,
Thought he was mighty fine.
John Henry drove his fifteen feet,
An' de steam drill only made nine,
Lawd, Lawd, an' de steam drill only made nine.

De hammer dat John Henry swung
It weighed over nine pound;
He broke a rib in his lef'-han' side,
An' his intrels fell on de groun',
Lawd, Lawd, n' his intrels fell on de groun'.

John Henry was hammerin' on de mountain,
An' his hammer was strikin' fire,
He drove so hard till he broke his pore heart,
An' he lied down his hammer an' he died,
Lawd, Lawd, he lied down his hammer an' he died.

All de womens in de Wes',
When dey heared of John Henry's death,
Stood in de rain, flagged de eas'-boun' train,
Goin' where John Henry fell dead,
Lawd, Lawd, goin' where John Henry fell dead.

John Henry's li'l mother,
She was all dressed in red,
She jumped in bed, covered up her head,
Said she didn' know her son was dead,
Lawd, Lawd, didn' know her son was dead.

John Henry had a pretty li'l woman,
An' de dress she wo' was blue,
An' de las' words she said to him:
"John Henry I've been true to you,
Lawd, Lawd, John Henry, I've been true to you."

Annie Christmas

Though some believe that the character of Annie Christmas is based on a genuine figure who lived in New Orleans, as with her male counterpart, John Henry, there has been no way to prove it. Whether she lived or not, the tales about her eventually reached legendary proportions, and they brought a feminine element to the overwhelmingly male-centered body of myth surrounding the growth of the nation. In some stories about Annie Christmas, she is depicted as a white woman; in others she is black, and there continues to be disagreement among folklorists and storytellers about which was the original character.

Once upon a time in New Orleans there lived a woman who could only be described as extraordinary. For starters, she was strong, stronger than any man; stronger, some said, than any horse or ox that worked the river hauling wagon loads of cotton and goods to and from the riverboats that brought the world to New Orleans and took New Orleans to the world. Though she's been dead a long time, if you hang around New Orleans to this day, you will hear somebody say of a man, "Why, he's as strong as Annie Christmas."

And then Annie Christmas was tall. Some said she stood seven foot; some said eight. Some said anywhere in between. She wore the clothes of a riverman and worked her own keelboat. She worked faster and longer than any man alive. "Said little and done much," that's what they said, for she did not speak except to call out a warning or make it known what she thought of any man who mocked her.

Oh, she'd been known to fight, and any man who fought her once knew better than to fight her again. Once a newcomer to New Orleans named Mike Fink was hanging around the dock with all the other rivermen waiting for an empty flatbed to arrive to take a load of cotton up to Natchez. He commented that her ladyship ought to be home darning cotton socks and not out making a fool of herself hauling cotton bales. He said this to her back while she was hunched

over a half-ton bale getting ready to hook it with a grapple. Without a word, Annie laid down the grapple, picked up the cotton, and stood up . . . and up . . . and up. At her full height, and with a half-ton bale of cotton stretched up over her head, she looked like Atlas holding up the world. And though some say Mike Fink was tall of stature, and some say he was short, on that day it probably didn't matter if he was tall or short in comparison to ordinary people.

Fink's eyes, that had been narrowed in sarcasm a minute before, were round, now, and popping. It was the only time anyone ever noticed him lose his wisecracking voice. For he sputtered and stuttered and put his stubby little arms out as if he was going to catch that bundle on the way down.

Annie spoke then. Her voice was soft as cotton fresh from the gin. "It seems clear to me, suh, that you have a somewhat narrow viewpoint on the subject of who should be where, when." That was all she said. And then she threw that bale with all her might, but not at Fink. She threw it down, straight down into the water off the dock by his feet. The tidal wave that swept Fink away was small, but powerful, and it carried him, still standing, to Natchez with his mouth open but no sound coming out, all the way. And that's why Mike Fink was never seen in New Orleans again.

"Not much of a fight," was all the rivermen could think of to say about the incident.

When she felt like it Annie would dress up. She would dress up *fine!* She had her dresses made by Miz Lacy Lusterfellow, who knew just where to tuck and sew to show off a figure like Annie Christmas. To make the midnight blue gown Annie wore when she wanted to look particularly pretty, Miz Lacy used an entire bolt of the finest China silk, which Annie had taken in pay for a week's work in August the year before. The dress had more gathers than the opera house curtains, and more bows about the bodice than the Christmas tree at the governor's mansion. And when Annie walked down the street she'd nod her feather-crowned hat to her friends, who would marvel aloud how a woman so big and so strong could look so ladylike, so *royal*, in a dress.

The only thing that could take Annie Christmas out was love. Strong as she was, she was powerless when that old bug bit her, and she was tireless in pursuit of a way to scratch that itch. Once she fell for a man, he'd just as well come along, 'cause she'd dog his tracks, rest her oars in the wake of his keelboat, or gamble the night away on his boat, as in the case of her last love, the gamesman in a riverboat gambling hall. Annie had twelve sons, and they were all as tall and black as she was. And when they all dressed up to go have themselves a time on the river, they were a sight to behold. Six sons escorted her on the right, and six sons escorted her on the left. She aimed to have more sons, so they said, but her last chance came and went on the night Annie Christmas died.

On this particular night, Annie and her sons rowed out on a flat boat to the *Lacey Mae*, a riverboat with a sweet name and a reputation for the fiercest gambling on the Mississippi. Annie fell in love that night for the last time, with a man named Easter, Jimmy Easter. She stood behind him while he played blackjack, and he had more luck than a copper penny. He knew she was there, but he ignored her something awful. He didn't know— how could he have known?—that she was his lucky charm. When he turned to collect his winnings, Annie put her hand on his shoulder and smiled. He smiled back and said, "Howdy, ma'am."

Jimmy Easter was nigh as tall as Annie and equally handsome. He winked at her, but didn't tarry, brushed by her shoulder and walked off to the roulette wheel to try his new found fortune there. Annie's girlfriend, Sis McQueen, saw what was coming and told Annie the truth, that Jimmy Easter was a married man and she'd better watch out. But Annie was smitten, and she strolled over to the roulette wheel and just *leaned* on Jimmy's arm. The closer she got, the more he won. It was a match made in gambler's heaven, and Jimmy seemed to be about to realize that when the door to the casino opened and in walked his wife, Charlene. It only took her a second to assess the situation, and she being the jealous type, she wasted not a word or a minute, pulled a gun, and shot Annie Christmas once through the heart.

What the rivermen said was, "River couldn't kill her; birthing twelve big strapping boys couldn't kill her; Mike Fink couldn't kill her; but love, careless love, that's what killed her."

Annie's sons knew what to do after that. Seemed they'd known this day would come. They dressed her in her midnight blue dress, and had a coffin made to fit her. They carried the coffin through the streets of New Orleans so her admirers could pay their last respects. They walked her to the river, and at the dark of the moon, put her on a keelboat. Then they stood, each taking a turn with the pole, and pressed themselves out of sight down the river, into the mist, singing a slow sad song, never to be seen again.

The Saga of Pecos Bill

As the popularity of America's new mythological heroes grew, writers invented new ones who were quickly embraced by the public. In 1923, Edward O'Reilly wrote "The Saga of Pecos Bill" using the formula that had proved so successful with Paul Bunyan and other demigods. That is, he strung together many of the tall tales that were circulating about cowboys in the early part of the century, creating one long story of the most remarkable cowboy who ever lived.

According to the most veracious historians, Bill was born about the time Sam Houston discovered Texas. His mother was a sturdy pioneer woman who once killed forty-five Indians with a broom-handle, and weaned him on moonshine liquor when he was three days old. He cut his teeth on a bowie-knife, and his earliest playfellows were the bears and catamounts of east Texas.

When Bill was about a year old, another family moved into the country, and located about fifty miles down the river. His father decided the place was gettin' too crowded, and packed his family in a wagon and headed west.

One day after they crossed the Pecos River, Bill fell out of the wagon. As there were sixteen or seventeen other children in the family, his parents didn't miss him for four or five weeks, and then it was too late to try to find him.

That's how Bill came to grow up with the coyotes along the Pecos. He soon learned the coyote language, and used to hunt with them and sit on the hills and howl at night. Being so young when he got lost, he always thought he was a coyote. That's where he learned to kill deer by runnin' them to death.

One day when he was about ten years old a cow-boy came along just when Bill had matched a fight with two grizzly bears. Bill hugged the bears to death, tore off a hind leg, and was just settin' down to breakfast when this cow-boy loped up and asked him what he meant by runnin' around naked that way among the varmints.

"Why, because I am a varmint," Bill told him. "I'm a coyote."

The cow-boy argued with him that he was a human, but Bill wouldn't believe him.

"Ain't I got fleas!" he insisted. "And don't I howl around all night, like a respectable coyote should do?"

"That don't prove nothin'," the cow-boy answered. "All Texans have fleas, and most of them howl. Did you ever see a coyote that didn't have a tail? Well, you ain't got no tail; so that proves you ain't a varmint."

Bill looked, and, sure enough, he didn't have a tail.

"You sure got me out on a limb," says Bill. "I never noticed that before. It shows what higher education will do for a man. I believe you're right. Lead me to them humans, and I'll throw in with them."

Bill went to town with this cow-hand, and in due time he got to enjoyin' all the pleasant vices of mankind, and decided that he certainly was a human. He got to runnin' with the wild bunch, and sunk lower and lower, until finally he became a cow-boy.

It wasn't long until he was famous as a bad man. He invented the six-shooter and train-robbin' and most of the crimes popular in the old days of the West. He didn't invent cowstealin'. That was discovered by King David in the Bible, but Bill improved on it.

There is no way of tellin' just how many men Bill did kill. Deep down he had a tender heart, however, and never killed women or children, or tourists out of season. He never scalped his victims; he was too civilized for that. He used to skin them gently and tan their hides.

It wasn't long before Bill had killed all the bad men in west Texas, massacred all the Indians, and eaten all the buffalo. So he decided to migrate to a new country where hard men still thrived and a man could pass the time away.

He saddled up his horse and hit for the West. One day he met an old trapper and told him what he was lookin' for.

"I want the hardest cow outfit in the world," he says. "Not one of these ordinary cow-stealin', Mexican-shootin'

bunches of amateurs, but a real hard herd of hand-picked hellions that make murder a fine art and take some proper pride in their slaughter."

"Stranger, you're headed in the right direction," answers the trapper.
"Keep right on down this draw for a couple of hundred miles, and you'll find that
very outfit. They're so hard they can kick fire out of a flint rock with their bare
toes."

Bill single-footed down that draw for about a hundred miles that afternoon; then he met with an accident. His horse stubbed his toe on a mountain and
broke his leg, leavin' Bill afoot.

He slung his saddle over his shoulder and set off hikin' down that draw,
cussin' and a-swearin'. Profanity was a gift with Bill.

All at once a big ten-foot rattlesnake quiled up in his path, set his tail to
singin', and allowed he'd like to match a fight. Bill laid down his saddle, and just
to be fair about it, he gave the snake the first three bites. Then he waded into that
reptile and everlastingly frailed the pizen out of him.

By and by that old rattler yelled for mercy, and admitted that when it
came to fightin', Bill started where he left off. So Bill picked up his saddle and
started on, carryin' the snake in his hand and spinnin' it in short loops at the Gila
monsters.

About fifty miles further on, a big old mountain-lion jumped off a cliff
and lit all spraddled out on Bill's neck. This was no ordinary lion. It weighed more
than three steers and a yearlin', and was the very same lion the State of Nuevo
León was named after down in old Mexico.

Kind of chucklin' to himself, Bill laid down his saddle and his snake and
went into action. In a minute the fur was flyin' down the cañon until it darkened
the sun. The way Bill knocked the animosity out of that lion was a shame. In
about three minutes that lion hollered:

"I'll give up, Bill. Can't you take a joke?"

Bill let him up, and then he cinched the saddle on him and went down
that cañon whoopin' and yellin', ridin' that lion a hundred feet at a jump, and
quirtin' him down the flank with the rattlesnake.

It wasn't long before he saw a chuck-wagon, with a bunch of cow-boys squattin' around it. He rode up to that wagon, splittin' the air with his war-whoops, with that old lion a screechin', and that snake singin' his rattles.

When he came to the fire he grabbed the old cougar by the ear, jerked him back on his haunches, stepped off him, hung his snake around his neck, and looked the outfit over. Them cow-boys sat there sayin' less than nothin'.

Bill was hungry, and seein' a boilerful of beans cookin' on the fire, he scooped up a few handfuls and swallowed them, washin' them down with a few gallons of boilin' coffee out of the pot. Wipin' his mouth on a handful of prickly-pear cactus, Bill turned to the cow-boys and asked:

"Who the hell is boss around here?"

A big fellow about eight feet tall, with seven pistols and nine bowie-knives in his belt, rose up and, takin' off his hat, said:

"Stranger, I was; but you be."

Bill had many adventures with this outfit. It was about this time he staked out New Mexico, and used Arizona for a calf-pasture. It was here that he found his noted horse Widow-Maker. He raised him from a colt on nitroglycerin and dynamite, and Bill was the only man that could throw a leg over him.

There wasn't anythin' that Bill couldn't ride, although I have heard of one occasion when he was thrown. He made a bet that he could ride an Oklahoma cyclone slick-heeled, without a saddle.

He met the cyclone, the worst that was ever known, up on the Kansas line. Bill eared that tornado down and climbed on its back. That cyclone did some pitchin' that is unbelievable, if it were not vouched for by many reliable witnesses.

Down across Texas it went sunfishin', back-flippin', side-windin', knockin' down mountains, blowin' the holes out of the ground, and tyin' rivers into knots. The Staked Plains used to be heavily timbered until that big wind swiped the trees off and left it a bare prairie.

Bill just sat up there, thumbin' that cyclone in the withers, floppin' it across the ears with his hat, and rollin' a cigarette with one hand. He rode it through three States, but over in Arizona it got him.

When it saw it couldn't throw him, it rained out from under him. This is proved by the fact that it washed out the Grand Cañon. Bill came down over in California. The spot where he lit is now known as Death Valley, a hole in the ground more than one hundred feet below sea-level, and the print of his hip-pockets can still be seen in the granite.

I have heard this story disputed in some of its details. Some historians claim that Bill wasn't thrown; that he slid down on a streak of lightnin' without knockin' the ashes off his cigarette. It is also claimed that the Grand Cañon was dug by Bill one week when he went prospectin'; but the best authorities insist on the first version. They argue that that streak of lightnin' story comes from the habit he always had of usin' one to light his cigarette.

Bill was a great roper. In fact, he invented ropin'. Old-timers who admit they knew him say that his rope was as long as the equator, although the more conservative say that it was at least two feet shorter on one end. He used to rope a herd of cattle at one throw.

This skill once saved the life of a friend. The friend had tried to ride Widow-Maker one day, and was thrown so high he came down on top of Pike's Peak. He was in the middle of a bad fix, because he couldn't get down, and seemed doomed to a lingerin' death on high.

Bill came to the rescue, and usin' only a short calf-loop, he roped his friend around the neck and jerked him down to safety in the valley, twenty thousand feet below. This man was always grateful, and became Bill's horse-wrangler at the time he staked out New Mexico.

In his idle moments in New Mexico Bill amused himself puttin' thorns on the trees and hems on the toads. It was on this ranch he dug the Rio Grande and invented the centipede and the tarantula as a joke on his friends.

When the cow business was dull, Pecos Bill occasionally embarked on other ventures; for instance, at one time he took a contract to supply the S.P. Railroad with wood. He hired a few hundred Mexicans to chop and haul the wood to the railroad line. As pay for the job, Bill gave each Mexican one fourth of the wood he hauled.

On another occasion Bill took the job of buildin' the line fence that forms the boundary from El Paso across to the Pacific. He rounded up a herd of prairie-dogs and set them to dig holes, which by nature a prairie-dog likes to do.

Whenever one of them finished a nice hole and settled down to live in it, Bill evicted him and stuck a fence-post in the hole. Everybody admired his foresight except the prairie-dogs, and who cares what a prairie-dog thinks?

He threw in with a bunch of Kiowa Indians one time on a little huntin'-trip. It was about the time the buffalo were getting scarce, and Bill was huntin' with his famous squatter-hound named Norther.

Norther would run down a buffalo and hold him by the ear until Bill came up and skinned him alive. Then he would turn it loose to grow a new hide. The scheme worked all right in the summer, but in the winter most of them caught colds and died.

The stories of Bill's love-affairs are especially numerous. One of them may be told. It is the sad tale of the fate of his bride, a winsome little maiden called Slue-Foot Sue. She was a famous rider herself, and Bill lost his heart when he saw her riding a catfish down the Rio Grande with only a surcingle. You must remember that the catfish in the Rio Grande are bigger than whales and twice as active.

Sue made a sad mistake, however, when she insisted on ridin' Widow-Maker on her weddin'-day. The old horse threw her so high she had to duck her head to let the moon go by. Unfortunately, she was wearin' her weddin'-gown, and in those days the women wore those big steel-spring bustles.

Well, when Sue lit, she naturally bounced, and every time she came down she bounced again. It was an awful' sad sight to see Bill implorin' her to quit her bouncin' and not be so nervous; but Sue kept right on, up and down, weepin', and throwin' kisses to her distracted lover, and carryin' on as a bride naturally would do under those circumstances.

She bounced for three days and four nights, and Bill finally had to shoot her to keep her from starvin' to death. It was mighty tragic. Bill never got over it. Of course he married lots of women after that. In fact, it was one of his weaknesses; but none of them filled the place in his heart once held by Slue-Foot Sue, his bouncin' bride.

There is a great difference of opinion as to the manner of Bill's demise. Many claim that it was his drinkin' habits that killed him. You see, Bill got so that liquor didn't have any kick for him, and he fell into the habit of drinkin' strychnine and other forms of wolf pizen.

Even the wolf bait lost its effect, and he got to puttin' fishhooks and barbed wire in his toddy. It was the barbed wire that finally killed him. It rusted his interior and gave him indigestion. He wasted away to a mere skeleton, weighin' not more than two tons; then up and died, and went to his infernal reward.

Many of the border bards who knew Pecos Bill at his best have a different account of his death.

They say that he met a man from Boston one day, wearing a mail-order cow-boy outfit, and askin' fool questions about the West; and poor old Bill laid down and laughed himself to death.

5

Life Lessons

~

Tale-telling offers a way of passing the time and entertaining one another, but some stories have a more serious purpose. They convey meaning and instruction that are important to the community that has generated the stories. Cautionary tales—or moralizing tales, as they are sometimes called—reinforce social values, sometimes with humor and sometimes with tales meant to frighten children and adults away from behavior that will harm them or disrupt community life.

Many stories that are not overtly moralizing have strong lessons embedded in them. Such stories have the power to persuade because they entertain as they teach, and their lessons are remembered long after a simple warning or admonition is forgotten. As a nation of immigrants, North Americans have taken their cautionary tales from many lands, and the values they support represent many cultures. Yet every such story, no matter what its source, has a life lesson to teach all of us, since the most important values—generosity, honesty, common sense—cut across time and cultural boundaries.

Looking for Trouble

This tale, which encourages common sense, is a traditional cautionary tale from the Sea Islands off the coast of Georgia and South Carolina, where Gullah is spoken. Because of their isolation, the people of the Sea Islands retained a rich body of lore until well into the twentieth century.

One day long ago, Alligator was floating in his home creek thinking how satisfy life is.

In those days, he's dress-up in a white suit good enough for Sunday all the time. He lives in the water with all the fish he can eat so he never has to work for a living. And he never, never meets up with trouble.

Well, Alligator is lazy in the sun-hot when here comes Bo Rabbit projecting along the creek shore.

"G'morning, Alligator. How're you today?" asks Bo Rabbit, stopping to pass the time of day and other sociabilities.

"Doing just fine, thank you kindly. How's everyone to your house?"

"Oh, we making out. But so much trouble, Alligator. So much trouble."

"Trouble! What's that, Rabbit? I ain't never seen trouble."

"You ain't never seen trouble! Great Peace! I can show you trouble, Alligator."

"I'd like that, Bo Rabbit. I'd surely like to see how trouble stands."

"All right," Bo Rabbit makes response. "Meet me in the broomsage field tomorrow morning time the sun dries the dew off the grass good and I'll show you trouble."

Next morning time the sun gets high, Alligator takes his hat and starts to leave the house. Miz Alligator asks him where he's going.

"I'm going to meet Bo Rabbit so he can show me how trouble stands."

"Well, if you're going to see trouble, I'm going, too."

"Hush up, you ain't going nowhere," says Alligator, high and mighty. "You best let me go see how trouble stands first. Then I can show you."

This makes Miz Alligator so mad she starts to arguefy.

They quarrel so loud till all the little alligators hear them and come sliding into the room, *hirr, hirr, hirr, hirr, hirr, hirr.*

All the little alligators holler, "If you're going to see trouble, we're going, too. If you're going, we're going, too."

They make such a racket that to save his ears, Alligator roars, "Quiet! All right, all right. You *all* can come."

They cross the marsh and time they get in the broomsage field there's Bo Rabbit sitting on top a stump waiting for them.

"G'morning, Bo Rabbit," they say. And all the little alligators make their curtseys, *sazip, sazip, sazip, sazip, sazip, sazip.*

Bo Rabbit tells them "G'morning" back. "You all come to see trouble this morning, isn't it so!"

"It's so," says Alligator.

"It's so," say all the little alligators.

"All right. Stand out in the middle of the field and wait. I'll go get trouble and bring it."

Alligator, Miz Alligator and all the little alligators slither into the field, KAPUK, *Kapuk, kapuk, kapuk, kapuk, kapuk, kapuk, kapuk.*

Bo Rabbit runs to the far edge and cuts him a hand of broomsage. Then he puts fire to it and runs it round and round the field till the fire runs round and round the field.

Miz Alligator sees the fire jumping up red and the smoke rising. "What's that yonder, Alligator?" She lives in the river and the wet marsh and never sees fire.

Alligator runs his eye around and shakes his head in puzzlement.

"I think that's the trouble Rabbit is bringing to show us," says Miz Alligator.

All the little alligators jump up and down and holler, "Ain't trouble pretty, Ma? Ain't trouble pretty!"

Soon the fire hot gets close and the smoke gets bad and all the alligators take out for one side of the field. They meet the fire.

They turn around to the other side. They meet the fire.

The fire gets so close it feels like it's going to burn them.

They all shut their eye and throw their head close to the ground and bust through the fire and never stop till, SPASHOW, Alligator jumps in the creek.

Right behind him, *Spashow*, Miz Alligator jumps in the creek.

Then all the little alligators come, *shu, shu, shu, shu, shu, shu,* in the creek.

As they scramble out, Bo Rabbit yells across the stream, "You've seen trouble now, Alligator. You like to see it again? I can show you."

"No, suh, Bo Rabbit. No, suh," says Alligator.

He looks at his suit. His white suit good enough for Sunday is gone.

He is blackish-green and rough and bumpy just the way he stands till yet.

"It's all Bo Rabbit's fault. Him and his Judas ways," says Alligator.

But even as the words come out his mouth, Alligator knows in his spirit that's not rightly so. He's the one asked to see trouble.

"I've learned one lesson for all my life," says Alligator. "Don't go looking for trouble, else you might find it."

The Bird That Was Ashamed of Its Feet

Children of all ages spend a lot of time scrutinizing themselves and agonizing over any-thing that doesn't seem normal. How do we, by the time we are adults, learn to appre-ciate what makes us unique? This Cherokee tale, adapted by storyteller Gayle Ross, offers all of us a new way to look at ourselves.

This is what the old people told me when I was a child, about the days when the world was new and all creatures still spoke the same language. Now, in those days, there was a bird called Meadowlark, whose feet grew so big that he was ashamed of them. While the other birds flew through the air and sang in the treetops, Meadowlark hid himself in the tall grass where no one could see him. He spent all his time staring down at his big feet and worrying about them.

"Provider must have made a terrible mistake," thought Meadowlark, turn-ing his feet this way and that. No matter how he looked at them, all Meadowlark could see was how big his feet were. "Perhaps Creator thought this would be a funny joke to play," said Meadowlark. "I'm sure anyone who saw my big feet would laugh at them, but I do not think this is funny at all." And so Meadowlark con-tinued to hide himself away in the tall grass.

One day Grasshopper was going about his business, making his way through the tall grass, when he bumped smack into Meadowlark, sitting on the ground and staring sadly at his feet.

"What are you doing here?" asked Grasshopper. "You are not one of those birds who live on the ground! You should be in the treetops with the other birds. Why do you not fly and sing as they do?"

"I am ashamed," answered Meadowlark. "These feet that Provider gave me are so big and ugly that I am afraid that everyone will laugh at me!"

Grasshopper looked down at Meadowlark's feet, and his eyes grew big with amazement. It was true; Meadowlark's feet were huge! Grasshopper did his best not to smile; he did not want to hurt Meadowlark's feelings.

Finally he said, "Well, it is true that your feet are perhaps a bit larger than those of other birds your size. But Creator does not make mistakes. If your feet are big, you may be sure that they will be useful to you someday. Big feet will not keep you from flying. Big feet will not stop you from singing. You are a bird and you should act like one!" And Grasshopper went on about his business.

After Grasshopper had gone on his way, Meadowlark sat and thought about his words. "Perhaps he is right," said Meadowlark. "The size of my feet cannot change the sound of my voice or the power of my wings. I should use the gifts Creator gave me." And so Meadowlark took Grasshopper's advice and flew out to sing. He landed in the top of a tree, threw back his head, and let his song pour from his throat. Meadowlark could really sing! Piercingly sweet and beautiful, the liquid notes of Meadowlark's song spread through the forest.

One by one, the animal people stopped what they were doing and gathered to listen to Meadowlark's voice. Raccoon, Possum, and Skunk; Deer, Bear, and Wolf; even Rabbit paused in his scurrying about to listen in wonder to this marvelous singer. The other birds flocked around Meadowlark, listening. Even Mockingbird fell silent, entranced by the melody that Meadowlark sang.

When Meadowlark began to sing, he forgot everything else, even his big feet. He closed his eyes and lost himself in the joyful song Creator had given him. When at last he finished his song and looked around, there were all the other birds and animals, staring at him. With a rush of shame, Meadowlark remembered his feet. Thinking that the others were staring at him because he was so ugly, Meadowlark flew back down to the tall grass and hid. And this time he would not come out.

Not very far from the tall grass where Meadowlark hid, there was a wheat field planted by the Human Beings. Now there was a Quail who had made her nest and laid her eggs in the middle of this wheat field. Every day she sat on her nest and waited for her eggs to hatch. As the wheat grew ripe and her eggs had still not hatched, Quail began to worry. Sure enough, one afternoon she heard the people talking about how they were going to come out and cut the wheat the very next day. Quail knew that her nest would be trampled and her eggs crushed, and she began to cry.

Now Grasshopper heard Quail crying, and he came to see what was wrong. "The men are coming to cut the wheat," Quail cried, "and my family will die!"

Suddenly Grasshopper had an idea. "Wait here," he told Quail. "I think I know someone who can help."

Grasshopper hurried to find Meadowlark. "Quail needs help to move her family," said Grasshopper, "and I think your big feet are the answer."

When Meadowlark heard of Quail's trouble, he agreed at once to try to help. He flew to Quail's nest. There he found that his big feet were just the right size to pick up Quail's eggs. Very carefully, Meadowlark lifted Quail's eggs and flew with them to the safety of the tall grass. There Quail built a new nest, and it was not long before the eggs hatched. As Meadowlark watched Quail tending her beautiful babies, he thought to himself, "My feet may be big and ugly, but they did a good thing. I should not be ashamed of them!"

And so Meadowlark flew out of the tall grass, back to the treetops where he began to sing. He is singing to this day, and his song is still so beautiful that everyone stops to listen.

A Boy and His Donkey

Every book of etiquette makes it clear that one fundamental rule of good manners is to take the smaller portion and leave the larger for others. We can tell our children this, but it is much more likely that they will remember it after reading this tale from the Hispanic Southwest.

Once there lived a very poor woman who lived alone with her only child.

One day the son, who was only ten, decided to seek work. "Mother," he said, "let me go out and look for work."

His mother would not permit him to go because he was too young. But the boy insisted that he should go out and look for work to help support her. He bothered her so much that one day she finally relented. She prepared a packsack with provisions for her brave young son, gave him her blessing, and sent him on his way. The lad then loaded the provisions on his donkey and set out to look for work. He didn't know which direction to take, so he wandered until he was far from home.

But the Virgin Mary, who was the boy's patron saint, and the prayers of his mother guided him. On the road he traveled he met a woman dressed in a blue robe.

"Where are you going, my son!" asked the woman, who was in truth the Blessed Virgin.

"I am looking for work to support my mother."

"You are a good son, but you must be very careful because there are many evil men on this road who may harm you," she warned him.

"They can't harm me," the boy answered, "because I have nothing they can steal."

The Virgin smiled. "Since you are determined to continue your journey, here, take these three apples. Whenever you meet someone who wants to travel with you, cut an apple in half, but always cut one half smaller than the other. Offer both halves to the person; and if he takes the bigger half then do not count that person as your friend. He is a bad person, and may harm you. But the person who takes the smaller half will be a good friend whom you can trust."

The boy tucked the three apples in his coat pocket and continued on his way. That evening he met a man who asked him if they could travel together as companions and the boy agreed. When they stopped to rest that evening the boy cut one of the apples in half, remembering to leave one half smaller than the other. He offered them to the man. The man reached for the bigger half.

This is not a good companion, the boy thought. And he was right because it was the intention of the man to steal the donkey once the boy was asleep.

That night, although he was very tired, the boy didn't sleep. When he was sure the man was asleep he got up very quietly, gathered his provisions and hurried to his donkey. He loaded his burro and fled.

When the thief got up to steal the burro he found both the boy and the donkey gone. The thief cursed his luck and wondered how the boy had known his intentions.

Later on his journey, the boy met another man. The man suggested to the boy that they could travel together since they were going in the same direction. The boy agreed. That evening he cut the second apple in half, again cutting one half smaller than the other. He offered them to the stranger and the man immediately took the bigger half. So the boy knew this was another sly man to beware of.

That night as soon as the man had fallen asleep the boy got up very quietly and carried his pack to where his burro was hobbled. He packed his provisions and was far away by the time the thief awakened to find himself alone with his evil intentions.

The very next day the boy met up with an old man.

"Where are you going, my son?" the old man asked.

"I am going to the city to look for work," the boy replied.

"There are many thieves on this road. They might harm you."

"They can't harm me," the boy answered, "because the prayers of my mother and the Blessed Virgin Mary protect me."

"Very good, my son," the old man nodded. "I am going in the same direction. Why don't we travel together?"

The boy agreed and they continued together. That evening when they had arrived at a campsite, the boy cut his last apple in half, again leaving one half smaller than the other. He offered them to the old man, and the old man took the smaller piece.

And so the boy knew that he had met a good companion with whom he could travel. That night he slept soundly, confident that he had met a good friend. When he awoke the sun was already high in the sky. He rubbed his eyes and looked around, but the old man was gone.

The boy leaped out of his bedroll and ran in search of his burro. But when he went down to the pasture he found them both. The old man had simply moved the burro to where there was better pasture. From that day on they traveled together and became good friends, and eventually the boy found work, and sent money to his mother.

Brer Possum's Dilemma

Storyteller Jackie Torrence was told this tale by her grandmother after she was bitterly disappointed by the betrayal of a friend. She says that, though it was a bitter lesson to learn that some people are ungrateful by nature, stories like this one comforted her.

Back in the days when the animals could talk, there lived ol' Brer Possum. He was a fine feller. Why, he never liked to see no critters in trouble. He was always helpin' out, a-doin' somethin' for others.

Ever' night, ol' Brer Possum climbed into a persimmon tree, hung by his tail, and slept all night long. And each mornin', he climbed outa the tree and walked down the road to sun 'imself.

One mornin' as he walked, he come to a big hole in the middle of the road. Now, ol' Brer Possum was kind and gentle, but he was also nosey, so he went over to the hole and looked in. All at once, he stepped back, 'cause layin' in the bottom of that hole was ol' Brer Snake with a brick on his back.

Brer Possum said to 'imself, "I best git on outa here, 'cause ol' Brer Snake is mean and evil and low-down, and if I git to stayin' around 'im, he jist might git to bitin' me."

So Brer Possum went on down the road.

But Brer Snake had seen Brer Possum, and he commenced to callin' for 'im.

"Help me, Brer Possum."

Brer Possum stopped and turned around. He said to 'imself, "That's ol' Brer Snake a-callin' me. What do you reckon he wants?"

Well, ol' Brer Possum was kindhearted, so he went back down the road to the hole, stood at the edge, and looked down at Brer Snake.

"Was that you a-callin' me? What do you want?"

Brer Snake looked up and said, "I've been down here in this hole for a mighty long time with this brick on my back. Won't you help git it offa me?"

Brer Possum thought.

"Now listen here, Brer Snake. I knows you. You's mean and evil and low-down, and if'n I was to git down in that hole and git to liftin' that brick offa your back, you wouldn't do nothin' but bite me."

Ol' Brer Snake just hissed.

"Maybe not. Maybe not. Maaaaaaaybe not."

Brer Possum said, "I ain't sure 'bout you at all. I jist don't know. You're a-goin' to have to let me think about it."

So ol' Brer Possum thought—he thought high, and he thought low—and jist as he was thinkin', he looked up into a tree and saw a dead limb a-hangin' down. He climbed into the tree, broke off the limb, and with that ol' stick, pushed that brick offa Brer Snake's back. Then he took off down the road.

Brer Possum thought he was away from ol' Brer Snake when all at once he heard somethin'.

"Help me, Brer Possum."

Brer Possum said, "Oh, no, that's him agin."

But bein' so kindhearted, Brer Possum turned around, went back to the hole, and stood at the edge.

"Brer Snake, was that you a-callin' me? What do you want now?"

Ol' Brer Snake looked up outa the hole and hissed.

"I've been down here for a mighty long time, and I've gotten a little weak, and the sides of this ol' hole are too slick for me to climb. Do you think you can lift me outa here?"

Brer Possum thought.

"Now, you jist wait a minute. If'n I was to git down into that hole and lift you outa there, you wouldn't do nothin' but bite me."

Brer Snake hissed.

"Maybe not. Maybe not. Maaaaaaaybe not."

Brer Possum said, "I jist don't know. You're a-goin' to have to give me time to think about this."

So ol' Brer Possum thought.

And as he thought, he jist happened to look down there in that hole and see that ol' dead limb. So he pushed the limb underneath ol' Brer Snake and he lifted 'im outa the hole, way up into the air, and throwed 'im into the high grass.

Brer Possum took off a-runnin' down the road.

Well, he thought he was away from ol' Brer Snake when all at once he heard somethin'.

"Help me, Brer Possum."

Brer Possum thought, "That's him agin."

But bein' so kindhearted, he turned around, went back to the hole, and stood there a-lookin' for Brer Snake. Brer Snake crawled outa the high grass just as slow as he could, stretched 'imself out across the road, rared up, and looked at ol' Brer Possum.

Then he hissed. "I've been down there in that ol' hole for a mighty long time, and I've gotten a little cold 'cause the sun didn't shine. Do you think you could put me in your pocket and git me warm?"

Brer Possum said, "Now you listen here, Brer Snake. I knows you. You's mean and evil and low-down, and if'n I put you in my pocket you wouldn't do nothin' but bite me."

Brer Snake hissed.

"Maybe not. Maybe not. Maaaaaaaybe not."

"No, sireee, Brer Snake. I knows you. I jist ain't a-goin' to do it."

But jist as Brer Possum was talkin' to Brer Snake, he happened to git a real good look at 'im. He was a-layin' there lookin' so pitiful, and Brer Possum's great big heart began to feel sorry for ol' Brer Snake.

"All right," said Brer Possum. "You must be cold. So jist this once I'm a-goin' to put you in my pocket."

So ol' Brer Snake coiled up jist as little as he could, and Brer Possum picked 'im up and put 'im in his pocket.

Brer Snake laid quiet and still—so quiet and still that Brer Possum even forgot that he was a-carryin' 'im around. But all of a sudden, Brer Snake commenced to crawlin' out, and he turned and faced Brer Possum and hissed.

"I'm a-goin' to bite you."

But Brer Possum said, "Now wait a minute. Why are you a-goin' to bite me? I done took that brick offa your back, I got you outa that hole, and I put you in my pocket to git you warm. Why are you a-goin' to bite me?"

Brer Snake hissed.

"You knowed I was a snake before you put me in your pocket."

And when you're mindin' your own business and you spot trouble, don't never trouble trouble 'til trouble troubles you.

The Red Rag Under the Churn

The Devil figures mightily in the cautionary tales of North America where many folk-tales teach the values of religious faith. Avoidance of the Devil is the obvious message in the following tale from Kentucky, but a more subtle message is implied: "Be suspicious when you are offered something for nothing."

One day a man went over to his neighbor's to see him about trading hogs. When he got there the old woman come to the door an' told him her man's off somewheres in the field, but would he come in an' wait a spell till he'd git back. He done so, and when he got hisse'f set down he took notice that she's doin' her churnin'. Hit come to him how quick she's gittin' her butter, too, a heap faster'n his old woman ever got hern. He asked her could he have a drink, an' quick 's she got out the door after him one he lifted up the churn and looked under it, and thar were a little bitty red rag, like off'n a flannel petticoat. He got out his knife and cut him off a piece, and put the rag back under the churn, against she got back with his drink. Then he told her he 'lowed he'd not wait longer, but go out an' see if he could find her man in the field.

But he never went ary a step after that man. He went home to his wife fast's he could ever git there. He says to her, "Sary, git up what cream you have, an' do some churnin' fer me."

She looked at him wonderin'-like, an' says, "What fer ye wantin' me to churn? I ain't got but a dab o' cream, an' they's heaps o' butter, down to the springhouse."

He just says to her, "Sary, you git out what cream they is, an' do a churnin' fer me right off!"

Well, when a man spoke to his old woman thataway, she done what he said. Leastways, in them days she did. She brought out her churn, an' her dab o' cream, an' was just fixin' to begin her churnin' when he says, "Here, Sary, let me hitch up your churn an' put this here little bitty red rag under it."

She looked at him funny-like, but she never said nothing. So he put his rag under the churn an' she begun. Well, will ye believe what I'm tellin' ye? They wasn't scarcely enough cream in that churn to make a splash, but right off she could tell hit was gittin' fuller'n fuller. Hit wasn't no time till the butter was comin' so fast hit scared her. She jumped up and grab up her churn an' started out the door, sayin' she didn't aim to git mixed up in no bewitchment. Her old man picked up the red rag and stuffed it in his pocket.

That evenin', when he'd done finished up his chores, he was just startin' from his milkin'-shed back to the house when all to onct they was a huge-big figger standin' square in front of him. The sun-ball was settin', and this figger looked plumb queer, with the red glare from the sun-ball lightin' up all the sky behind him.

Hit come up, a-bowin' and smilin', and helt out his hand with a little book in it to the man. He says to the man, "Sign your name right here, if you please."

The man was feelin' mighty queer by this time, but he pulled hisse'f up the best he could an' says, "If you're aimin' fer me to sign your book, bring it over here to me your se'f!"

The feller looked at him surprised an' says, "Why, I can't come over to you."

Then he saw as how they was a circle plumb round him, an' hit come up clost to where the figger was standin', but not quite. So he reached over and took the book and opened it. They was writin' at the top of the page an' hit said, "WE, AND ALL THAT WE POSSESS, BELONG TO THE DEVIL." Below hit was the names of all his neighbors, an' the name of the woman what had the red rag under the churn headed the list!

Well, he looked acrost at the figger, an' hits eyes were glarin' at him like coals of fire, but he says, "I ain't goin' to sign nothing like that! I don't belong to the devil!"

The figger glared at him worse'n ever, an' says, "Hit's strange if ye don't belong to the devil. Ye have took part in witchcraft! What about that there red rag under your churn?"

Right then the man he felt somethin' movin' in his pocket, an' fore he could bat his eyes twict, out come the purtiest little bitty red bird, an' hopped up on his wrist. Hit cocked one eye up at him an' then flew acrost an' lit plumb on the shoulder of that awful-lookin' figger. An' all the time hit were lettin' out the horridest loud chuckles, like a demon laughin' at him.

The man he turned to the book real quick an' writ somethin' down on the other side of the page, an' signed his name. He writ, "WE AND ALL THAT WE POSSESS BELONGS TO THE LORD." Then he reached the book back to the figger. He give just one look at it, an' then he—he—, well, I 'low he jist went up in smoke! Leastways they was a flash, like a fire, an' a smell of brimstone, an' the man fell to the ground in a sort o' fit.

Soon's he come to hisse'f he got up an' run in to his wife. He told her what had happened to him, an' said they was aimin' to pack up an' leave thar the very next mornin'. He wasn't aimin' to stay where all his neighbors belonged to the Devil!

I reckon they moved right off. Leastways they hain't no one lived there up on the side of the hill since I can recollec'. An' will ye believe what I'm tellin' ye? Right thar where the figger stood, they hain't nothin but sage-grass growed from that day to this. I reckon that's the reason they've allers named that thar patch of sage-grass THE DEVIL'S GARDEN.

The Two Wagoners

In the largely Catholic Hispanic culture, stories whose characters include God and the saints are frequent. Although capable of miracles, they are presented in folktales as quite human; sometimes they are even roguish. But generally the tales they inhabit are meant to instruct people in the right relationship with the deity.

One hot summer day two men with wagons were delivering firewood to the villagers of the Villa Real de Santa Fe. When they came to the steep and narrow path which climbed La Bajada hill, the carts got stuck. Try as they might, the two pairs of oxen couldn't pull the heavily loaded carts up the steep hill.

One of the wagoners worked diligently with his oxen, cracking his whip over their backs and cussing and coaxing them to pull harder.

His *compadre* in the second cart didn't seem too concerned about the predicament. He calmly lay down in the shade to take a nap.

God will help me out of this dilemma, he thought to himself. I'll just say a few prayers before I take my nap!

Now it so happened that the Lord and St. Peter were on their way to Santa Fe that same day. They often traveled the old Camino Real to watch over their flock and perform good deeds for worthy people. When they came upon the two wagoners the Lord said, "Come now, St. Peter, let's help this honest man push his wagon up the hill."

So they put their strong shoulders to the wagon of the man who was working so diligently and they soon had it up the steep grade and on its way to Santa Fe.

The Lord and St. Peter then continued on their way. St. Peter, who had been reflecting on the ways of the Lord, finally stopped and said, "Lord, I am perplexed. Why did we help the man who was cursing in his work, but didn't help the man who remembered you in his prayers!"

"Well, St. Peter, I can see you have some things to learn about human nature and the way of the Lord. The man we helped did not curse from his heart. His language was that of affection for his oxen. He is a good man who works hard and is concerned with the well-being of his family. But the second man is a lazy one who thinks that I will solve all his problems if he only mumbles a few prayers before he sleeps. He is a hypocrite who remembers me only when he is in trouble. He can stay where he is!"

Annancy and the Yam Hills

This African American story was recorded in the 1890s and recounts the prodigious greed of the famous African trickster-spider, Annancy. Annancy is still a major character in tales told in North America. In some areas the name has been changed to Nancy, and the character takes on female traits. Like tricksters in other cultures, Annancy roams the world doing pretty much what he pleases. Sometimes he gets away with his deceptions, and sometimes, as here, he doesn't.

A long time before time dere was a Queen, who was bery wicked; an' she was a witch, an her name was Five; but she didn't like dat name, so she say, who eber say Five, mus' fall down dead!

An' one time, it was bery hungry times, an' all the rivers were from bank to bank—an' nobody could get across to go to market side. An' Annancy get to be bery hungry, so he was cunning an' go an' build five piles of yams by de riber side. An' he build a nice little house dere, too.

An' when de rainy season over, de people day come fetch water at de ribber. An' by dis time Annancy was getting more an' more hungry. So when anybody come along him would say:

"I beg you, come tell me how many yam hills I have here; I can't count bery well."

So den de friendly ones would come to where de yam hills was an' count dem.

"One, two, three, four, five"—an' when dey say "five" dey fall down dead, and den Annancy eat dem!

So time go on an' on; an' Annancy lib bery well, an' in plenty, till one time Guinea Fowl come along, on her way to de grand market; an' Annancy say:—

"Oh, Missus Guinea Fowl! I beg you come count my yam hills for me. I make some, an' I don't know how many. Do come tell me!"

So Guinea Fowl come to where de yam hills dem was. An' den she go an' sit upon one of dem an' say:

"I see, one, two, three, four an' de one I sittin' on!"

"Cho!" say Annancy; "you don' count right at all!"

An' Guinea Fowl say again, "One, two, three, four, an' de one I sittin' on!"

An' Annancy say again, "Cho! you don' count right, at all!"

So den Guinea Fowl say, "How you count it, den?"

An' Annancy say: "One, two, three, four, f-i-v-e!—five!"

An' him fall down dead, an' Guinea Fowl eat him up.

Dis story show dat "Bein' greedy choke de puppy!"

Words of Wisdom

———

An almost identical version of this Hispanic story has been recorded in Kentucky from Italian immigrants, and yet another version comes from Ireland. What seems nonsensical at first makes more sense after you have a bit of experience.

———

Once there were three poor men. Two of them had large families, but the third had only his wife and one son who was studying for the priesthood. One day they discussed the poverty of their small village and the job of feeding their families, and the three decided that it was best to leave their depleted farms and look for work in the city. So they prepared provisions and set out to look for work.

After they had traveled some distance they met an old man who asked them where they were going. They explained their situation and told him they were looking for work.

"Well," the old man said, "suppose I make you an offer. Which would you prefer to take: a bagful of money, or three wise pieces of advice that would serve you in life!"

"We'll take the money, of course!" two of the men said without any hesitation.

The man with the one son thought awhile and finally said, "I believe I will take the words of wisdom."

The old man gave the full sacks of money to the first two men, then he turned to the third and said:

"Don't leave the well-traveled road for the path. Don't ask about what does not concern you. And, don't jump to conclusions about what you hear and act too hastily."

Then he said goodbye to the three men and disappeared. Immediately the two who had chosen the money turned to the third man and exclaimed, "Oh, what a foolish thing you've done! What good is that advice going to do you?"

The man smiled. He knew the advice of the old ones was not to be taken lightly. "It may be that the three rules will serve me better than the gold will serve you. And I will gladly part with my wealth, so I am going to give you free the first piece of advice: As you return home, *don't leave the well-traveled road for the path.*"

"Bah! What do you know!" they answered and went off laughing. And to get home sooner they decided to take a path through the forest instead of the road. On the trail they were assaulted by thieves who killed them and took their gold.

The man who had been given the advice continued his journey until he came upon a very large ranch house where he asked for lodging for the night. The gentleman of the house invited him in and gave him supper. After supper, the master of the house took the man to meet his wife. She was very frail and thin, a mere skeleton. The man felt like asking why she was so thin, but at the same time he remembered the second proverb for guiding his life, so he remained quiet. The man then asked for work and was given a job.

Now it so happened that his host was a rich man who owned much land and had many servants, and in all his years he had never met a man who minded his own business. When anyone saw his wife they invariably asked why she was so thin and then he would become angry and run them off. If his rage was aroused enough he would have them killed. He had purposefully instructed his servants to feed her only leftover food, bones and pieces of dry tortillas, and that is why his poor wife was so thin. He had made a solemn vow not to better her condition until he met a person who would not ask why he kept his wife in such a state. On the other hand, if he met such a person, that person would acquire all of his wealth.

Now, the master thought, this last man I hired has not stuck his nose in my business; I will ask him why.

"Señor," he said to the worker, "why haven't you asked me why I keep my wife as I do?"

"Sir," the man replied, "a husband and a wife's business is their own, and I do not ask about what does not concern me."

"Well spoken," the master answered. "At last I have found a man who doesn't meddle in the lives of others. From this day forward you shall be the owner of everything I have, and I will ask my wife's forgiveness and treat her well."

The rich man gave the worker everything he had and then he and his wife left for another city. The man, now that he was the new owner of a vast ranch, decided to go fetch his family. He made preparations, packed his pistol and hurried home.

Now, he had been gone a long time, so when he arrived he decided to surprise his wife. He went to the window and peeked in and what he saw made his blood boil! A young priest had just embraced his wife! He immediately thought of killing his wife and reached for his pistol, but then he remembered the third piece of advice and calmed himself. He listened closely and heard his wife speak to the young priest, and then he recognized this man as his son.

The third maxim had served him well. He entered the house and greeted his family and they cried with joy. And the fortune which the rich man had left them was more than enough for the husband and wife to live well the rest of their lives.

So now you've heard my story
Of do's and of don'ts
And men who mistreat wives.
If you don't like my cuento
Tell your own to make us wise!

The Golden Rain

Kindness and generosity almost always pay off in folktales. Likewise, characters who are mean and selfish always receive their just deserts. Aunt Lizbeth Fields of Kentucky transforms this timeless fairy tale into a story for the children of her community to take warning by. Much of Aunt Lizbeth's archaic language reflects the Old World origins of the tale as well as of her ancestors.

In all the years I was a granny midwife I never tended but one woman that birthed twin babies, and them as like as two peas. It was different with the twins in an olden tale I aim to tell you while I wait for Dicie to get her business tended to.

The twin girls in the olden tale weren't no ways like each other. One of them was ugly as homemade sin and lazy and idlesome. T'other was pretty as a picture and helpsome and work brittle. Their mammy favored the ugly, idlesome girl and made a pet of her. The pretty, helpsome girl they made do all the work around the place. She had to spin and weave and pack water from the spring. They never let her rest or have a minute's peace.

One day they got so mad at her that they drove her off out of the house and made her sit by the spring and spin yarn. Maybe she liked better to be out away from the house where she couldn't hear them quarrel at her. She spun so fast she stuck her finger with the spindle and made the blood come. She stooped down to wash off the blood with spring water, and she fell into the spring.

She fell down and down through the water and on down past the water. When she came to herself and looked about, she was in a fine meadow, all over green and pretty with flower blooms and with birds a-singing. Falling straight down for such a far piece had made her feel scatter-wit. She sat there till she gathered up her wits, and then she got up and set out walking across the meadow.

First she came to a little house with some bread baking in the oven. The bread said to her, "Please take me out of this here hot oven or I'll burn up. Hurry, for I'm already a-scorching." She took the bread out of the hot oven and set it to cool. The bread said to her, "Thank you, mam, and put a piece of good fresh bread in your pocket to eat on while you are a-traveling."

Next she came to some walnut trees, all bending down clear to the ground with a heavy load of nuts. The walnut trees said to her, "Please to shake our limbs and make some of the nuts fall off so we won't break down with such a heavy load." She shook off nuts till the walnut trees' limbs raised up some. The walnut trees said, "Thank you, mam, and take some nuts for your journey."

Last she came to a little house where a little old woman was a-working. "Please," the old woman said, "come in the house and cook me some supper; I'm all tired and wore out and I can't cook me a bite to eat."

She fixed the old woman and herself a good supper. She washed up the dishes and cook pots and shook up the old woman's feather bed so she would rest easy. Weeks and months passed by and she went on living at the old woman's house, doing all the house work and spinning, and weaving goods to make the old woman some new wearing clothes. She hoed out the garden and tater patch and sang song ballads while she was a-working.

After a time she got homesick and wanted to go back for a visit. Seems like she was lonesome for her kin, no matter how bad they had treated her. The old woman asked her how much wages were owing, and the girl said, "You don't owe me nary penny."

To show her thanks the old woman made a shower of gold around the girl. The golden rain fell on her till she was all over covered with gold. She went back home like that, and they mirated over how she was all over covered with gold. She let them pick off her gold and hide it away to spend for things, and she told them where she had been and what took place.

The ugly, idlesome girl wanted to have a shower of gold fall on her. So she set a spinning wheel by the spring and stayed there a while. She never got no blood on her finger, for she never spun no yarn. She just stood up (after a time) and jumped into the spring.

It happened the same way with her, only she wouldn't help the things that begged her to. She walked right on and let the bread burn black as a cinder, and she let the walnut trees break down with such a heavy load of nuts. At the old woman's house she said she wouldn't do a lick of work lessen she got high wages. The old woman agreed to that. The girl turned out lazy and hateful and just sat around and collected her wages. After she stayed long as she figured she had to for the gold to rain down on her, she left the old woman's house to go back home. No shower of gold for her, though. It rained down sticky, black tar all over her, and she never could wash it off. Though she scrubbed and scoured till she wore the skin off of herself, she never could clean herself up; and she had to live that way, all black and sticky, to the end of her days.

Why Men Have to Work

This African American story offers modern Americans a cautionary tale about selfishness toward the environment. Though it is an ancient tale with mythological elements, it is freshly relevant given modern attitudes toward nature.

The sky used to be very close to the ground. In fact, it wasn't any higher than a man's arm when he raised it above his head. Whenever anybody got hungry, all he had to do was to reach up and break off a piece of the sky and eat it. That way, no one ever had to work.

Well, it was a fine arrangement for a while, but sometimes people would break off more than they could eat, and what they couldn't eat they just threw on the ground. After all, the sky was so big there would always be enough for everybody to eat. What did it matter if they broke off more than they actually wanted?

Maybe it didn't matter to them, but it mattered to the sky. In fact, it made the sky angry to see itself lying on the ground, half-eaten, like garbage. So one day the sky spoke out and said, "Now look-a-here! Can't have this! Uh-uh. Can't have you people just breaking off a piece of me every time your stomach growls and then taking a little bite and throwing the rest away. Now if y'all don't cut it out, I'm going to move so far away no one will ever touch me again. You understand?"

Well, people got the message. In fact, they were pretty scared, and for a while they made sure that no one ever broke off more of the sky than he could eat. But slowly they began to forget. One day, a man came by and broke off a chunk big enough to feed forty people for a month. He took a few little bites, licked around the edges, threw the rest over his shoulder, and walked on down the road just as happy and dumb as anything you've ever seen. Well, the sky didn't say a word, but with a great roar, the sky lifted itself up as high as it could, and that was pretty high.

When the people realized what was happening, they began crying and pleading with the sky to come back. They promised that they would never do it again, but the sky acted like it didn't hear a word.

The next day, the people didn't have a thing to eat, and they had to go to work to feed themselves, and that's why man is working to this very day.

A Bundle of Troubles

One of my favorite African American tales, "A Bundle of Troubles," reminds us not to think too much about that grass on the other side of the fence.

One night Mose went to bed 'bout bowed down with his troubles.

Seem like all of 'em was a-hoppin' on him at oncet. He turned and twisted, but by 'n by he went to sleep and then he had the dream.

Seem like, in the dream, ever'body had all a-sudden started miratin' and fussin' 'bout their troubles. Seem like they couldn't talk 'bout nothin' else. Fin'ly, the debbil, he got tard of all this loose talk 'bout troubles, caze most of 'em was blamed on him. Then one Sadday, 'thouht nobody 'spectin' him, he 'peared uptown, jes as the streets was most crowded, and he rung a bell to call all they 'tensions to him.

When ever'body gathered 'round, he say like this:

"I bin hearin' a powerful lot 'bout all you folkses' troubles. Yo'all thinks you is got more troubles as anybody. And I's a-gittin' mighty tard a-hearin' 'bout nothin' else. Yo'all nussin' your troubles so hard you ain't got no time for no real sinnin'.

"I tell you what I's a-gonna do. I's a-gonna take up all of you troubles. Ever'body what has got troubles, jes wrop 'em up in a bun'le and bring 'em down to the depot check-room right away and I'll take 'em up and rid each and ever'body of you troubles. Now go home and wrop them troubles up and hurry down to the depot with 'em."

Well, it didn't take Mose more'n a minit to git home. He say he warn't runnin' 'zactly, but he was a-passin' a lot of folks what was.

He got the biggest thing he could find to hold all of his troubles, which was a big paper box with "Saunders Tripe" printed on the outside. Mose didn't think it would begin to hold all his troubles, but he started in a-packin' anyway.

First went in his old rhumatiz, and then his cawns.

"Yo'all bin hurtin' me for many the year," he say, "and I's sho glad to part company with you."

Then went in the lan'lord, and the sto'keeper what Mose owe for his fertilize. Then there was his back church dues what he hadn't paid, and that yeller gal over at Marse John Simmons' place. I don't know why he put her in, but he did. Then he throwed in his sore tooth, and his boy what got drunk all the time, and the old plow what never would foller a straight furrow. Then went in his old black skin, all his gray hair, and his wife's naggin', and the hatchet what would fly offen the handle. He throwed in his old mule, Bess, what kicked the daylights outen him ever time she got a chancet, and that sportin' nigger what was a-slippin' 'round his youngest gal.

He throwed in a heap more tribalashuns, and it seem like the box jes' wouldn't hold all of 'em, but there was allus a lil room at the top.

By'n by he had 'em all in, and then he took a big breaf and a piece of old plow line and tie them troubles up hard and fast in the box. He made a nice bun'le and throwed it on his wheelbar' and started for the depot.

It took him a long time to git there, caze the streets was packed with folks all loaded down with bun'les. There was old Sis Thompkins what didn't anybody know ever had a trouble in her life, and what was allus a-laffin', and a-jokin', and a-goin' on. She was loaded down with such a big bun'le that she had three of her lil gran'chillun a-helpin' her tote it. There was the preacher with a good-size load. There was even white folks, and Mose was surprise at that, but they seem to have the biggest bun'les of all. There was old Cunnel LeRoy, the biggest man in the town; even he had a bun'le. It warn't a very big bun'le, 'bout the size of a dozen eggs wropped up, but it was a bun'le just the same.

When Mose got to the depot, the check-room was piled up to the ceilin' with bun'les, and the debbil had three-four of his imps a-helping him with the checkin'. Mose put down his bun'le, and a perlite lil imp put a check on it and handed Mose a stub.

"What fo' you gimme this check?" say Mose. "I don't want the bun'le back—no time atall."

"'Tain't you check," say the perlite lil imp. "It's somebody else's check. You see it's like this: Next Chusday all yo'all what's checked a bun'le of troubles comes back here with these checks and you gets somebody else's bun'le of troubles. Ever'one of you has been a-sayin that you troubles was worser yit, so the Old Man he gonna let each'n of you trade and git somebody else's troubles."

"Well," say Mose. "I sho won't mind that. Maybe I git some nice easy troubles like dander, or a good-lookin' wife, or too much money." And then he put out for home.

Long 'bout cain't-see time, when Mose was a-settin' on his porch, he got to thinkin' 'bout the propersition, and the more he think 'bout it the lessen he likes it. He 'members somethin' 'bout ole Cunnel LeRoy, and some of the other folks, too. Seem like it jes warn't workin' out like he had thunk. By'n by he got down his hat and his walkin' stick and he went down to the depot to see how things was a-comin'. When he got there, first thing he heerd was somebody laffin', and he looked 'round the corner of the pile of bun'les and there was the debbil and the imps a-laffin' fit to kill. Seem like they had jes heered the bestest joke anybody ever told.

"Now look here," say Mose to hisself, "When the debbil gits to laffin' somebody bound to git the worst of it. I ain't never heerd of the Old Boy a-doin' anybody a favor yit lessen he gits the best of the deal."

So he went up to the debbil, perlite-like, and he say, "Mister Debbil, mebbe I make a mistook today. I left a big bunch of troubles with you, but I ain't so sure now that I wants to part with 'em. They bin with me so long I thinks that I's growed kinda fond of 'em. Wonder could I get 'em back 'thouht nobody axin' me no questions?"

The debbil he open his mouf wide and laff. And when he laff it was worser as when he frowns. His eyes didn't have no whites in 'em and was all shiny like they bin polished. His funny skin was a-twitchin and his tail was a-lashin' back'rds and for'rds.

"Br'r Mose," he say, 'tween laffs, "I's powerful sorry to tell you, but the check for you bun'le is in somebody else's hands now, and I don't see how you can git it back."

"Well, then," say Mose, "I won'er iffen you can show me what kinda lookin' bun'le this here check of mine calls for?"

"To be sho," say the Old Boy, and he looked at the check, and went 'round comparin' it with the checks on the bun'les.

"Here it is," he fin'ly say, and he holds up the lil bun'le of troubles of Cunnel LeRoy. "Looks like a mighty nice lil bun'le of troubles you gonna git Chusday, Br'r Mose. I congratulates you. Jes a lil bun'le of white folks troubles. That ought'n worry a old darky like you."

When Mose see that bun'le he scairt most to death.

"Please, suh, Mister Debbil," he say, "please, suh, gimme my old bun'le of troubles back. That's it right over there by that lil green imp, in the box marked with the tripe. I bin a-thinkin' it over and my troubles ain't so bad. I kinda miss the ole cawns and the rhumatiz, and the game tooth. By rights I owes the lan'lord, and the sto'keeper, and it wouldn't be right not to pay 'em. That yeller gal ain't gonna bother me no more, caze she's gittin' crazy 'bout somebody else. I kin take a firmer hand with the chillun, and I don't mind being mule-kicked, or throwed by the plow, and I kinda misses the old woman's naggin already. To tell the truf, I don't believe they was troubles after all—jes lil worries, and I misses 'em tubble. Won't you please to give 'em back, suh?"

The debbil he laff agin, and he laff and laff. And Mose begin to back off a lil way. Then the debbil look mad, and he say: "Take you bun'le of troubles, Br'r Mose," he say, "but don't you ever let me hear you fussin' 'bout 'em agin, or I'll give you some sho-nuff troubles."

Mose grab up his troubles and toss 'em up on his shoulder like they was no more'n a box of feathers. It didn't take no wheelbar' to git 'em away from that depot.

Why didn't Mose take old Cunnel LeRoy's troubles when he had a chancet? I axes him that.

Mose say he see a coffin in that bun'le, and he 'members jes in time that the Cunnel's trouble was a lil old cancer of the stummick.

The Robe

———·—·——

La Llorona is a ghost who haunts many areas of the North American Southwest region as well as regions of Central and South America. Legend has it that La Llorona lived in Aztec times, though many tales place her much more recently. The story goes that her children were drowned; in some accounts she drowned them because she didn't want them; in some her husband forced her to drown them; and in others the drowning was an accident. Whatever the cause of her sorrow, La Llorona, "the weeping woman," roams the countryside crying for her children and warning others against wrongdoing. This story is not a traditional tale, but it is likely to provide a cautionary story in this young man's family for generations.

———·———

As a young boy growing up in the Belen area in the early 1950s, there were many times when I used to hear the story of *La Llorona*. There were several versions, but the one I used to hear the most often from my grandmother was that *La Llorona* had lost her two children and desperately needed to find them, and that she might see a child who looked like one of hers, and she would start screaming in agony. The reason she was always near the river was because that's where she had lost them, supposedly by drowning. My grandma also used to say that *La Llorona* had the ability to judge others because she lived in another world where the past, present, and future were one.

My understanding of *La Llorona* came into play during the summer of 1956, when Billy Segura moved into the neighborhood. Billy and I were both 12 years old and we hit it off right away. I liked Billy because he was afraid of absolutely nothing. He brazenly smoked Pall Malls, cussed up a storm, and dismissed as "stupid" all of the things that I had been taught to value from birth. Not only that, he talked about getting himself tattooed when he was 16 and joining the Navy. Billy was from Los Angeles and knew everything—a real sophisticated kind of a guy, I thought. My parents differed on this appraisal and forbade me to associate with him in any way whatsoever.

I was an obedient, well-behaved kid and I tried to oblige my parents but it was pretty useless in the face of Billy's constant insistence that we break the rules whenever possible. He also berated me for being "chicken" and for allowing my parents and grandmother to "push me around." This was around the time of the Korean conflict and there was a lot of publicity in the papers about American soldiers being brainwashed by the Koreans. Billy warned me about losing my ability to even reason in the face of their manipulation. I was putty in his hands.

I began climbing out of my bedroom window some nights to meet Billy and his wayward friends down by the river, or at the dump, or wherever they decided to congregate. Most of his friends were older kids—some of them even had their own cars and they carried chains or tire irons around the way some women carry purses. They had nicknames like "Killer" or "Loco" or; "Hitter," and I found out that one of the major reasons they all met so late at night was for the purpose of acquiring parts to their automobiles at minimal, if any, cost.

I began to wise up at some point and realized I was in over my head. I knew it was a matter of time before I would be placed on assignment as a "runner" or something illegal. I was also growing tired of this deception and I was still young and impressionable enough to fear my grandmother, fear *La Llorona*, fear my parents, and fear punishment. One hot night in August, I snuck home with a new resolve—I would not see Billy Segura or his weird friends anymore. I carefully removed the screen, climbed into my bedroom in the usual way, replaced the screen, and got into bed.

As I lay back against the cool pillow, relieved that I had finally made this decision to straighten out my twisted and corrupt life, I happened to look down toward the end of my bed, and there she was, the light of the half moon showcasing her like a Renaissance painting in a museum—*La Llorona*, seated in my rocking chair, as motionless as a statue. As I lay there in a state of complete terror, my eyes riveted to her darkened but distinctive form, a cloud moved across the moon and plunged us both into near total darkness. As the minutes—and then hours—ticked by on my trusty little alarm clock, *La Llorona* continued her vigil, staring at me in final judgment of my deeds. I knew, then, that it was probably too late to do anything—it was your classic example of the sinner repenting, only to find out that Judgment Day had already arrived, that the Grim Reaper—or, in this case, *La Llorona*—was already at the door.

I could see that she looked almost exactly as I had always pictured her, with the exception of a long braid that fell over her left shoulder. And, despite the heat of that endless summer night, she wore her dark cloak securely wrapped around her with a hood that almost completely covered her pale, twisted, and ancient face. Her mouth lay slackly open as if prepared to emit a silent scream, and I could see tiny little fangs glistening in the dim moonlight. As I lay there waiting for death or whatever fate *La Llorona* had chosen for me, I thought of my loving family, of this wonderful house we lived in, of the beans and chile and tortillas that I would never taste again in the awful netherworld that I would call home for all eternity. And I wondered why *La Llorona* was not sitting in Billy Segura's bedroom instead of mine. What had I ever done to deserve this?

And so, I have come to the end of my story. As you can see, I am still here. Of course, it was not *La Llorona* sitting in my rocking chair that August night. It was my bathrobe, a dark brown corduroy thing thrown carelessly over the back of the chair, a robe that my mother had made on her Singer sewing machine. It was an unusual bathrobe because it had a gold braid that served as a tie around the waist, which used to be a pull for some old draperies we had in the basement. And it had a hood that I could wear over my head on those cold nights when it was necessary to make a trip to the outhouse.

To this day, I regard the dawn as the most exciting, revealing part of the day, when a person is most susceptible to learning the truth about life.

What happened to Billy Segura? I have no idea. His family moved back to Los Angeles a few months later. I am glad I knew him for that brief period, though—the best lessons are always learned early in life.

6

Tricks and Tricksters

The trickster is one of the most enduring characters in the oral traditions of North America. Tales chronicling the exploits of Rabbit and Coyote originated around ancient Native American campfires, and the characters still influence Native American culture. In a less serious vein, but testifying to the lasting quality of the trickster, people enjoy seeing similar characters pulling similar tricks on the Saturday morning cartoons. In many of the best-known tales, the hero-trickster is a small, weak creature who gets the better of his stronger antagonist through wit and deception. We love the trickster because he (rarely she) flouts the laws of polite society, challenges the high and the mighty, and wins! He does what we would all like to do if we only dared.

European immigrants brought to North America tales in which a human trickster outwits other people, and such stories have never waned in popularity. Elements from trickster stories turn up in the Jack Tales (a fine example of which appears in this chapter), in tales about outsmarting the Devil, and in tales in which one member of a culture group consistently gets the better of everybody else, as in the stories of the Yankee Peddler. In some stories, such as those about Big John the Conqueror, the ability to pull the wool over the eyes of the unsuspecting has elevated characters in North American lore to legendary status. Though the tales below are from oral tradition and generally out of the past, the contemporary trickster is everywhere. Look for him at the movies!

Brother Rabbit Breaks Up a Party

When they were brought to America, African slaves lost almost everything but their folklore. It is significant that the central figure in the tales they preserved is Brer Rabbit, who is small and weak and in constant danger, but who manages to stay alive by using his wits. When Joel Chandler Harris published the Uncle Remus stories in 1880, he helped to fuel an interest in understanding and preserving African American traditions. Since then, the stories of the fruitless efforts of Brer Fox to outwit Brer Rabbit have been retold, updated, and republished in countless forms.

"One time," said Uncle Remus, "Brer Fox, he took and asked some of the other creatures to his house. He asked Brer Bear, and Brer Wolf, and Brer 'Coon, but he didn't ask Brer Rabbit. All the same, Brer Rabbit got wind of it, and he allowed that if he didn't get to go, he expected he'd have as much fun as the next man.

"The creatures that did get the invite, they took and assembled at Brer Fox's house, and Brer Fox, he asked them in and got them some chairs, and they sat there and laughed and talked, until by and by, Brer Fox, he fetched out a bottle of rum and lay her out on the side board. And then he sorter stepped back and said, says he:

"'Just do step up gentlemens, and help yourselves.' And you better believe they helped theirselves.

"Well, while they was drinkin' and drammin' and drammin' and goin' on, what do you expect Brer Rabbit was up to? You can just as well make up your mind that Brer Rabbit was monstrous busy, 'cause he was sailin' around fixin' up his tricks. Now, a long time before that, Brer Rabbit had been at a barbecue where there was a fit of playing the pipes and drums. And all the while all the folks was down at the spring eatin' dinner, Brer Rabbit, he crept up and ran off with one of the drums. There was a big drum and a little drum, and Brer Rabbit he snatched up the littlest one and ran home with it.

"Now, then, when he heard about the other creatures going to Brer Fox's house, what did Brer Rabbit do but get out this rattlin' drum and make his way down the road towards where they were. He took that drum, and he went down the road towards Brer Fox's house, and he made it talk like thunder mixed up with hail. It talked like this:

"'*Diddybum, diddybum, diddybum-bum-bum—diddybum!*'

"The creatures, they was a drinkin' and a drammin' and a goin' on at a terrible rate, and they didn't hear the racket, but all the same, here comes Brer Rabbit:

"'*Diddybum, diddybum, diddybum-bum-bum—diddybum!*'

"By and by Brer 'Coon, who always has got one ear hung out for the news, he up and asked Brer Fox what was that, and by that time all the creatures had stopped to listen. But all the same, here came Brer Rabbit:

"'*Diddybum, diddybum, diddybum-bum-bum—diddybum!*'

"The creatures, they kept on listenin,' and Brer Rabbit kept on gettin' nearer, 'til by and by Brer 'Coon reached casual-like under the chair for his hat and says, says he:

"'Well, gents, I expect I better be going. I told my old woman that I wouldn't be gone a minute, and here it is a long way in the day.'

"With that, Brer 'Coon, he skipped out, but he hadn't got much further than the back gate, for here came all the other creatures like they was running a foot-race. And old Brer Fox was working in the lead—he was that scared.

"Yessir! there they all were, and there they all went. They took short cuts, and they scrambled over one another, and they didn't rest 'til they got in the bushes.

"And meanwhile, old Brer Rabbit, he kept comin' on down the road:

"'*Diddybum, diddybum, diddybum-bum-bum—diddybum!*'

"And bless gracious! When he got to Brer Fox's house, there wasn't nobody there! Brer Rabbit is that audacious that he hunted all around 'til he found the air hole of the drum, and he put his mouth to that hole and sang out, says he:

"'Is there anybody home?' And then he answered himself, says he:

"'Law, no, honey. Folks all gone.'

"With that, old Brer Rabbit broke loose and laughed. He did! Fit to kill himself. And then he slammed Brer Fox's front gate wide open and marched up to the house. When he got there, he kicked the door open and hailed Brer Fox, but nobody was there. And Brer Rabbit, he walked in and took a chair, and made himself at home with puttin' his feet on the sofa and spittin' on the floor.

"Brer Rabbit didn't sit there long, though, before he caught a whiff of that rum. And then he *saw* it on the side-board, and, of course he stepped right up and dropped about a tumbler full somewhere down in the neighborhood of his goozle. Now, Brer Rabbit is mighty like some other folks I know. He took one tumbler full, and it wasn't long before he took another one, and as you know when a man does this a-way, he proceeds to get rummy.

"Now, all this time the other creatures was down in the bushes listenin' for that diddybum, and makin' ready for to light out from there at the drop of a hat. But they hadn't heard no more fuss for a while. And by and by Brer Fox, he says he's going back and look after his plunder. And the other creatures say they believe they'll go along with him. They started out, they did, and they crept towards Brer Fox's house. But they crept mighty careful, and I'm bound if somebody didn't shake a bush and make a racket, and all stopped stock still and listened. Yet they still didn't hear no fuss, and so they kept on creepin' 'til they got in the house.

"Well! When they got in there, the first sight they saw was old Brer Rabbit standin' up by the rum bottle, mixin' up a toddy, and he wasn't so stiff-kneed, neither. He sort of swang from side to side, and he looked like he was mighty limber, which goodness knows a man gets to be limber when he drinks the kind of liquor that Brer Fox provided for them creatures.

"When Brer Fox saw Brer Rabbit makin' free with his doins that way, what do you expect he did? What he didn't do, he didn't cuss; he didn't holler; and he didn't chase Brer Rabbit away like you'd think he would.

"In fact, to be sure, he was glad, because he saw right away that he had a good chance to catch Brother Rabbit once and for all.

"So he stood there, Brer Fox did, and he watched Brer Rabbit's motions. By and by he hollered out, says he:

"'Ah yi! Brer Rabbit!' says he. 'Many a time you've done made your escape, but now I got you!' And with that, Brer Fox and the other creatures closed in on old Brer Rabbit.

"Seems like I told you that Brer Rabbit had gone and taken more rum than what was good for his wholesomeness. Yet his head wasn't swimming so bad that he didn't know what he was doin.' And 'bout the time he laid eyes on Brer Fox, he knew he had done got himself in close quarters. As soon as he saw this, Brer Rabbit made like he was down in the cup even deeper than he was. And he took and staggered around like a town gal standin' in a canoe. It seemed like he was just as limber as a wet rag.

"So he staggered up to Brer Fox, he did, just as sassy and audacious as you please. And he rolled his eyeballs around, and slapped Brer Fox on his back and asked how he be. Then when he saw the other creatures, he hollered out, he did:

"'Put up your dukes, gentlemens! Put up your dukes! If you'll just gimme hand-room and come one at a time, the tussle'll last longer. Now you all come on,' says he.

"Ole Brer Rabbit talked so crazy that the other creatures had more fun than you can shake a stick at. But by and by Brer Fox said they better get down to business. So then they all closed in on Brer Rabbit, and there he was.

"Now, in them days, ole man Bear was a judge amongst the creatures, and they all asked him what they was goin' to do with old Brer Rabbit. And Judge Bear, he put on his specs and cleared up his throat and said that the best way to do with a man that kicked up such a racket and run the neighbors out of their own house and went in there and leveled the pantry was to take him out and drown him. And old Brer Fox, which was sittin' on the jury, he up and smacked his hands together and cried and said, says he, that after this he was going to believe that Judge Bear had got ahold of some lawyer-books, because that was exactly what they say when a man levels his neighbor's pantry.

"Then Brer Rabbit, he made out like he was scared, and he hollered and cried, and he begged 'em, in the name of goodness, 'Don't fling me in the spring branch. Oh! don't fling me in the spring branch! 'Cause y'all know I don't know how to swim!' But then he hung down his head like he was meeting his fate and said sadly, but if y'all are just dying for to pitch me in, then for mercy's sake, give me a walkin' cane, so I can have somethin' to hold onto while I'm a'drownin'.

"Ole Brer Bear scratched his head and said, says he, that as far as his remembrance goes back, he ain't come across nothin' in the lawyer-book to the contrary of that, and then they all agreed that Brer Rabbit could have his walkin'-cane.

"With that and a cheer, they caught up Brer Rabbit and put him in a wheelbarrow and carried him down to the branch, and flung him in.

"They flung him in, all right," continued Uncle Remus. "And Brer Rabbit lit on his feet, same as a tomcat, and picked his way out with the help of the walkin'-cane. The water was that shallow that it didn't more'n come over Brer Rabbit's slippers. And when he got out on the other side, he hollered back, says he:

" 'So long, Brer Fox!' "

Tío Conejo and the Hurricane

It is almost impossible to trace the path of folktales as they travel from culture to culture, and this tale demonstrates why. It is a Latino story, but its roots are in the original Brer Rabbit stories. (In Spanish, Tío Conejo *means "Uncle Rabbit.") Mary Ann Brewer, who tells this tale, says that it is popular in many places where hurricanes are frequent: in Mexico, Texas, North Carolina, and in the Caribbean. Wherever he lives, whether he is Uncle Rabbit, or Brer Rabbit, or simply Rabbit, the animal who is the smallest and weakest in the forest is the classic trickster who does more than just protect himself. When he has a chance to make a clean escape, Tío Conejo remains to bedevil his nemesis for the sheer joy of it.*

A long time ago, all the animals in the jungle got along with each other, except for one, Tiger, better known as Señor Tigre. Señor Tigre vowed to eat all the small animals he could get his claws on, and he loved to chase after Rabbit, better known as Tío Conejo.

But Tío Conejo was quick and smart, and he loved to play tricks on slow, gullible Señor Tigre. Like the time when Tío Conejo was cleaning out some vines and making a rope out of them. It was hot, and the sun was blazing down. Tío Conejo wasn't paying any attention, when who should come sneaking up behind him? Why, his favorite enemy, *el gato malo y tonto*, that mean dumb cat, Señor Tigre.

"OK, Tío Conejo, I've caught you now. You are one dead rabbit!"

Señor Tigre was too close. Tío Conejo knew he didn't have time to get away. He had to think fast. "OK, Señor Tigre. Just eat me up right now. I don't want to be around when—it happens!" Tío Conejo gave a little shiver of fear and rolled his eyes dramatically.

"What's going to happen, Tío Conejo?"

"Oh, Señor Tigre, haven't you heard? A terrible hurricane's coming. It'll be here any minute. This sudden heat is a sure sign."

"*¿El huracán? ¡A mi no me gustan los huracanes!*" Señor Tigre replied with a shaky voice.

"I know you don't like hurricanes. I don't like them either. That's why I'm making this rope. I'm going to tie myself down to something so I don't blow away." Tío Conejo held up his rope for Señor Tigre's inspection.

"That's a good idea, Tío Conejo. But you just wait a minute! I want you to tie *me* down. I don't want to blow away either."

"Oh, Señor Tigre, I like the way your mind works. Let's see what we can find to tie you down to." Tío Conejo's eyes danced as he grabbed Señor Tigre by the paw and led him through the jungle. Suddenly, Tío Conejo stopped short. "Oh, Señor Tigre, look at this big tamarind tree. I bet it has stood right here through lots of hurricanes. Let's tie you to this!"

"OK, *pero, bien fuerte.*"

"Oh yeah . . . good and tight, I'll tie you good and tight!" Tío Conejo couldn't help but smile.

So Tío Conejo tied Señor Tigre to that tamarind tree with his long rope of vines, wrapping it around and around Señor Tigre's chest. "*¿Bien fuerte, Señor Tigre?* Tight enough?"

But Señor Tigre was still uncertain. "*Un poquito mas.* Just a little tighter, Tío Conejo."

So Tío Conejo grabbed the rope with both paws and pulled with all his might. "*¿Bien fuerte ya?* Tight enough now?"

Señor Tigre's eyes nearly bulged out of his head. He managed to gasp out, "*¡Bien fuerte!*" But when he looked at the other end of the rope, Tío Conejo was nowhere to be found. *¡Tío Conejo se fué como una chispa!* Tío Conejo was outta there!

Now it should come as no surprise that Señor Tigre was not the most popular guy in the jungle. It took him well into the next day just to find someone who was willing to untie him. He finally talked a couple of monkeys into letting him loose. Just as they untied him, he grabbed one of the monkeys and started to pop it into his mouth. At that moment he heard a voice up on the tree.

"Uh-uh-uh! That's no way to eat a monkey, Señor Tigre. Don't you know how to eat a monkey?"

"Well, I *thought* I knew how to eat a monkey."

"No, Señor Tigre. You've got to throw that monkey up into the air, close your eyes, open your mouth, and let the monkey fall in. That's how you eat a monkey!"

Señor Tigre shrugged his shoulders. "OK," he said. He scratched his head and closed his eyes. Repeating the instructions to himself, *"Cierra los ojos, abre la boca, tira el chango,"* he threw the monkey up in the air. But the monkey caught a branch of the tree, and he was gone.

Tío Conejo was waiting in that tree. He had a big tamarind seedpod, and as soon as he got a good aim, he threw that big old seed right down Señor Tigre's throat. Oh, Señor Tigre was in terrible shape. He was coughing and sputtering, trying to get his breath. Finally, he blew that tamarind seed through the air. Then he ran back into the jungle, yelling for Tío Conejo.

Now, some people say that he's still out there—that somewhere in the thick, green, Latin American jungle lurks a slow, dull-witted, big cat with a bad temper. They say you can hear him as he runs through the jungle, yelling for Tío Conejo. "Tío Conejo, someday I'm going to catch you! You are one dead rabbit! *¡Tu eres un conejo muerto!"*

But you'll never hear Tío Conejo answer back. He's nowhere to be found. *¡Tío Conejo se fué como una chispa!* Tío Conejo is outta there!

Coyote Tricks the White Man

Folktales almost always have a function beyond their entertainment value. Stories about Brer Rabbit in the African American slave culture, for example, offered encouragement to people to find subtle ways to rebel. Some Native American tales took on the same function as white settlers became more and more a threat. In this example, where the white man is the butt of the joke, the point is unmistakable.

Coyote was walking down a road when he saw somebody riding toward him on horseback. When the rider came up Coyote saw that it was a white man. Coyote kept looking at him, already thinking up some way to cheat him.

The man pointed toward Coyote and said, "I'm looking for the cleverest coyote. Are you the one that tricks all the people; are you that clever one?"

Coyote said, "No, I am not that one."

But the white man insisted, "You are the man that cheats the people." Coyote kept denying that he was the clever one. "Hurry up," said the white man, "cheat me, perform some trick on me."

Coyote said, "Oh, I'm not that kind of man. They just call me that."

The white man said, "I know about you; let's have a match."

Finally Coyote said, "It's true, I'm that one, but my medicine for cheating people is at home. I left it way back west and it would take me a long time to go get it."

The white man said, "Well, you go get it."

Coyote answered, "I'm pretty tired. I've traveled a long ways. If you want to have a match, you lend me your horse and I'll go get my medicine."

The man got off his horse and said, "All right, you go get your medicine."

Coyote picked up a little stick and went to the opposite side from the white man in order to get on the horse. Coyote then jabbed the horse as he pretended to try to get on him. The horse gave a snort and jumped away from him. "Your horse is afraid of me because I have no hat," Coyote said.

"All right, I'll give you my hat," the man said.

Coyote pretended to get on the horse, jabbing him again. "Your horse is afraid of me because I have no coat," Coyote explained. The white man gave Coyote his coat.

Coyote again caused the horse to snort and jump. "Your horse is afraid of me because I have no boots." The man gave Coyote his boots.

Again Coyote tried to get on the horse, but as usual the horse appeared to be afraid. "Your horse is scared of me because I have no pants." The man took off his pants and gave them to Coyote.

Coyote did the same thing to the horse and said, "I haven't any gun." The man strapped his gun on Coyote. This kept up until the white man did not have a stitch of clothes.

When Coyote got all the white man had, he got on the horse and rode away, leaving the man with nothing on. After riding a short distance he turned and said, "Say, white man, you know it now. I am a clever Coyote; this is how I cheat people." The white man called him to come back, but Coyote did not listen and rode off and left him there. He took everything the man had.

Big John the Conqueror

Big John the Conqueror represented a human version of Brer Rabbit, having all the survival skills of that famous trickster, and then some! Although there is no firm evidence that he ever lived, stories about Big John were widespread among slaves, and they demonstrate how the slaves used the character as an escape valve in the face of oppression.

Every night Big John used to go up to the Big House and stand in the chimney corner and listen to what Old Massa talked about. That way he learned a lot about what was goin' to happen. If he heard Old Massa say he was gonna kill hogs the next day, Big John would slip back to the quarters and tell the other niggers, "Tomorrow we kills hogs."

"How you know that?" they asked him.

"I can tell fortunes, that's how," said Big John. "Ain't nothin' hid from me."

And the next mornin' when Old Massa come out and told all the niggers to get ready for a big hog killin', they decided Big John was a fortune teller for true. From then on they believed anything he told them.

One day when Big John was hangin' around the back door of the Big House, he seen his Mistress throw the water out of her wash basin, and in it he saw her diamond ring. But before he could pick it up, a turkey gobbler gobbled it down.

Soon the whole house was raisin' a ruckus lookin' for the lost ring, so Big John went to Old Massa and told him he knew where it was. Old Massa promised him if he could find the ring he would make him a present of a fine fat shoat. So Big John told him to kill the gobbler and he would find the ring.

At first Old Massa didn't want to kill his prize gobbler, and he told Big John that if he was foolin' him he would kill him sure. But when he killed the gobbler, there was the ring. From then on Old Massa thought Big John was a fortune teller too.

One day Old Massa was braggin' to some white folks that he had a nigger who could tell fortunes. One man disputed his word, so Old Massa said, "I'll bet you forty acres of good bottomland my nigger can tell fortunes!"

" 'f you so sure, what you spuddin' for?" asked the man. "Why don't you make a real bet? I'll bet you my whole plantation."

"Since you really wants to make a bettin' thing outa my statement," said Old Massa, "let's make it worth my time. We'll bet our whole plantations and every horse and mule and hog and nigger on the place."

So they agreed on it, and decided to prove the thing out a week from that day. Old Massa took Big John aside and told him about the bet, and said, "I bet everything I got in this world on you, and if you make me lose I'll kill you!"

The provin' day came and Old Massa was up bright and early. He was up so early he had to saddle his own horse and then go wake up Big John. Big John climbed on a mule, and off they rode to the provin' ground. When they got there it looked like everybody and their brother was on hand to see the sight. The other bettin' man had the privilege of fixin' the proof, so Big John was led away a little piece. Then they brought him back and showed him a great big old black iron washpot turned upside down, and they asked him what was under it.

Everybody knew but Big John. Old Massa told him he better think good if he wanted to live. Everybody kept quiet waitin' to hear what Big John would say. He looked hard at the pot and walked around it three or four times, but he didn't have the least idea what was under it. He began to sweat and scratch his head and Old Massa looked at him and began to sweat too. At last Big John decided he might just as well give up and get the killin' over with.

"You got the old coon," he said.

When he said that Old Massa threw his hat up in the air and let out a whoop, and everybody else was yellin' with surprise, cause that's what was under the pot,—a big old coon. So Old Massa went off to Philadelphia to celebrate, but before he left he give Big John his freedom and a hundred dollars and left him in charge of the plantation.

Old Massa and Old Miss had no sooner got on the train than Big John sent word to the niggers on all the plantations, "Massa is gone to Philamayork and won't be back for three weeks. He done left me in charge of everything. Come on over to the Big House for a big time." While the invite was bein' carried round, he told some of the hands to go into Massa's lot and kill hogs till you could walk on 'em.

That night Big John really spread a scrumptious table. Everybody that could get hold of white folks' clothes had 'em on. Big John, he opened up the whole house and took Old Massa's big rockin' chair and put it on top of Massa's bed. Then he climbed up and sat down in it to call the figures for the dance. He was sittin' in his high seat with a box of Massa's cigars under his arm and two in his mouth when he seen a couple of poor-lookin' white folks come in.

"Take them poor folks out of here and carry them back to the kitchen where they belongs," Big John said. "Don't allow 'em back up front again."

"Nothin' but quality up here."

He didn't know that they was Old Massa and Miss, who had slipped back to see how he would behave while they was gone. They washed the dirt off their faces and came back up front where Big John was still sittin'.

"John," said Old Massa, "after I trusted you with my place you done smoked up my fine cigars and killed all my hogs and let all these niggers in my house to act like they was crazy. Now I'm goin' take you out to the persimmon tree and hang you. You is entitled to a good hangin', and that's what you gon' get."

While Old Massa was gone to fetch a rope, Big John called his friend Ike to one side and said, "Ike, Old Massa is gonna take me out and hang me to the persimmon tree. Now I want you to hurry out to that tree and climb up in it. Take a box of matches with you, and every time you hear me ask God for a sign, you strike a match."

After a while here come Old Massa with a rope, and he led Big John out to the tree. He tied a noose in the rope and put it around Big John's neck and then threw the other end of the rope over a limb.

"I got just one favor to ask of you, Old Massa," said Big John. "Let me pray before I die."

"All right," said Old Massa, "but hurry up and get it over with, cause I never been so anxious to hang a nigger in my life."

So Big John kneeled down under the tree and prayed, "O Lord, if you mean for Massa not to hang me, give me a sign."

When he said that, Ike struck a match and Old Massa seen it and began to shake. Big John kept on prayin', "O Lord, if you mean to strike Massa dead if he hangs me, give me a sign." Ike struck another match and Old Massa said, "Never mind, John, you done prayed enough—the hangin' 's off!" But Big John prayed right on, "O Lord, if you means to put Old Massa and all his family to death unless he turns us niggers loose, give me a sign." This time Ike struck a whole handful of matches, and Old Massa lit out from there as fast as he could run.

And that's how the slaves was freed.

Jack and the Giants' New Ground

—·—·—

The Jack Tales are sometimes called American fairy tales because, though they are set in the ordinary coves and hollows of the backwoods, they are nonetheless peopled with the kings, queens, and fantastical beings common in European lore. Though Jack (or sometimes John) is known in folktales throughout the world, the tales most identified with North America are those told in the Appalachian region of the eastern United States. Popular culture was slow to come to the mountains, and modern tellers remember hearing the Jack Tales from their parents and grandparents who told them while the entire family worked at tedious tasks such as carding wool and weaving cloth. Skilled storytellers took an hour or more to finish a long rambling tale. Here, Mrs. Maud Long, of Hot Springs, North Carolina, evokes that earlier time when there was no need to hurry through a story.

—·—·—

A long time ago Jack and his folks lived way back in the mountains and they were just as poor as people could be. Will and Tom, the two older brothers, were just fine workers—they helped in everything. But Jack was just so lazy—half the time they couldn't get a lick of work out of him. Now, of course, this made for a lot of quarreling and fussing with the two older brothers and his father and mother.

So one day Jack said, "You know what I'm going to do? I'm going to clear out of this place. I'm going out into the world and see if I can't find me a fortune. I'm tired of this little old rocky farm."

So his mother fixed him up a poke of vittles and he threw 'em over his back and away he went. He walked and he walked, and the sun just a-beating down on him so hard. He got hungry and ate up his poke of vittles, and went a-walking on, and the sun getting hotter and hotter every step he took. And yet it wasn't twelve o'clock. And he thought, "I wonder where I'm gonna get a bite of dinner . . . for I sure am getting hungry."

Just then he noticed a nice-looking road that turned off from the main highway and he thinks to himself, "I'll just follow this a little way and see where it leads to." And pretty soon he came to a great big rock wall with a gate of pure gold. "Hm-m-m," said Jack to himself, "they's well-doing folks a-living here. I just wonder if they'd give me a bit of dinner. I believe I'll holler and find out."

"Hello-o-oo!"

Pretty soon a man came out on the porch and said, "Hello, stranger. What are you doing, what are you looking for?"

"Well, I'm a-lookin' for a job of work," says Jack.

"Well, I don't know as I'm hiring anybody right now, but come on in anyway, stranger, and sit a while."

Jack pushed that gate open and walked right in. And the man reached around and brought out two chairs, and says, "Come on, sit down, I reckon you can rest a little while, can't you? You're not in much of a hurry."

"No," Jack says, "I guess I can rest a little while anyway." So he took out his old corncob pipe and leaned back and went to smoking. Looked around after a while and he says, "And what did you say your name was, Mister?"

"Why, I'm the King. What's your name?"

"Jack's my name. Now, Mister King, I'm just mighty glad to know you. I'm mighty glad. And I know with all of this land that you have around here, you've got a sight of work. Don't you want to hire somebody?"

"Well," the old King says, "now Jack, I'd like to know, are you a good worker?"

"Oh, yes sir," Jack says, "I'm the finest worker there is back home."

"Well, can you plow?"

"Sure I can."

"Well, can you clear a new ground?"

"Why, you know, King, that's just all I do back home, I just clear new ground."

"Well, can you kill a giant?"

"Huh?" says Jack. Dropped his old pipe and he reached down and picked it up. Said, "Well, I ain't never killed one yet, but I guess I could try."

"Well, now," the King says, "if you can clear a new ground and if you're a giant killer, you're just the man I've been looking for. But I tell you, Jack, I have a new ground at the top of that mountain yonder that I've been trying to get cleared for a year. I've sent more than a dozen men up there, and they've every one been killed by that giant. Because you see, down in that other holler, there lives a family of giants that claim that new ground is theirs and they won't let anybody clear it. Well, if you can go up there and kill them, and then clear that new ground, Jack, I tell you, you're the man I'm looking for. Besides paying you good wages for clearing that new ground, I'll pay you a thousand dollars for every giant head you bring here to the house. And I'll give you ten cents a hour for every bit of work you do besides. And that's a good price."

"Yes, sir," Jack says, "that's a good price and that just suits me fine. I'll be ready to go up there and see what I can do."

"Yes," the King says, "after you eat a bite of dinner. Now come on in, I think the old woman has us some dinner ready. And let's see if we can't eat a little, and then you can go up there and see what you can do."

Jack went in to the table and, my!—it was just loaded with good things to eat. Chicken and ham and pie and cake, and biscuit and butter and honey. Oh, Jack just ate such a dinner!

But he looked across and the old King was still eating, and the Queen just piled his plate up full of food again and, lord, Jack didn't want those folks to think that he couldn't eat as much as the King.

So he reached down under the table and drew up that old leather apron that he always wore, fastened it good in his pants-belt, and drew his belt right good and tight to hold it down good and strong, and he begun eating all over again. He'd take a bite and then he'd slip a whole lot down into that leather apron. Poured four or five glasses of milk down in there, bread and chicken and cake— just everything.

After a while, the King pushed back his chair and said he was through. And Jack pushed back his chair, went out on the porch and he said, "Now I guess, bedads, I'd better be about that giant killing."

"Yes," the King said, "go on down yonder to the woodpile and you'll see there some axes. Pick you up the sharpest-edged looking one you can find, and go on. Up on the top of the mountain there, you'll find the tree with a chip or two taken out of it, where the other fellows have tried to begin chipping. But just about the time you begin a-whacking, Jack, right then the giants will be a-coming."

Well, Jack went on down to the woodpile, looked back and waved to him and said, "I'll be back in time for supper."

Picked him up a little old bit of a tommy-hatchet there, and the King said, "Jack, Jack! you'll need one of them big axes! Don't take that little old thing."

"No," Jack says, "bedads, this axe is just what I want." Stuck it in his belt and went a-climbing on to the top of the mountain.

Now when Jack got up there, he was sure worried. He didn't know what he was going to do. Gracious sakes, he didn't want to begin a-hacking on that tree, for those giants'ud come a-running up on him. And he knew that if he didn't hack some, the King would know that he hadn't been doing any kind of work and he wouldn't give him any supper. Well, he thought and he thought. What could he do? He just didn't know.

He looked around and he saw a tall slim poplar tree, the highest thing on the mountain. Climbed into the very tip top of that, took off that little old tommy-hatchet from out of his belt and begun hacking at the little bitty limbs. Ka-whack! Ka-whack!

He hadn't made more than six whacks till he heard something coming through the underbrush, and he looked down there and, gracious sakes alive, there was that two-headed giant that the King had told him about! (Yes sir, this one just had two heads, but the twins had three heads apiece, the old mother had three heads, and the old daddy had four.)

"Oh, boy," Jack says, "there comes $2000, but do you reckon I'll ever get 'em?"

He just kept right on a-whackin', though, just like he didn't know a thing was down underneath.

The old giant came right up to the very tree where he was a-whackin' and

looked up at him, and he says, "Howdy, stranger, what in the world are you doin'
up there?"

"Ah," Jack says, "bedads I'm clearing the new ground."

"Clearing the new ground!"

"Yes, I'm clearing the new ground for the King."

The giant said, "Now lookee here, stranger, what's your name?"

"Jack's my name, bedads."

"Well, Jack, you must be plumb crazy. Clearin' a new ground and a-begin-
nin' at the top of the tree. I never heard tell of no such."

"Why," Jack says, "that's the way we clear the new grounds back home all
the time."

"Well," the giant says, "listen, Jack, we're not havin' that new ground
cleared. No siree, we're not! This new ground belongs to us, and the King or
nobody else is goin' to clear it. Now you just come down on out of that tree and
go on home with me for supper."

Well, the old giant thought Jack wouldn't understand what he meant. But
Jack did. But he came sliding down the tree, but he stayed well up in the limbs
above that old giant's reach. He looked down at him and he said, "I tell you, I've
always heard that giants is powerful strong. How 'bout it, sir?"

"Well," the old giant said, "some of us is and some of us ain't. Now as for
me, I can kill any thousand Englishmen that ever dare face me, just barehanded."

"Well," Jack says, "I tell you what, I bet you I can do something that you
can't do."

"Huh," the old giant says, "what is that?"

"Why," says Jack, "I can squeeze milk out of a flint rock."

"Now you can't do it, and I know it!"

"Well," Jack says, "just a-hunt me up a flint rock down there and chunk it
up here, and I'll show you."

So while the old giant was hunting around to find an old flint rock, Jack
took a little old knife—the sharp point of it—and jabbed a little old hole in that
little leather apron. The giant threw him up the flint rock and Jack caught it in his

hand, squeezed it right up tight next to that little old hole in that leather apron, and drip, drip, drip went the milk right down at that old giant's feet.

"Well," he says, "lands sakes, Jack, do that again."

So Jack pushed it up good and tight against the little old apron and squi-i-i-r-rt the milk came out just like you was a-milking a cow.

"Well," that giant says, "throw that rock down here to me. If you can do that, I can do it."

Jack threw the rock down to the giant, and he squeezed down on it and he didn't get a drop of milk. And he squeezed again, and there didn't any milk come. And the old giant got so mad, he just squeezed down with all his might and just ground that flint rock into powder in his hands.

"Well," Jack says, "I can do something else you can't do, too, giant."

"Now," the giant says, "what can you do this time?"

"Why, laws a-massy, I can just take my knife and rip my stomach right open, sew it up again, and I'm just as good as new."

"Hah, now," the old giant says, "now I know you're lying, Jack."

"All right," Jack says, "bedads, just watch me."

Took his knife and he ripped open that little old leather apron and out came pouring milk and chicken and everything. And Jack just took him a little old rawhide string that he had, and punched him some holes, and sewed that old leather apron right back up again.

The old giant says, "Jack, for lands sakes, throw me down that knife. I know if you can do that, I can do it."

Jack threw him down the knife and the old giant picked it up and r-rripped open his stomach, and blood and everything come flying out—and first thing you know the old giant just reeled around there and keeled over dead.

Jack slid down that tree, took his little old tommy-hatchet, hacked off those two heads, and went a-dragging them down to the King's house.

Well, when the King saw him coming he says, "Land a-sakes, Jack, if you're not the finest killer I ever saw! You're sure the man I've been a-lookin' for. And here's your $2000 for those two heads. Now come on in, Jack, and eat you some supper and rest up a bit."

Well, Jack went in and he had him a good supper. And he had a good bed to sleep in and, oh!, he had $2000. "Ho," Jack thinks to himself, "boys, as soon's I can get away from here, I'm a-lightin' back out home."

After breakfast he said to the King, "Now I tell you, I'd better be going home. The folk's are missing me powerful back there, and I betcha my pappy's a-wanting me to help him set out tobacco. I'd better just be goin' on back."

"Oh, no," the King says, "Jack, you can't go back now. Why, gracious sakes, you're the finest giant-killer that there is. No sir, you go back up in that new ground and kill me some more of those giants. That's what you do. Why, I believe you can destroy the whole bunch of them."

"Well," Jack says, "bedads, I guess I can go back and try."

So he started back up the mountain.

Oh, my, how he wished he could get out of there without passing back by the King's house. He didn't want to mix up with those giants any more.

But he didn't have much time to think, because just about the time he reached there, a-coming up the holler he heard tramp! break! scrape! down through the thicket there. He looked and there came the twins with the three heads, just a-stepping over those big old rocks and thickets, coming just a-brushing up that mountain.

"Law," Jack thought, "what will I do? what will I do?" He was just shaking all over.

He saw a great old big hollow log over there, and ran into that just as hard as he could go, scooping his shirt-tail up full of rocks as he went in. Got in there and laid down. It was so big, why, he could stand right up in it. He just crawled down among some of the big old leaves and things that had blown in there, and lay as still as a mouse.

When those two giants came up and saw their brother lying there with his heads cut off, oh, my land, such taking on you've never heard! They screamed and they cried, and they said, "Oh, what will Pappy and Mammy say when they know about this! And don't we wish we knew who did it! Look, the ground's not tore up a bit. It don't look like there's been a sign of a fight, and yet his head's whacked clear off and gone. Oh, if we could just find the feller that did that, wouldn't we go for him! You know, he could have killed a thousand Englishmen if every one of them had come at him at one time. Now who do you reckon could have done that? Well," they said, "we'd better pick him up and take him on down home."

And one of them said, "You know what, Mammy sent us up here for some firewood. We'd better not go back without it either. But let's just pick the handiest thing there is. Let's just take this hollow log over there. That'll be just fine."

All right, one of the twins got at one end of it and the other at the other.

Of course Jack got jostled around a good bit laying in there, but finally they kind of got it up on their shoulders and settled down a little bit.

The giant in front had it just laying right up on his shoulders, just right with his head showing right square to Jack.

Jack waited until they got down the hill a little ways.

He picked him out one of those pretty good sized rocks and with all his strength—kavim!—he took the old giant right in the back of the head.

The old giant stumbled a little and he said, "Looky here, don't you be a-rocking me! Goodness knows we've got enough carrying this old log with brother laying on top of it. Don't go a-rocking me now, sir!"

"Oh," the other giant said, "why I didn't touch you with no rock. What's the matter with you? I've not got a rock anyway." He said, "Go on down that mountain."

Well, they started on down the mountain a little.

Traveled a little bit further, and Jack picked him out a little bit bigger rock. And ka-whack! he took him right in the back of the head. Oh, boy, that hurt, I know!

The old giant stumbled around and he said, "Now listen here, that's the second time you've done it. You hit me with another rock, and if you don't take a lickin' it will be because I can't give it to you. Now you mind what you're doing."

His brother said, "Well, what in the world are you a-talkin' about? I've not hit you with no rock."

Well, they just fussed and quarreled and gave each other the lie and everything you could think about. They finally started on down the hill, though, carrying the big old log with the brother laying on top.

Well, Jack reached around in among his rocks and got a real sharp-edged one, the biggest one of the whole bunch. And just let go with it—ka-wham!—right in the same spot. And just cut that old giant's head till the blood begun to ooze down there. Oh, it just almost knocked him down!

And he threw down that log and he took back at that other giant, and he said, "I tell you, I told you I'd whip you if it was in me if you hit me with another rock—and you've cut the blood out of my head!"

And such a fight you've never seen.

Why, they clawed and kicked and bit and pulled hair, and finally they just got clinched so tight, they rolled over and over on the ground. They kicked up great trees and rocks, and they just fought until they were so weak they couldn't even let go of each other.

When Jack saw them in that kind of a fix, he just crawled out of the end of that old log and—ka-whack, ka-whack, ka-whack, ka-whack, ka-whack, ka-whack!—the six heads of those giants were off.

Jack took the six heads and he went a-walking back down to the King's house.

Well, there was $6000 more. Oh, boy, Jack was feeling good.

The King says, "Now, Jack, you've killed all the young ones. There's just the old man and the old woman, and I know good and well you can go back up there and get them."

"Well," Jack says, "I tell you, this is enough. I guess I'd better be going for home, sure. I know my folks is worried about me by now. They're expecting me back to the house. I'd better go on."

"Not now, Jack," the King says, "go on back up there and kill the rest of those giants. And then the only thing in the world you'll have to do will be to clear that new ground."

"Well," Jack says, "bedads, I'll go on back up there and try."

So back up the mountain he started. And this time he didn't climb no trees. He wasn't a-shaking, he wasn't scared. He just took his little old tommy-hatchet and he begun a-hacking on that tree—ka-whack, ka-whack! And my land, it sounded like thunder coming up that mountain—this old big giant with four heads, just right charging on him. And he saw his boys lying there dead, their heads cut off.

He said, "Huh, stranger, howdy. What's your name?"

Says, "Mister Jack is my name, sir."

"Well," he says, "Mister Jack, do you know anything about who's killed my boys here?"

"Yes, sir," Jack says, "you're looking right at the man now. I killed 'em. Come up here sassin' and a-cussin' me around. I'm not takin' that off of anybody. And you want to be mighty careful, sir, what you say to me or I'll fix you the same way."

"Oh, yes," the old giant pappy says, "come on, Mister Jack, and come on down to the house with me and meet the old lady. Why no, I'm not going to sass you nor say nothing bad at all. I'm going to be powerful careful of what I say."

"Well," Jack says, "bedads, I don't care if I do, then. Let's go." And down the mountain they started to the old giant's house.

The old giant said when he got pretty close, he said, "Now, Jack, you'd better wait out here and let me go in, for when I tell the old woman about these boys being killed and your being out here, she's a-going to take on powerful. Law, they's no telling what she might do. So, Jack, you just stay out here and wait on me a little while, and I'll go in. And then if it's all right, why, we'll be glad to have you come in for some supper."

"Well," Jack says, "bedads, I'll just wait out here on you."

He just waited until the old giant got in the house and

he went a-slipping up to the door as fast as he could and put his ear right to the keyhole, and he heard the old man say, "Old woman, they's a little old man out there named Mister Jack. Jack's killed all three of our boys. He's cut their heads off. You've never seen such a fight in your life as they fit up on that mountain . . . it's just cleared up pretty near!" And he said, "This Mister Jack says he done it. Now I don't know whether he did or not. He don't look powerful strong to me, but out there's the boys. I brought 'em down. They're laying out there in the yard."

Well the old woman *did* throw a fit. She screamed and she cried and she raved, and then she said she'd kill Mister Jack. . . .

"Now, now, now," the old man said, "don't you go out there. He's killed those three boys. Now don't you dare go. Old woman, you're a-kind of weak and feeble compared to them. Don't you go out that way. You just wait. I'll test out Jack's strength, I'll see if he's as strong as he says he is."

So the old woman calmed down a little.

And the old giant said, "I'm going out and find out about him, and you just kind of straighten up the house in here—and get the oven good and hot! I think maybe we might have him for a little supper."

So Jack went a-pounding back out into the yard and was a-standing out at the edge, just like he was a-walking up to where the old giant and the house was.

The old giant came out and he reached down in the yard and he picked up four great big old buckets. You've never seen such things! Slung 'em on his arm and said, "Come on, Jack, let's go down here to the creek and bring the old woman up a little bit of water so she can get her some supper."

So they went down to the creek and the old giant reached in with one hand and he dipped up one big piggin full, and he reached in the other hand and he dipped up the other. And he said, "Now, Jack, over there's your two buckets."

Jack didn't pay him a bit of attention. He just rolled up his britches-legs and rolled up his shirt-sleeves way up to his elbows, and he went a-wading right out into the middle of that creek, feeling around in under a big old rock that was out there.

And the old giant says, "Jack, what in the world are you doing out there?"

"Why," he says, "bedads, just as soon as I can find a place to take hold of, I'm going to tote this creek up there to the old woman so we won't have to be a-toting loads of water up there. She can just come out there and get it when she wants it."

"Oh, law, no," the old giant says, "don't be getting this creek up there, Jack. No, no, don't do that." Says, "Land sakes, don't you know it would ruin my cornfield. And besides, the old woman's getting kind of old and tottery. She might fall in and get drowned. Come on, come on back to the house."

"Well," Jack says, "bedads, if I can't take the creek up there, I'm not taking no little old piggin of water."

"Well," the old giant says, "just leave the creek alone, Jack, and you don't need to mind about the little old buckets of water. Come on. These two's enough for her anyway." And on back up to the house they went.

The old man went in the house again, and he said, "Land sakes, old woman, I had the hardest time in the world getting Jack not to bring that creek up here. Lord, he's the mightiest man I ever did see or hear tell of. I just had to beg him to leave it down there." Said, "Now listen, you see if you can't do something with him. I'll get him to come on in the house here, and you see if you can't get him in that oven over there. I'll go out, and I'll be out here somewhere. Well, wait," the old man said, "wait a minute. Let me . . . let me try him first with throwing that crowbar. Just wait a minute, I'll see what he can do with that."

So he comes on back out. And Jack had heard every word that he said, but he was standing way off down in the yard just like he hadn't heard a thing.

The old man says, "Come on, Jack, this is what me and the boys used to do while the old woman was a-getting supper. We'd pick up this crowbar here and see who could throw it the furthest. Now come on, I'll give it a send way out yonder in the field, and you go out there and get it and bring it on back over here. Throw it on back over here to me."

So the old man picked up this great old big crowbar—why, it must have weighed a half a ton!—and give it a sling through the air. Went about a hundred and fifty feet out there.

Well, Jack went a-running on out to where the old crowbar lit up in the ground. Just standing there. He didn't even pay a bit of attention to the old giant. He cupped his hands up to his mouth and shouted: "UN-N-CLE! UN-N-CLE!"

"Ah!" the old giant says, "what'd you call me 'Uncle' for?"

"Oh," he says, "I'm not a-talking to you, I'm not a-talking to you at all . . . UN-N-CLE! . . . I'm a-hollerin' to my uncle way over yonder in Ohio. Why I've got a uncle over there that's a blacksmith, and he needs this here crowbar about making some horseshoes. The very thing. I'm just getting ready to throw it over to him, and I want him to be ready to catch it. UN-N-CLE!"

"Listen, Jack, Jack, don't throw that crowbar away! Why, that's all the one I've got. Don't do that. Now take your hand off of that crowbar and come on back here. Come on to the house and let's go on in. I think the old woman's got some supper ready. If she hain't, she pretty soon will have."

So the old giant took Jack into the house and said, "Now, old woman, here's Mister Jack, and he's going to come and have a little supper with us. I'll go out and split you up a little bit of wood while you go on finish the supper."

Well, the old woman she made like she was real glad to see Jack, and she picked up a comb and a washrag and said, "Come on here now, Jackie, let me comb your hair and wash your face and get you nice and cleaned up, ready for supper."

"Oh, no, bedads," Jack says, "I can wash my own face, and I can comb my own hair, too."

"Oh, no, no, now," the old woman says, "come on and just let me do it. This is the way I always fixed up my own boys. Now come on and let me do it, Jackie. Just get right up there on that shelf, and I can just reach right over and get you without having to stoop over a bit."

And Jack looked—and he saw that that shelf was right where it could be tipped right off into the old oven.

Well, Jack he acted like he'd like to get up on the shelf and he couldn't.

And he'd wiggle off and he'd get always off on the wrong side.

And the old woman said, "Well, Jack, didn't you ever sit on a shelf before in your life?"

"No, sir," Jack says, "bedads, I never did. I don't know a bit more know how to sit on this shelf than anything. You get up here and show me."

"Well," the old woman says, "I'm kind of heavy to get up on that little shelf. But you just put your shoulder right under the edge of it there and hold it up so it won't break, and I'll get up there and show you how to sit on a shelf."

So the old woman, the old giant, got up on that shelf, and Jack just gave his shoulder a little hunch and a good push and right into that old oven he threw the old giant mother. And he worked around there with a great old big iron hook and he finally pulled the lid on it. Went over and hid in behind the door.

After a while the old man pushed open the door, come walking in, and says, "Old woman, old woman! Jack's a-burning, I smell him, I smell him!"

Jack didn't say a thing.

The old man run over and pulled the top off of that big old furnace there . . . "Law have mercy," he says, "that's not Jack. That's my old woman, and she's burned to a coal! There's your three heads, there's your three heads! That's her!"

"Yes," and Jack stepped from behind the door. And he said, "Mind what you say to me, I'll just sure put you in there, too."

"Oh, yes, Jack, I'm a-minding what I say to you. I'm not going to say a thing in this world out of the way. No, sir, Jack, I'm not!" But he says, "Listen, Jack. Help me get out of this country some way." He said, "Here you've killed the boys and now you've killed the old woman . . . just help me get out of the country."

"Well," Jack says, "I'd be glad to, sir, but, you know, I'm afraid it's a little too late."

"Too late? What do you mean?"

"Why," Jack says, "the King's a-sending a thousand soldiers down here right now, maybe two or three thousand of them. And they're going to kill you just as soon as they get down here."

"Oh, Jack, Jack! Can't you hide me somewhere? Can't you do something for me, Jack?"

"Yeah," Jack says, "get into that old big chest over there and I'll see what I can do."

So he got the old giant down in the chest, and Jack ran out on the back side of the house. And he took up big sticks of wood, and he thumped and he beat on the old house, and he hollered and he whooped. And you'd have thought there was two or three thousand men out there, the noise Jack was a-making.

And he was a-fussing with them: "Now go on back, go on back. I tell you I've done away with all of them. You go on home and tell the King he didn't need to send you over here. Go on back, every one of you!"

But he acted just like they'd pushed right on into the house. And Jack came on in the house, throwing over the chairs, and breaking up the tables, and ker-whacking and ker-banging. And finally Jack acted like he was just driving them every one back out, and he took up a big stick and he said, "Now, if you don't get out of here, I'm going to do you just like I did the giants. Get out, I tell you! I've already killed the old giants."

Finally it went like they'd all went off and the noise kind of died down. And Jack went over to the chest and raised up the lid a little bit, and said, "Now crawl out there," he said, "the last one of 'em's gone. You get out of there easy like, and get away from here."

The old giant came out. He was just a-trembling and a-shaking. "Oh, Jack," he said, "what'll I do for you, what'll I do? Here you've saved my life from all them three thousand Englishmen." Said, "I know they'd a-killed me, they'd a-tore me limb from limb. Now, Jack, now, Jack, what do you want me to do?"

Jack says, "Mister, just start right over that mountain and don't let me see you stop anywhere. Just keep a-walkin' and that'll be all I ever ask of you. Just don't you ever come back here!"

The old giant said, "Jack, I'll be so glad to get away from here I'll never want to come back." And great steps he went taking right over that mountain.

And the last Jack saw of him, he just tipped the ridge and went right down on the other side.

Well, Jack looked around. There was the three old heads of the old woman giant. He could take them in . . . but, boys, what was he going to do about the old man? He'd sent him away.

Took those three heads back down to the King, and the King says, "Now, Jack, I just owe you $3000 more, but I sure can't pay you a thing for them giant's heads that went walking off over the mountain. You just lost $4000 right that-away."

"Well," Jack says, "bedads, this is plenty to do me and my folks the rest of our lives anyway." And he says, "Now listen, King, I'm kinda tired and wore out fightin'. I'm goin' on back home, and tomorrow I'll send Will and Tom to clear that new ground for you."

The Boy That Was Foolish-Wise

The following story was told in the 1920s by Uncle Tom Dixon of Kentucky. Collector Marie Campbell writes of Uncle Tom's beautiful speaking voice and his love of "lingering" over a tale. This story is clearly related to the Jack Tales, but notice that there are no Old World elements included here.

What I'm starting to tell now ain't much of a tale. Mostly it's just a pack of foolishness about a boy that hired out to a farmer and acted foolish-wise and outsmarted the farmer. The boy's two brothers had been hired out to the farmer for a year and a day, and they came back home all wore out and sick from slaving in the garden and corn patches—and no wages in their pockets. The farmer cheated them out of the last penny.

The boy that had stayed at home and worked around the place got mad. "I'll show that farmer," he said. "I'll collect your wages for you, and I'll outsmart him so he can't cheat me out of what will be owing."

He went and hired himself to the farmer, and he laid down a hard bargain. He said, "You'll have to pay me twenty [dollars] for a year's working, and some more things I want to set straight; it's a bargain that every time I won't do what I can do I lose a month's wages, and every time I'm stopped from doing what I was told to do you pay me an extra month's wages."

The farmer agreed, thinking all the time that he'd figure some way to get out of living up to what he promised.

The first day the boy worked, he never got much to eat. He stole a half a goose and made out to keep from starving.

The next day he had a scant bite for breakfast, so he called for his dinner and ate it right after his breakfast. He asked for his supper and ate that too, along with breakfast and dinner. Then he went out and asked the farmer, "What do you tell your work hands to do after supper?"

The farmer said, "I tell my work hands to go to bed after they eat their supper."

The boy went to bed and lay there all day, resting up from slaving the day before. The farmer found out he weren't working, and hunted and found him in the bed.

He made the boy get up out of the bed, and the boy collected an extra month's wages according to their bargain, for the farmer had told him to go to bed and then made him get up.

The day after that, the farmer told the boy to keep the old brindle cow out of the corn patches. There he sat all the morning minding Old Brindle, and keeping her out of the corn patches while the other cows and the sheep and hogs were tromping down the young corn.

The farmer saw how things were, and he hollered at the boy, "Leave Old Brindle be and chase them other critters out of the corn patches!"

The boy let Old Brindle alone for a while and chased the other critters out of the corn patches. He collected another extra month's wages for being stopped from doing what he had been told to do.

Another day the farmer told the boy to make a path across a swampy place. The boy said, "What made the path over the mountain?"

The farmer said, "Sheep's feet made the path over the mountain."

The boy sharpened his pocket knife and started to cut off the sheep's feet, saying, "I reckon sheep's feet made a path over the mountain, they can make a path across a swampy place. Reckon I'll just have to cut off all the sheep's feet and strow them along in the miry places, like filling up mudholes with rocks." The farmer made him stop, and that was another extra month's wages.

Things went on like that for some time, with the boy collecting an extra month's wages every day of his life. The farmer couldn't stand it no longer, and he told the boy he was fired. The boy said he wouldn't quit, but the farmer begged him to. After some time, the boy agreed to go home if the farmer would pay him the wages owing to his brothers. The farmer paid the brothers' wages, and then he said, "Now you are fired. You got to quit working for me and go home."

"There goes another extra month's wages," the boy said. "You hired me to work for you, and now you're making me stop what you hired me to do."

And the farmer was bound to pay.

The Arkansas Traveler

Pity the poor traveler on the back roads of America! Stories of the taciturn farmer who simply will not give a straight answer have made their way into jokes and popular songs. In some regions of the country, especially where there are a lot of tourists, the local people revel in such tales as "The Arkansas Traveler," letting the trickster do what they are, in fact, too polite to do.

A tall, well-dressed stranger made his way through the backwoods of Arkansas, a place where the roads weren't but dirt paths and the cabins scarce as hens' teeth. Suddenly he came to a small clearing, in the middle of which sat an old cabin. It had sagging walls and a mighty poor roof, and out on the porch, sitting on a whiskey barrel playing the fiddle, was an old, bearded man. The stranger, who has come to be known as the Arkansas Traveler, heard the old fellow playing the same notes over and over again as if he couldn't bear to part with them. The Traveler rode up, and all during their conversation the old man continued right on playing those same notes.

Arkansas Traveler: Hello, stranger.

Fiddler: Hello, yourself.

T: Sir, can you tell me where this road goes to?

F: It ain't never been any whar since I've lived here. Least it's always thar when I git up in the mornin'.

T: Well, I'm supposed to take it to where it forks. How far is it to there?

F: It don't fork at all, but it shore splits up like the devil.

T: Have you any spirits here?

F: Lots of 'em. Sal saw one last night by that ol' holler gum tree, and it nearly skeered her out of her skin.

T: You don't understand what I mean, sir. Have you any liquor?

F: Had some yesterday, I did, but ol' Blue he got in and lapped it right up out of the pot.

T: No, I don't meant pot liquor. I mean whiskey. I'm wet and cold and would like some whiskey. Have you got any?

F: Oh, sure I do. Certain. Why, I drank the last this very day.

T (growing more annoyed): Well, I'm as hungry as I am thirsty. I haven't eaten since this morning. Might you have something to eat?

F: Stranger, thar ain't a damned thing in the house and that's a fact. Not a mouthful of meat, not even the dust of a meal round here.

T: Can you give my horse something?

F: Got nothin' to feed him on.

T: Sir, I'm not likely to get to another house tonight and I would be very grateful if you would let me sleep in yours. I'll tie my horse to that tree and will just have to do without anything to eat or drink.

F: Cain't. See, my house leaks. Thar's only one dry spot in it and me and Sal sleeps on that'n. As for your horse, that thar tree is the ol' lady's persimmon tree. You cain't tie to it, 'cause she don't want it shuk off. She aims to make beer off it.

T (staring hard at the fiddler): Why don't you repair your roof and stop the leaks?

F: It's been rainin' all day long.

T: Why don't you do it when the weather is dry?

F: It don't leak then.

T: How far is it to the next house?

F: Stranger, I don't know. I ain't never been thar.

T: Well, do you know who lives here?

F: I do.

T (waiting to hear): Who, then?

F: I do.

T: If I may be so bold, what might be your name?

F: It might be Tom and it might be Dick, but it lacks a damned sight of it.

T: This place of yours is pretty quiet. Seems the only thing alive is you. How do you do for a living here?

F: Perty well, thank you. How do you do yourself?

T: I mean what do you do for a living, sir?

F: Keep a tavern and sell whiskey.

T (exasperated): I told you that was what I wanted!

F: Stranger, hear tell of this. I bought a bar'l more'n a week ago. Me and Sal we went shares. But after we got the bar'l here, we found we only had one bit 'tweenst us, and Sal she didn't want to use her'n first, nor me mine. I had me a spiggin' in one end and she had her a spiggin' in t'other. So, you see, Sal takes a drink out of my end and pays me the bit fer it. Then I'd take one out'n her'n and give her the bit back. My, we was getting along fust rate, 'til Tom, damned skunk that he be, bored a hole on the bottom to suck at and the next time I went to buy myself a drink from Sal, they weren't none thar.

T (giving up): Well, sir, I'm sorry your whiskey's all gone.

The Arkansas Traveler had finally gotten the message and turned his weary horse away from the porch determined to follow the road until he found a place more hospitable. He heard those crazy fiddle notes going over and over, and couldn't resist a parting shot at the old man on the porch.

T: My friend, why in the hell don't you play the balance to that tune?

F: It's got no balance to it.

T: I mean that you aren't playing the whole tune, just part of it.

F: Stranger, kin you play the fiddle?

T: Yes, a little, sometimes.

F: Well, you don't look like a fiddler to me, but if you think you got a tune in you or if you think you kin pull any more out'n the tune I been playing, you kin just git down and try.

The Traveler climbed off his horse and stepped up onto the man's porch. He took up the fiddle and played those same notes, only he added a whole music book more. He played the whole tune, and then some.

F: Stranger, take a half a dozen chairs and set down here. Sal, stir yourself round like a six-horse team in a mud hole. Go round in the holler whar I killed that buck this mornin', cut off some of the best pieces, and bring 'em up for me and this gentleman directly. Raise up the board under the head of the bed and git that old black jug I hid from Tom (the skunk ain't so smart as he'd have me think), and give us some whiskey. Thar's plenty in that. Mose, drive ol' Blue out of the bread tray, then climb up in the loft and git that rag that's got the sugar tied in it. Dick, carry the gentleman's hoss 'round the back and under the shed and give him some fodder and corn, as much as he can eat.

Mose: Daddy, thar ain't enough knives for to set the table.

F: Whar's big butch, little butch, ol' case, cob-handle, granny's knife, and the one I handled yesterday? That's enough to set any gentleman's table with. Damn me, stranger, if you cain't stay as long as you please, and I'll see to it that you git all the plenty you need to eat and drink. Will you have coffee for supper?

T: Yes, sir.

F: Play away, stranger. You kin sleep on the dry spot tonight.

T (after playing steadily for two hours): Friend, can you tell me about the road I'm to travel tomorrow?

F: Tomorrow! Stranger, you won't git out'n these diggings fer six weeks and a day. But when it gits so you can start, you see that big sloo over thar? Well, you have to git cross that, then you take the road up the bank, and in about a mile you come to a two-acre-and-a-half corn patch; the corn is mightily in the weeds, but you needn't mind that one bit, just ride on. About a mile and a half, maybe two miles from that, you'll come to the damnedest swamp you ever struck in all your travels; it's boggy enough to mire a saddle blanket. Thar's a fust-rate road near about six feet under thar.

T: How am I to get at it?

F: You can't git at it nary time till the weather stiffens down some. Well, about a mile beyon', you come to a place whar thar's two roads. You can take the right-hand road if'n you want to, and you'll follow that a mile or so 'til you find it runs out. So then you got to come back and try the left hand road. When you git about two miles down that-a-one, you'll know fer certain you're on the wrong path, for thar ain't any road thar. You'll then figure you're mighty lucky if'n you can find your way back to my house, whar you can come and play that tune fer as long as it suits you.

The Yankee Peddler

One of the masters of deception in American folklore is the Yankee Peddler. Tales of his shrewd business deals were published in newspapers all over the country during the nineteenth century and thus went from oral tradition to the printed word. Then they were read and retold in backwater towns as if the events had happened locally. Like many tricksters, the Yankee Peddler is regarded with a mixture of scorn and admiration.

THE YANKEE FINISHES HIS MEAL

There was once this stagecoach route in Texas that ran through a little town called Camden, where a notorious tavern was situated. A stage full of folks was nearing Camden one evening when one man aboard remarked to another, "We aren't but five miles from town."

"Pesky glad to hear it," said a Yankee-lookin' feller. "I'm as hungry as a hound."

"Sorry for you, then," answered the other man. "I'm as hungry as you, but we won't get three mouthfuls down before the stage is ready to leave. It's an old trick at the tavern."

"Trick or no trick," said the Yankee, "I'll have a hearty dinner."

"You might at that," said the man, "but you'll lose your seat on the stage for sure."

The Yankee smiled and looked at everyone. "I'll bet you supper for this whole group that I get my dinner and I don't lose my seat."

"I hate to steal your money, but I'll take that bet, because I know this tavern too well. You can throw cigars and wine into the deal too, for we'll be in Columbus later on this evening in time for a real supper."

Sure enough, when the stage got to Camden,

the dinner that was supposed to be for the passengers wasn't ready yet. When it was, a man stood at the door and taxed folks four bits apiece as they went in to eat. But before the passengers could get four bits' apiece worth of food down their throats, the tavern-keeper came in shouting that the stage was ready, mail was behind time, and the driver wouldn't wait a minute not even for his own grandmother. The travelers raced outside as fast as they could, no one wanting to miss his seat on the stage and get stuck in Camden, except for the Yankee, who stayed where he was and continued to eat. Plate after plate, he made those vittles walk down his throat most amazingly fast.

"You'll lose your seat, friend," said the tavern-keeper.

"Don't care much. I want the dinner I paid for, and then some," replied the Yankee, eating his way through a turkey that no one else had had time to touch. "And to finish up," he said to the tavern-keeper, "I guess I'll take a bowl of bread and milk."

The keeper went out of the room and presently came back and put the bowl down before his customer.

"Thank you kindly," the Yankee said. "I reckon I'll need a spoon, though, to eat this stuff with; cain't be eatin' bread and milk with my fingers."

"Spoon, sir!" said the keeper, his eyes popping out of his head. "There were a dozen spoons on the table just a while ago, and they were real silver spoons at that!"

"Well, there may have been," said the Yankee, "but you cain't blame them folks on that stage, now, can you? They weren't goin' to pay four bits an' come away with nothin' to show for it."

"Thunder and lightning!" roared the keeper. "If I don't bring the whole lot of those thieves to justice, then there's not a snake to be found in Virginny!" and he rushed to his horse out back.

About a half an hour later, after the Yankee had finished every scrap of food on the table, the same stage returned rattling and clattering. The Yankee got up, went outside, and climbed aboard the stage among the passengers.

"Hold on! Hold on, stranger!" yelled the keeper, who had brought the stage back with the sheriff. Quite a crowd had gathered. "I want you to point out the robbers that took those spoons. Now I got the law and some friends and they'll help me straighten these thieves out for good."

"Well, mister," drawled the Yankee, "I guess if you look in your coffeepot, I calc'late you'll find them spoons. Seems I made a mistake. Goodbye, and thanks for the best meal I ever got for four bits. And don't be tellin' this to the next stage, neither."

Away went the stage, the driver cussin' because his stage was late, the passengers roarin' with laughter, and behind them a tavern-keeper who was madder than a blind hornet.

RAZOR-STROP TRADE

"I reckon I couldn't drive a trade with you to-day, Square," said a "ginooine" specimen of a Yankee peddler, as he stood at the door of a merchant in St. Louis.

"I reckon you calculate about right, for you *can't*," was the sneering reply.

"Well, I guess you needn't git huffy 'beout it. Now here's a dozen ginooine razor-strops—worth $2.50; you may have 'em for $2.00."

"I tell you I don't want any of your traps [tricks]—so you may as well be going along."

"Wal, now look here, Square, I'll bet you five dollars, that if you make me an offer for them 'ere strops, we'll have a trade yet."

"Done!" replied the merchant, placing the money in the hands of a bystander. The Yankee deposited a like sum.

"Now," said the merchant, "I'll give you a picayune [sixpence] for the strops."

"They're your'n!" said the Yankee as he quietly pocketed the stakes.

"But," said he, after a little reflection, and with great apparent honesty, "I calculate a joke's a joke; and if you don't *want* them strops, I'll trade back."

The merchant's countenance brightened.

"You are not so bad a chap, after all," said he; "here are your strops, give me the money."

"There it is," said the Yankee, as he received the strops and passed over the sixpence. "A trade is a trade; and, now you are wide awake, the next time you trade with that 'ere sixpence, you'll do a little better than to buy razor strops."

And away walked the peddler with his strops and his wager, amidst the shouts of the laughing crowd.

How Pedro Urdemalas Got Into
and Out of Heaven

In the Hispanic Southwest, a cycle of tales grew up around one Pedro Urdemalas, who exhibits all the lawless traits of Coyote. Since the trickster finds his greatest delight in flouting the power of authority, it follows that in a largely Catholic society, Pedro would match his wits with the highest authority of all. In the following hilarious example, the original collector of the tale, Frank Goodwyn, includes the dramatization offered by the tale-teller.

It seems that Pedro Urdemalas, swindling his bosses out of fabulous sums, had lived a long life on earth. When it was over, he climbed the clouds to heaven and knocked on the golden gate.

"Who is it?" asked Saint Peter, who was Pedro's *tocayo*. That is, they had the same name.

"This is your *tocayo*, Pedro Urdemalas. Let me in."

"Where is your passport? Where were you born?" To Nicolas [who told the story], Saint Peter was a customs officer, the golden stairs were the bridge across the Rio Grande, and Pedro was himself trying to get home again.

"I was born in a valley between two hills." Imitating Pedro, Nicolas made his voice thin and plaintive as the baa of the freshly branded calves that had not yet found their mothers.

"What was the name of the valley?" Imitating Saint Peter, Nicolas made his voice heavy and demanding as the bawl of bulls plaguing the worried mothers of the calves.

"Oh, it has many names, *tocayo*." Nicolas squinched his shoulders and stuck out his upward-turned palms in imitation of

Pedro. "Different people gave it different names. I think it ran east and west. All kinds of good things were there. Watermelons, beans, grass for the cows, corn for the hogs, oats for the horses. And a river ran through it, with water which went all the way from its head in the hills to its mouth in the sea. When there was rain, everything grew green, but when it was dry, the grass died and the cows and hogs and horses became thin."

Nicolas shook his fist and told me that Saint Peter's angry yelling shook the stars. "Stop wasting my time! What do I care for watermelons, beans, grass for the cows, corn for the hogs, and oats for the horses? Am I a cow or a hog or a horse? No! I am a saint! A spirit! And spirits do not eat, for there is no body to need eating. Only spirit, thin as the air. Nor do I care for your rivers or hills, nor for your green grass of rainy weather or your dead grass of dry times. I am here by command of Dios, to see that no man passes in without permission from the bosses. If you do not know the day and place of your being born, you cannot get a passport, and without a passport you cannot pass this gate. It is the law."

"But I was born a long time ago, *tocayo*. I cannot remember."

"That is your bad luck. Not mine."

"But please, *tocayo*. Have pity on a poor *pelado* who wants only to get a glimpse of your beautiful place, so that he may tell the others of his land what it is like. Nobody from Texas has ever seen inside heaven. Just one little peep is all I ask, *tocayo*."

Now Saint Peter, being a man of mercy, opened the gate just a little. Instead of looking, Pedro stuck his finger in. Quickly, Saint Peter tried to shut the gate, but Pedro cried, "Ouch! *Tocayo*! My finger got caught in the gate! Please do not cut it off! Open the gate a little more, so I can get it out."

Saint Peter, who could not bear to see a man suffer, opened the gate a little more. Instead of taking his finger out, Pedro stuck his whole hand in.

"Ouch! *Tocayo*! You will cut off my hand! Open the gate just enough for me to get it out."

This was not going as Saint Peter had intended, but his kindness of heart would not let him do otherwise than open the gate a bit more for Pedro to get his hand out. This time Pedro stuck his whole arm in.

"Ouch! *Tocayo*! Now you have caught my arm! You should not be so careless with your gate!"

Saint Peter, who would not think of cutting off a man's arm, opened the gate a little more. Instead of taking his arm out, Pedro took off his big straw hat and threw it into heaven. It went bouncing and rolling over the clouds behind Saint Peter.

"Oh, what a shame, *tocayo*!" Pedro lamented. "It seems that I can never have anything but bad luck. The wind has blown off my hat! It is the only one I have, and hell is such a hot place, I am told. Almost as hot as Texas when the Texans are branding calves. You cannot send me away without a hat. Please let me come in and find it."

Now as all the world knows, Saint Peter has no hair himself. He could not bear to think of a man going bareheaded in hell, to say nothing of Texas. So he let Pedro in to find his hat. Pedro, very happy, went running over the clouds behind his hat. Saint Peter looked at the sun, which was his clock. Thirty minutes passed, then thirty hours, then thirty days, but still there was no sign of Pedro.

One day an angel came and knelt before the throne of Dios, our Señor, saying, "Sir, I lost a feather from one of my wings. Do you think there could be a thief around here?"

"Hush!" whispered Dios. "You must not mention thieves in this holy place! You will ruin my good reputation! Go back and play on your harp, and maybe you will find your feather. Here is a fresh cloud that I have just made. You may use it for a pillow." He tossed the new cloud to the angel, who took it and flew away pacified if not happy.

Next day a second angel came. "Our Sir, I lost a ring from my finger. Are you sure that no—"

"Hush! Do not say that word. Go back and play on your harp and maybe you will find your ring. Here is a fresh cloud, one of the softest I have ever made. You may cushion your knees on it when you kneel before the cross." For even angels must kneel before the cross of Christ.

Next day a third angel came. "Our Sir! I lost—"

"Hush!" said Dios. "I know what you are going to say. We will go and talk to Saint Peter. We must find out what kind of persons he has been letting in lately."

So they went to see Saint Peter, but he only shook his head. Then he thought a moment and said, "Now that I remember, a man from Texas named Pedro Urdemalas came in after his hat some time ago. He has not yet gone back out. I suppose he has not found it."

"Pedro Urdemalas!" gasped Dios, turning pale, for Pedro Urdemalas was known everywhere to be terrible for his deviltry.

"Pedro Urdemalas!" echoed the angels, also turning pale.

"Find him," commanded Dios, "and throw him out."

They hunted and they hunted but they never found Pedro. One by one the angels came back dragging their tired wings, bringing the bad news of failure.

Saint Peter scratched his bald head and tried to be helpful. "He may have slipped out through the cellar."

"My cellar!" screamed Dios, shaking his long beard with such thundering terror that the foundations of the sky almost came loose. "And I've got fifty gallons of good mescal down there! Go get him, you deadbeats! Hurry! Don't stand there like idiots! Get him out of here!"

The angels scattered like a flock of frightened turkeys, rushing in every direction at once, lifting up big clouds and little clouds to look under them, sometimes stopping and panting a moment behind a half-formed star, temporarily hidden from the wrath of Dios. After a long time they came back with sweat dripping from their wings. They had found nothing.

At last Dios, who knows all things, thought of a plan. He sent an angel to the earth after a Texan. Soon the angel returned, carrying a Texan by the collar.

"Bring him a chair," said Dios.

They brought the Texan a chair and he sat down beside the golden gate.

Dios asked, "Do you know a song called 'La Cucaracha'?"

"Oh, sure," said the Texan. "Everybody in Texas knows that song." He crossed his legs and used his hat to brush the stardust off his boots.

"Sing it," said Dios.

The Texan put his hat on one side of his head, tuned his guitar—for, as you know, all good Texans have guitars—and began to sing: "The *cucaracha*, the *cucaracha*, he will pace along no more. . . ."

The angels had never heard such a song before. They were very quiet.

"Again!" commanded Dios.

The Texan sang again. Nothing happened.

But the third time he sang, a straw hat went spinning into the sky beyond the faraway clouds. Dust began to rise in that direction, and the angels heard somebody yell, "Long live Mexico!"

Dios pointed his long, bony finger. "Yonder he is. I knew that he would not be able to stay quiet when he heard that song." Then Dios reached over the clouds, lifted Pedro out by the back of his neck as a mother cat lifts kittens, held him out over the edges of heaven, and dropped him back down to the earth, where he still works cattle in the Texas sun.

Bobtail and the Devil

———

The notion of outsmarting the Devil is very popular in the folklore of North America. In many tales, especially in the southeastern United States and in African American lore, the Devil is presented as just another scurrilous character who wants to cheat the hero, and the hero must use his wits to win. In the following tale, the Devil is just plain dumb and lazy.

———

Well, oncet upon a time there was two people lived in the world. Of these two people it was always questioned by other people which one was the smartest, Bobtail or the Devil. Now Bobtail he was just a Bobtail, just a-running around, and the old Devil he had other things. So one day Bobtail said, "Well, Devil," says, "we can't decide which one is the greatest. So I tell you what le's do. Le's raise a big patch of potatoes." The Devil agreed to do it.

Well, they planted 'em a big patch of potatoes. Bobtail planted him a big patch in his lot and the Devil planted him a big patch in his lot. Now Bobtail, he took and put manure on his potatoes. But the Devil he was lazy and sorry—he just run around, getting anything for nothing—and he didn't put anything on his.

Well, when digging time come Bobtail went and dug his potatoes. He had old big potatoes. The old Devil he had just little old small ones. He didn't like that much. So he—as the Devil is—he thought he had been cheated. He said, "Well, Bobtail," said, "you had your choice. Now I don't think it was fair. Le's raise some hogs."

Well, Bobtail said, "O.K., we will."

So Bobtail and the Devil got their hogs and they begin to raise hogs. They put 'em all in a lot together. Well, they fed their hogs, fed 'em corn, just anything they could feed 'em. When killing time come—when the hogs got up big enough—the question come up how they was going to divide 'em. Well, Bobtail says to the Devil, says, "Devil, I'll give you the first choice," says, "you take out you a hog and then I'll take out mine and we'll divide 'em."

So the Devil he went in and he looked over the hogs. As the Devil is, he wanted to cheat him, you know. So he retch down and picked up the biggest one he could find, an old big fat one. It went, "Weeeeeeennh!" and he picked it up and throwed it over the fence. Bobtail went down and he picked up his'n. It squealed right big and he throwed it over his fence into his lot. The Devil looked around and he picked the next biggest one he could find and he throwed it over the fence. Bobtail picked up another and put it over his fence into his lot. Well, there was just one more hog left, and the Devil said to himself, "Now I've got it on Bobtail, I've got it on him—that's sure!" So he picked up this small hog and throwed it over in his lot. The Devil was pleased. Bobtail he kindly scratched his head, you know, and he said to himself, "I've been cheated!"

But he got to looking around directly, and the Devil he was looking around. And then the Devil hollered at Bobtail, said, "Bobtail!"

Bobtail said, "Yes, Devil, what do you want?"

"Looks like your hogs are in your lot, but I haven't got any hogs."

Bobtail said, "Why?"

Said, "I've fooled around and my fence has got holes in it and my hogs have got over in with your hogs."

Bobtail said, "Ah, that's all right. You see, when I picked up my hogs," said, "I twisted their tails," said, "I know mine."

As far as I know the Devil is still looking yet, trying to find them straight hog tails.

7

The Fool

~

In the lore of all lands there are famous characters who are fools, and North America has its fair share. Two kinds of fool dominate this group of tales. There is the simpleton who is invariably foolish—a noodle, a silly, who can always be counted upon to do the wrong thing. Then there is the wise fool, the one presumed to be too stupid to take seriously, but who, in the end, surprises everyone by coming up with the clever idea that wins the day. Both types of tales have high entertainment value in oral traditions.

Some of these tales will be familiar as jokes, for there is a close relationship between jokes that have been popular in North America and traditional tales about fools. In a less politically correct era than this one, characteristics of the fool were given to members of ethnic groups partly to emphasize the stereotypes of an outsider culture. Telling such tales in order to appear superior to another group seems part of human nature. When I was young my friends and I, being North Carolinians, told our noodlehead tales about, who else, South Carolinians. Later, I met South Carolinians who told identical tales with numbskulls from, you guessed it, North Carolina. No one likes to be the butt of noodlehead stories, but it seems that plenty of people like to tell them.

The Three Sillies

This classic noodle story, known throughout the world, is well told in a Southern version by Lee Drake. Other versions give different reasons for the daughter's distress: An ax is stuck in the ceiling and might fall on her someday; she can't decide what to name her firstborn child; or she can't figure out who the father of her children will be. This tale attaches another well-known story, usually told separately, about the foolish wife who is saving money for hard times and loses it all when she meets a man on the road who says his name is Mr. Hard Times. There are many variants of this tale because it is so easy to incorporate new jokes about fools.

This boy was goin' to see his girl, and he had promised to marry this girl. So he 'cided he would have dinner with the girl before he married her. That's back a long time ago. Instead of goin' to town and buyin' syrup [molasses] like they do these days, they made it, and they kept it in barrels. And when they wanted syrup on the table, they'd take a container out and turn the keg up over it and let the syrup come out; and it would come out slowly, y'know, until it filled the container up, and then they'd take it back to the kitchen.

So they had dinner fixed—mother, father, and everybody—for this guest. And this boy, they called him in and they got to the table and the mother says, "Oh, Sister, we forgot something. We don't have any syrup on the table." Says, "Sister, will you go draw some syrup?"

Sister say, "Yes, Mother, I'll go draw some syrup." So she went out there to draw the syrup, and she turned the keg up over the container and let the syrup start runnin' in. And she put her hand to her jaw, and she was thinkin'. She says, "Lawd, I'm tryin' to think what Brother's oldest son is named." And she set there and thought.

And so she stayed so long, her mother say, "Lemme go see what's wrong with Daughter." Say, "She's stayin' too long." So she goes out. She say, "Daughter, what are you doin'?"

Daughter say, "Mother, I'm just tryin' to think what Brother's oldest son is named." So Mother, she started helpin' think, too! She stays a long time.

So Father, he say, "Let me go see what's wrong with Mother and Daughter." So he goes out. "What are you all doin'?" he says.

"We . . . Sister's jus' tryin' to think what Brother's oldest son is named, and I was jus' here tryin' to help her think."

So this boy he still sit there, he sit there. He 'cided he would go out and see what all of 'em was doin'. So he went out there and looked. Syrup done run all out on the groun'! And he says, "Hey, what are you all doin'?"

Mother say, "Daughter was jus' tryin' to think what Brother's oldest son is named, and I started tryin' to helpin' her think."

And Father say, "Well, I tried to help them think what Brother's oldest son is named."

The fellow that was goin' to marry the daughter say, "Damn!" Says, "I'm goin'. I don't want no dinner." He say, "Now, if I find three more fools like y'all, I'll marry your daughter. Unless that, I won't." And he left.

So he went on down the road. He got down the road, he saw a lady goin' 'round and 'round the house with an empty wheelbarrow, 'round and 'round the house. So he stood and watched the lady. He say, "Lady, what you doin'?"

She says, "I jus' washed off my back porch, son, and," says, "it ain't no sunshine around there," says, "I'm tryin' to roll some of this sunshine around there to dry the back porch."

He say, "I'll be damned!"

He went on up the road a little further and a man had a pretty, nice brick house, pretty lawn with fine grass on it. And the man had a rope th'owed across the housetop and he was jus' swingin' down on that rope for all he's worth. Jus' sweatin' up everything. Boy asked him, "Hey, mister," say, "what are you doin'?"

He say, "Son, I'm goin' tell you somethin'." Say, "I got some old oxen 'round behind the house there." And say, "They so poor, I'm tryin' to pull 'em over on the grass."

He say, "Mister, take the rope off and drive the oxes around." And say,

"They'll come on around."

He told him, "I hadn't thought of that." He took the rope and drove 'em on around, and they went to eatin'.

He say, "Damn, look like I'm goin' to have to marry that gal anyway." He say, "I'm goin' to leave the road; I'm goin' down through these woods."

So he went down through the woods, turn off the road so he wouldn't meet nary another fool. He got thirsty and wanted some water. He say, "Well, there's an old spring down here; I'm goin' to stop at this spring and get me some water." Got to the spring. Happened to look up: man had a hog by its back legs jus' pushin' him, y'know. Juggin' him like he's tryin' to push a wheelbarrow or somethin'. Says, "Hey, mister, what are you doin'?"

He say, "I got a hog here and he's so poor, he won't even root." He says, "I'm tryin' to make him root."

He say, "Mister," say, "put him down; he'll go out there and go to rootin'." So he put the hog down and he went on out there and jus' started to rootin' and eatin' up everything, sticks and all.

He says, "I'll be damn. I guess I'll go back and marry her." He turned around and went on back. And he married the girl.

So he told her, "Honey," says, "here's ten dollars," and say, "I want you to keep this for Mister Hard Times, hear?"

She say, "Okay, Honey."

And he says, "I got a big old ham of meat in there." Says, "That's to go on these cabbage greens during the summer." He says, "Okay?" That means the cabbage greens they was goin' to raise, y'know.

So they went on, made it up 'til the summer, y'know. They had nice greens and everything, plenty to eat. Then things got kind of hard, and he wanted some of that ham meat that he had told her to go in the greens. So he asked her, says, "Honey," say, "you say you don't have anything to eat." Say, "How 'bout some of that ham meat I told we goin' to put in them greens this summer?"

She say, "Honey," says, "when those cabbage first come up," says, "I cut it [the ham] up in little thin slices and put a thin slice on every head."

So that made him mad. He says, "I shouldn't a married this fool at the start with." He say, "Where my ten dollars?"

She say, "Next day after we got married," say, "Mister Hard Times come by here and I give it to him."

So he quit her, and that's the end of that story.

Two Tales of Foolish John

———•·•———

One of the most famous and long-lived fools in North American folklore is found among the French-speaking people in the American South. In the Creole and Cajun cultures of Louisiana and Missouri he is often known as John Sot, or Jean Sotte. He is probably related to our old friend Jack, often journeying far and entering into contests that he, unlike Jack, loses more often than not. For he is usually presented as an utter fool with no redeeming intelligence. In the following two tales, Foolish John shows his colors as an authentic noodlehead, keeping company with the three sillies in the previous story.

———•———

THE DOLLARS AND THE FROGS

Foolish John's mother and father were very poor people. Foolish John, who was the eldest, was their sorrow instead of their solace. The more they tried to correct him, the more he showed himself to be stupid and no account. What I am going to relate will give you a good idea of what his parents had to tolerate and forgive in him. My goodness, what they went through!

One day Foolish John's mother sent him to his uncle's to borrow ten dollars. She warned him to take good care of the money, because there would be ten one-dollar bills, not to lose a single one. Foolish John assured his mother that he understood the errand very well, leaving on the run.

While returning from his uncle's house, Foolish John passed near a pond, where the frogs, springfrogs and bullfrogs, were carrying on a racket, like nobody's business. Foolish John stopped to listen. He heard the tiny voices of the small springfrogs, saying: "You have eight! You have eight! You have eight!" [*"Tu as huit!"*] The silly lad believed the creatures were making fun of him, meaning that he didn't know how to count the money he had in his pocket. He became furious and replied: "You lie! Mama says I have ten, do you hear!" The springfrogs continued more loudly: "You have eight! You have eight! You have eight!" Beside himself, Foolish John cried out to them: "If you know so much about it, here, look!" and he threw the bills out upon the water to the frogs. "Count them for yourselves, if you wish," continued he. "There you are—one, two, three, four, five, six, seven, *eight*, nine and ten! Well now, is that not right? You see that you were wrong. Now return them all to me. I must be off. Mama is waiting for me."

Naturally the springfrogs paid no attention at all to him, and the pretty dollar bills went floating off upon the water like so many leaves in the breeze. Foolish John, poor thing, did not know what to do. He stepped into the water of the pond, while saying: "I'll get them in a little while. Mama needs that money more than those springfrogs and bullfrogs." But just then a huge bullfrog, seated by a cypress tree, began to go: "No bottom! No bottom!" ["*Pas de fond!*"] Foolish John, who did not know how to swim and was afraid to get drowned in a deep pond, was frozen with fear. He stopped instantly and began to back up toward the bank of the pond. As soon as he felt the good, firm ground under his feet, he hastened homeward to relate his adventure to his mother. The poor woman! One can imagine what her sorrow was on learning what had happened to her money—borrowed money at that, which had to be returned without having spent it!

Now don't tell me, my little children, that in such a fool there was not something to make an angel lose patience.

FOOLISH JOHN AND THE RAIN

Foolish John had just put on a nice, clean suit of clothes and was ready to go somewhere for his mother.

"Foolish John," warned his mother, "be careful not to get caught in the rain with your nice, clean clothes. It looks like bad weather. Don't forget to duck out of the rain if it begins to fall."

"All right, Mother," answered Foolish John as he set out on his way. However, he had hardly reached the bayou bridge when a great peal of thunder brought down a shower of rain. Foolish John realized he was in the rain and wanted to get out of it, remembering what his mother had told him. He saw no shelter nearby as he stood on the bayou bridge. So he thought and thought. Finally he jumped from the bridge into the bayou, in order to get out of the shower. As he stood in the muddy bayou water, his hat remained over the water on his head that stuck out of the bayou. He took off his hat and held it under the water.

When Foolish John reached home, his mother saw him all wet and covered with mud from head to feet.

"Foolish John!" she exclaimed. "Didn't I warn you to keep out of the rain? You are not only wet but all covered with mud."

"Well, Mother," explained Foolish John, "you told me to duck out of the rain if it came. When it did, I ducked into the bayou. I even held my hat under the bayou out of the rain."

Fido est mort (Fido Is Dead)

It is easy to see how Jean Sot got to be the principal character of this delightful joke-tale, versions of which are told elsewhere in the world, including France, England, and other regions of the United States. This version was told to Barry Jean Ancelet by Revon Reed in Louisiana.

And then, the tale which makes me feel like laughing—He [Jean] had gone to work for a man who had a big plantation, a big planter, a rancher. He left to go on vacation. He put Jean Sot in charge of the farm, with the servants, the blacks, and the others, and his wife and his wife's mother, his mother-in-law in other words, and he went on a vacation.

And after a week, he decided to call Jean Sot on the telephone. He called him. He said, "Uh, Jean Sot, how is everything over there?"

"Oh, sir! Everything is going very well, sir," he said. "All is well."

"Are you sure that everything is okay?"

"Well, there's just Fido," he said, "Fido is dead. The little dog."

He said, "Fido is dead?! How did he die!"

"Well, sir," he said, "he died while eating some burnt, uh, mule meat."

"Oh, no!" he said. "What happened, Jean Sot! How did this happen?"

"Well, sir," he said, "your barn caught fire. The mules couldn't get out of their stalls. They burned." He said, "Then, the little dog went and ate some of that burnt mule meat. It gave him a stomach ache, and he died."

Then, the other fellow grabbed his head on the other end of the telephone. He said, "How did the barn catch fire, imbecile? Tell me quickly!"

"Well," he said, "the barn caught fire because of the house that had caught fire before."

He said, "How did this happen, Jean Sot?"

"Well," he said, "you see, sir, your mother-in-law had a heart attack and she died suddenly and she was enshrouded with candles all around and," he said, "one of the candles ignited the curtains and, before we knew it, the house was on fire and the barn caught fire and the mule burned and Fido ate some of the burnt meat and he died. Otherwise, everything's fine."

"And what killed the poor old woman!"

He said, "Well, it's her daughter, your wife." He said, "When she found out that she had secretly run off with one of the workers on your plantation, that she had eloped with one of the servants, it killed the poor mother."

And with this, the other fellow fell into a fit. He did not know what was going on anymore. It all started with Fido who had eaten some burnt meat, but Jean Sot did not want to say too much all at once.

The Devil and the Lord Dividing Souls

Fear of the local graveyard has made a fool of many a person. This is an African American version of a tale that is widely told throughout North America.

Here's a story about two slaves. Long years ago, they worked for the old master, and the old master never would give 'em enough to eat. And so, why, so they didn't git enough to eat, they would steal stuff and take home, and they would cook it at night after they git home. They would do all their stealing at night after they done gone home.

And so one day they had a lot of potatoes, and they knowed people didn't fool around the graveyards at night. And so they took these potatoes and carried 'em in the graveyard. Both of 'em had a sack apiece, and had two great big uns they laid down at the gate 'cause they was so tired when they got there with those big bags of potatoes apiece. And they went on inside. They was goin' to divide the potatoes up. Neither one of them could count, and the way they had to do to divide anything they had, they always say, "You take this one and I'll take that one."

So here come up another slave; he stayed at this other master's house. He'd go off at night, but he'd come back and spend the night 'cause he had to tote the old [crippled] master everywhere he went. He came by this graveyard that night and he heard this, "You take this one and I'll take that one. You take this one and I'll take that one." He stopped; thought that might have been a ghost or somethin'. And he stopped still and listened, see was it his heart beatin'. He felt his heart right tight, see was it his heart beatin'; and it wasn't his heart beatin'. Still he heard this sound: "You take this one and I'll take that one. You take this one and I'll take that one." So old John 'cided he'd run on up to the house and tell Boss about this God down there dividin' up souls!

So he went on up to the house. "Hey, Boss! Hey, Bossman!"

"Yes, John; what is it, John, what is it?"

He said, "God and the Devil down here dividin' up souls at the graveyard!"

He said, "Aw no, John, ain't no such thing!"

"Yes it is, yes it is. You don't tell me, 'cause I heard 'em!"

He says, "Okay, take me down there and let's see God and the Devil dividin' 'em up. I want to hear it, too."

So John picks him up and take him on down there. Sit him down 'side the gate. And so, sho' nuff, he heard this noise. "You take this one and I take that one. You take this one and I'll take that one." Sound went on for a long time.

Old Boss reach over and touch John: "You, you was right, John. You was right! You was right!"

Later on they got through dividin' up what they had in there. They had two real large potatoes they left at the gate; they was so tired, they just dropped them at the gate. One say, "Oh, you forgot somepin'."

He says, "What is it?"

"You know. You remember dem two we drop at the gate, don't ya?"

So John cut out! See, he didn't take time to pick up Old Master that time. So when John got to the house, Old Master was already in there, done slammed the door in his face!

Pat and the Devil

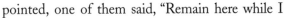

Pat and Mike are two Irishmen whose antics are famous in folktales among Irish immigrants to North America. In Ontario, where Pat is a well-known fool, he becomes the main character in a variant of the previous graveyard story. The following tale from Ontario was told by Mr. G. N. Waugh and published in The Journal of American Folklore *in 1918.*

There was once a country parson badly crippled with rheumatism, who had an Irishman employed to carry him about on his back.

Quite late one evening the parson was being brought home, when he discovered that he had forgotten his sermon at the church. Shortly before this, so it happened, a wealthy parishioner had died, and willed that all his money was to be buried with him. A couple of rascally fellows were about to dig up the body and steal the money, being totally unaware that the dead man's relatives had already removed the coin. When they dug the body up, the thieves found nothing but hickorynuts, which had been substituted by the relatives. Not so easily disap-

pointed, one of them said, "Remain here while I steal a sheep from the farm over there." Pat and the parson were then returning for the sermon. The thief in the churchyard, thinking it was his companion returning with the sheep, cried out, "Is he fat or lean?" Pat dropped the parson at once, saying, "Fat or lean, be jabers! you can have him," and he quickly ran for home. Getting up, the parson also ran, never again to be bothered by rheumatism.

Pat, ever after, thought it was the Devil he had seen in the churchyard, cracking nuts on a tombstone.

The Riddle Test

In "The Riddle Test" from Nova Scotia, Pat, from the previous story, suddenly crosses the line between the fool and the wise man. Usually depicted as an unmitigated fool, here he turns tables and makes a fool of the boss.

There was an Irishman out looking for a government job. So he went up to one fellow, an' he said, "Look a here, I've been voting for you all me life. I ought to get a job of you." So the man said, "I guess we've got something for you to do, but before I give you the job you have to answer three questions. Now you go home and consider the questions, then come back tomorrow with the answers. And if you answer them correctly you get the job." Pat said, "Go on with your questions." The man said, "The first is, the weight of the moon. The second is, how many stars are in the sky. And the last is, what I'll be thinking on when you come." So the next morning the Irishman come back. He found the old fellow in. He said, "Well, Pat, I guess you thought of what I told you. Now let's hear your answers. The first question was, 'How much does the moon weigh?' Well, how much?" The Irishman said, "One hundred weight." . . . "One hundred weight! Why how do you make that out?" Pat said, "Well, the moon has four quarters, and four quarters make a hundred, don't they?" The man said, "I guess you're right. Well, now, answer the second question. How many stars are in the sky?" The Irishman said, "Seven billion, eight thousand million, four hundred and fifty-two thousand." The man said, "How now, how do you make that?" "Well," said the Irishman, "if you don't believe me, you can go count them yourself." "That's right, that's right," said the old fellow. "We'll let that pass. But how about the last question. What am I thinking?" . . . "Well, you think that I'm Pat, but I'm his brother Mike!" . . . It wasn't Pat. He had sent his brother Mike to answer the questions.

Jean Sotte and the Riddle

———••———

Riddles are often used in tales as tests that separate the wise from the foolish. One of the oldest recorded riddles to come down through oral tradition was posed to Oedipus by the Sphinx, "What goes on four legs in the morning, two legs at noon, and three legs at night?" That question crops up in this next story of Jean Sotte. Here, however, as in the previous tale, the fool manages to blur the distinction between the wise and the foolish, surprising everyone and winning the day. The following story, though clearly of European origin, was collected among former slaves and told in the Creole dialect. The folklorist Alcée Fortier then translated the tale.

———•———

There was once a fellow who was so foolish that everybody called him Jean Sotte. He was so simple that everyone made fun of him. He would light the lamp in daytime, and put it out at night; he would take an umbrella with him only when it was very dark. In summer he would put on a great coat, and in winter he would go nearly naked. In short, he did everything contrary to common sense. King Bangon, who loved to play tricks, heard of the sayings and deeds of Jean Sotte, and sent for him to amuse his friends. When Jean came to the king all began to laugh, as he looked so awkward. The king asked him if he knew how to count. Jean replied that he knew how to count eggs; that yesterday he had found four and two. "How much does that make?" said the king. Jean went to count the eggs, and on returning said there were four and two.

"Exactly," said the king, "but tell me, Jean Sotte, they say that Compair Lapin is your father. "

"Yes, he is."

"No, no," said some one else; "I think it is Compair Bouki."

"Yes, yes," said Jean Sotte, "it is he also."

"No, no," said an old woman who was passing; "it is Renard who is your father."

"Yes," said Jean Sotte, "all of them; they are all my fathers. Every time one of them passes by me he says, 'Good-morning, my child.' I must believe, then, that they are all my fathers."

Everybody laughed at Jean Sotte; then the king said: "Jean Sotte, I want you to bring me to-morrow morning a bottle of bull's milk. It is to make a drug for my daughter, who is sick, and has a sideache in her back."

"All right," said Jean Sotte, "to-morrow morning early I shall bring it."

King Bangon then said:—

"On the first of April, in one month, you will come. I want you to guess something. If you guess, I will give you my daughter in marriage, but if you try three times, and do not succeed, my executioner will have to cut your neck."

"All right," said Jean Sotte, "I will try." And then he went away, pretending to go and get the bull's milk.

When he reached home, he related to his mother all that had happened, and the old woman began to cry, and could not be consoled, because, however foolish her boy was, she loved him, as he was her only child. She forbade him to go to the king, and threatened to tie him in her cabin, or to have the sheriff throw him in prison. Jean Sotte paid no attention to his mother, and started before day-break, with his axe on his shoulder. He soon arrived at the house of the king, and he climbed into a big oak tree which was before the door. He began, *caou, caou, caou*, to cut down the branches with his axe, and he woke up everybody in the house. One of the servants of the king came out to see what was the matter; and when he saw Jean Sotte on the top of the tree, he said: "But what is your business there? Fool that you are, you are disturbing everybody."

"It is not your business,—do you hear!" said Jean Sotte. "Are you the watch-dog to be barking thus in the yard? When your master, King Bangon, comes, I will tell him what I am doing here."

The king came out, and asked Jean Sotte what he was doing there. He replied that he was cutting the bark to make some tea for his father, who had been delivered the day before of two twins.

"What!" said the king, "for whom do you take me, Jean Sotte. Where did you ever hear of a man in childbirth? I think you mean to make fun of me."

"How is it that yesterday you asked a bottle of bull's milk? If you were right, I am also."

The king replied: "I believe that you are not so foolish as you want to make people believe. Go to the kitchen, and they will give you your breakfast. Don't forget to come on the first of April, that we may see which of us will be the April fool."

On the first of April Jean Sotte mounted his horse and went out without his mother seeing him. Compair Bouki, who is deceitful and evil-minded, said: "I shall prevent Jean Sotte from going because I know he is so foolish that they will cut his neck and keep his horse. It is better that I should profit by it, and take his horse. Don't you say anything; you will see what I shall do."

He took a large basket full of poisoned cakes, and put it on a bridge where Jean Sotte was to pass. "If he eats those cakes, he will die, and I shall take the horse."

Bouki knew that Jean Sotte was greedy and that he would surely eat the cakes. Compair Lapin liked Jean Sotte, because one day, when he was caught in a snare, Jean Sotte had freed him. He did not forget that, and said: "I want to protect the poor fellow," and before daybreak he waited on the road for Jean Sotte. When he saw him, he said: "Jean Sotte, I am coming to render you a service, listen to me: don't eat or drink anything on your way, even if you are dying of hunger and of thirst; and when the king will ask you to guess, you will reply what I am going to tell you. Come near; I don't want anybody to hear."

Compair Lapin then told him what to say. "Yes, yes, I understand," said Jean Sotte, and he began to laugh.

"Now," said Compair Lapin, "don't forget me when you marry the king's daughter; we can have good business together."

"Yes," said Jean Sotte, "I shall not forget you."

"Well, good luck, pay attention to all you see, look on all sides, and listen well."

Then Jean Sotte started, and a little while afterwards he arrived at a bridge on the river. The first thing he saw was the basket full of cakes which Compair Bouki had placed there. They smelled good and they were very tempting. Jean Sotte touched them and felt like biting one, but he remembered what

Compair Lapin had told him. He stopped a moment and said: "Let me see if they will do harm to my horse." He took half a dozen cakes and gave them to his horse. The poor beast died almost immediately and fell on the bridge. "See, if I had not been prudent, it is I who would be dead instead of my horse. Ah! Compair Lapin was right; a little more and I should have been lost. Now I shall have to go on foot."

Before he started he threw his horse into the river; and as the poor beast was being carried away by the current, three buzzards alighted on the horse and began to eat him. Jean Sotte looked at him a long time, until he disappeared behind the point in the river. "Compair Lapin told me: 'listen, look, and don't say anything'; all right, I shall have something to ask the king to guess."

When Jean Sotte came to the king nobody was trying to guess, for all those who had tried three times had been put to death by the king's executioner. Fifty men already had been killed, and everyone said, on seeing Jean Sotte: "There is Jean Sotte who is going to try, they will surely cut off his head, for he is so foolish. But so much the worse for him if he is such a fool."

When he saw Jean Sotte the king began to laugh and told him to come nearer. "What is it," said he, "that early in the morning walks on four legs, at noon on two, and in the evening on three legs?"

"If I guess, you will give me your daughter?"

"Yes," said the king.

"Oh! that is nothing to guess."

"Well, hurrah! hurry on if you don't want me to cut your neck."

Jean Sotte told him, it was a child who walked on four legs; when he grew up he walked on two, and when he grew old he had to take a stick, and that made three legs.

All remained with their mouths wide open, they were so astonished.

"You have guessed right; my daughter is for you. Now, let anybody ask me something, as I know everything in the world; if I do not guess right I will give him my kingdom and my fortune."

Jean Sotte said to the king: "I saw a dead being that was carrying three living beings and was nourishing them. The dead did not touch the land and was not in the sky; tell me what it is, or I shall take your kingdom and your fortune."

King Bangon tried to guess; he said this and that and a thousand things, but he had to give it up. Jean Sotte said then: "My horse died on a bridge, I threw him into the river, and three buzzards alighted on him and were eating him up in the river. They did not touch the land and they were not in the sky."

Everybody saw that Jean Sotte was smarter than all of them together. He married the king's daughter, took his place, and governed the kingdom. He took Compair Lapin as his first overseer, and hanged Compair Bouki for his rascality. After that they changed Jean Sotte's name and called him Jean l'Esprit.

Jean Sot and Bull's Milk

———•–•———

Different storytellers choose to emphasize different details in the stories they tell. In this fine example of a Cajun folktale, the teller expands on one brief episode from the previous Creole tale, creating a different story altogether.

———•–•———

Down around Mamou, there was once a boy who was so foolish that everybody called him Jean Sot, Foolish John. He and his *maman* were dirt poor, and he was less than no help at all. It seemed like Jean Sot just couldn't do anything right. Everything he touched ended in ruin, and he believed any silly story he was told. His *maman* would shake her head and sigh, "Oh, that boy must have moss between his ears!"

The people in his village loved to tease and play jokes on him. They'd say, "Jean Sot, the sky is fallin'!" The poor thing would run and hide, sure the world was ending for true. But their best joke was to ask, "Hey, boy, whatcha gonna be when you all grown up?"

Jean Sot loved that question. He would grin from ear to ear and say, "Me, I'm gonna marry the prettiest girl and be the richest man in all the parish." How the people laughed and laughed!

In time, the foolish boy became a foolish young man. One day as he was walking down the road, he passed by a big, fancy house. A beautiful girl was sitting up on the *galerie*, combing out her golden hair. She had the face of an angel but the brains of a duck. She was every inch as foolish as Jean Sot! Wouldn't you know, those two took one look at each other and fell right in love.

Jean Sot begged her to marry him. The girl says, "Oh, yes, *cher, mais oui!* But you must ask Papa for my hand!" The foolish boy ran to the girl's daddy, little knowing that this was the richest man in the parish, and asked to marry his daughter. But the rich man knew all too well about Jean Sot, and he had not the least intention of seeing his only child marry a fool, much less a poor one. Still, he thought it might be a good joke to play along and see just how foolish Jean Sot could be.

"Hmm," says the rich man, pretending to think it over, "I don't know if you are good enough for my daughter. Maybe you can prove yourself to me?"

"Oh, *oui*, Papa, anything you say!"

"Well, then, take this silver flask and fill it up for me."

"What do you want?" asks Jean Sot. "Wine, whiskey?"

"*Non*," says the rich man, keeping a straight face. "Take this flask and fill it up with . . . bull's milk. That's right! If you can fill this flask with the milk of a bull, then you can marry my daughter, and all my wealth will be yours someday."

So Jean Sot eagerly took the flask, and away he went down the road to find a bull to milk. He ran until he came to the countryside. There in a pasture, sure enough, was a big ol' mean-lookin' bull.

He walked right up to that bull and looked him over, trying to figure where to get started. But ol' bull was getting madder and madder, pawing the ground, shaking his horns. The next thing you know, he was charging and Jean

Sot was running for his life. He just barely escaped!

That evening Jean Sot thought harder than he'd ever thought in his life. Suddenly, it came to him. The girl's father had tricked him! Now, after a lifetime of being the target of everyone's practical jokes, even Jean Sot had learned a little something, you see. He thinks, "The time has come to show them all." Soon he had made a plan.

Late that night, with a little hatchet in hand, he went back to the rich man's house and shimmied up a slippery willow tree growing beside the man's bedroom window. He perched on a limb and took to chopping on that tree, chip-chop, chip-chop, chip-chop. All the while he's moanin' and groanin', "Oh, *mon pauvre papa!* Oh, my poor *papa!*"

Before long, the whole neighborhood comes running to see what all the commotion's about.

The shutters of the rich man's window fly open and he hollers out, "Jean Sot, is that you? What the devil are you doin', choppin' on my tree and moanin' to raise the dead in the middle of the night? I know you're foolish, but I didn't know you was crazy too!"

"Oh, my poor *papa*, he's havin' such a hard time of it," says Jean Sot. "This bark'll make a good tea, don't ya know, and help 'im get stronger."

"What's the matter with your *papa*, boy?" asks the rich man, taken aback. "Is he sick-sick? Has he got the fever?"

"Oh no, it's much worse than that!" says Jean Sot. "Never has a poor man had it so rough. You see, tonight my papa gave birth—to twins!"

"*Mon Dieu!*" the rich man exclaims. "Did he have boys, or girls, or one of each?"

With that, Jean Sot started in to laughin' so hard he nearly fell out of the tree. The neighbors were slappin' each other on the back and sputterin'. Well, the rich man realized he'd been had, and he starts to cussin'.

"Of all the . . . Jean Sot, you better get outta that tree and quit tellin' lies 'fore I get my shotgun after you!"

"I don't think I'd be talkin' 'bout lyin' if I was you," says Jean. "I don't want to call you a liar, but if you say a bull can give milk, then my *papa* can give birth to twins, for true!"

The rich man was ashamed. His neighbors had witnessed the whole thing, and so he was forced to hold up his end of the bargain or be ridiculed as a greater fool than Jean Sot.

And so, just as he had predicted, Jean married the prettiest girl and became the richest man in the whole parish. The people started thinking that he must really be smart-smart after all. They even made him captain of the Mardi Gras riders. It just goes to show that even the greatest of fools can sometimes become a leader.

The Mule Egg

Contemporary storyteller Doc McConnell carries on an age-old tradition when he takes a traditional tale and plugs in characters from his own experience. In this case it is his brother, Steamer, who becomes the main character in the tale of a gullible child.

I'd like to tell you a story about my brother Steamer. Now, ol' Steamer liked a lot of different things. Vienna sausage. Frog legs. Girls. Goin' to town. But best of all, he liked mules. He said that a mule was all a mountain boy should ever need.

He said, "Why, a mule'll plow all day long. He won't talk back. You can't push 'im off a bluff. He don't eat much, and he don't cost much to keep. Any man needs 'im a good mule."

Steamer would take any kind of mule.

He said, "If I could jist git me a little baby mule, I'd even take the runt of the litter. Jist a little ol' mule about twelve inches long with nice floppy ears, soft, fluffy fur, big, strong hind legs. Why, if I had me a little baby mule, I'd feed it and take care of it. And when it'd git up about waist high, I'd put my little harness on it, hook it up to my toy plow, and I'd plow ever' corn patch in Tucker's Knob."

That's all Steamer would ever talk about. He even begged Mama and Daddy to put 'im a baby mule in his sock at Christmastime.

Well, one day Steamer went down to John Mauk's General Store and begun to look around. John asked 'im, "Steamer, did ya ever find yourself a little baby mule?"

Steamer said, "No, I didn't. You don't know anybody that's got any little baby mules, do ya?"

John said, 'No, I don't know nobody that's got a baby mule, but . . ."

And about that time, Steamer looked over on the shelf and saw John's shipment of big, ol', brown, round, hairy coconuts, a whole basketful of 'em. Steamer looked at them things and said, "John, what in the world are those big, ol', brown, round, hairy things over there!"

He said, "Why, Steamer, them things is mule eggs. Ain't you never seen a mule egg before?"

Steamer said, "A mule egg?"

John said, "Yeah, you know how an ol' hen sits on a hen egg and hatches out little baby chickens? Well, these old mare mules sit on them big nests full of mule eggs, and that's where you git little baby mules."

And ol' Steamer says, "Where in the world did you ever find that many?"

John said, "Well, there was an old mare mule that had a nest down there in the brier patch, and we gathered 'em up this mornin'. Folks is always askin' for a good mule egg. *You* need one of them mule eggs, Steamer."

"You mean I could hatch it out myself?"

John said, "Why, Lordy, yes, son. You could hatch it yourself. Jist fix yourself a little nest, and sit on that ol' mule egg for 'bout two weeks, jist like an ol' hen. But don't ever let the egg git cold. You have to keep it warm all the time, or it won't hatch, Just sit on that egg for two weeks, don't ever git offa it, and when two weeks is up, that mule egg will pop open and there'll be a little ol', hairy, long-eared baby mule jist like you've always wanted."

Well, ol' Steamer was excited. "What will you take for one of them mule eggs!"

John said, "I'd have to have thirty-five cents for one, I guess."

So ol' Steamer picked up some pop bottles and pumped a little gas for ol' John and he gave 'im one of them mule eggs. Steamer carefully carried it home and showed it to Mama.

Well, Mama went along with Steamer—helpin' 'im git an ol' tobacco basket and some straw, settin' up Steamer's nest in our woodshed behind the house.

Ol' Steamer laid that mule egg right on top of that pile of straw, climbed on top, and sat down. And Mama brought Steamer an ol' quilt because she jist knew he was a-goin' to git chilly sittin' out there in the shed for two weeks.

Well, ol' Steamer started sittin' on that ol' coconut, thinkin' it was a mule egg, and he started countin' the days. One, two, three . . . And when Steamer would git hungry, Mama would bring his meals out to 'im. Four, five, six, seven, and finally, eight days had passed. Ol' Steamer was gittin' excited 'cause it wasn't goin' to be long 'til that mule was a-goin' to hatch out and he was a-goin' to have 'im a nice, fluffy, long-eared, baby mule.

Steamer counted the days. Nine, ten, eleven, twelve, thirteen, fourteen, fifteen, and finally, eighteen days come and went. Two weeks had already passed and no baby mule. He couldn't figure out why that baby mule hadn't kicked open that shell, so he held it up to his ear to see if he could hear 'im kickin' inside. He didn't hear a sound.

Well, Steamer got mad, and out there behind that woodshed he threw that ol' mule egg as hard as he could down into the brier patch—hopin' it would bust open and, if there was a baby mule inside, it would git out.

Well, sittin' out there in that brier patch was a floppy-eared jackrabbit. And that ol' mule egg hit that jackrabbit on the side of the head, addled 'im, and that rabbit jumped from the brier patch and commenced to runnin' 'round in circles and, finally, run off across the cabbage field.

When Steamer saw that ol' floppy-eared jackrabbit, he thought it was his baby mule and commenced to chasin' it, hollerin', "Come back! Come back! I'm your mammy! And your pappy, too!"

Steamer chased that ol' jackrabbit 'til he was jist give out, and he watched 'im run over the hill and out of sight.

"Oh, go on then," yelled Steamer. "I don't want ya. I can't plow that fast nohow."

The $50,000 Racehorse

Carrying on her family's storytelling tradition, Hannah McConnell Gillenwater tells this tale that she heard from her uncle "Steamer" McConnell, who was the subject of the previous story.

When I was a girl, I was my dad's shadow. Everywhere he went, I tagged right along. One of my favorite places to go was John Mauk's country store in Stony Point, Tennessee.

I remember that store's screen door and how the hinges would squeak. John kept those old wood floors oiled, and I can still recall the smell. That was *the* store in Stony Point, complete with a pot-bellied stove. All the gentlemen would sit around that stove, and it'd be red-hot at the bottom. They'd sit there, chewin' and spittin'. I'd sit there too and listen to the stories they had to tell.

Now, John Mauk was quite a character. Long before I was even a gleam in my daddy's eye, they say that John was probably the meanest man in Hawkins County. He never would go to Sunday school, church, or revival meetings—in fact, he'd cheat you blind. He'd charge you a little more than he should and keep his finger on the scales when he weighed out fruit or vegetables. He was a pretty ornery fellow.

Well, John was getting up in years, and the people in the community were starting to worry about his soul and what would happen to him in the hereafter. There happened to be a traveling Baptist revival coming through Hawkins County, and some of the little old ladies down at the Baptist church commenced to praying for old John. They started tellin' him, "John, you need to come to this revival." Well, they hounded him, and the men of the church hounded him too, until finally he said, "All right, I'll come."

It was on the last night of the revival that John Mauk came, and he got religion. He said, "I've turned over a new leaf. From here on out, I'm going to be living at the foot of the cross." He got such a good case of religion that afterward, every time he went to ring up a sale in his store, he'd quote a verse of Scripture.

Well, this particular day in October—the sun was shinin' down, but there was a definite nip in the air—we were all sittin' around the stove in John's store, and I was listening to stories and wantin' a chew of tobacco, but they wouldn't let me have one. And in the door came this little girl.

John said, "Well, howdy, honey. What can I do for you today?" She said, "I want some candy." So John handed the big old glass candy jar down to her, and she filled her pockets full, gave him her money, and left. She must have gotten 15 cents' worth of candy for a nickel. We couldn't believe that he'd been so kind to that kid. Old John never had liked young 'uns much.

He went around to the cash register and looked up into the heavens. Then he rang up the sale, and he said, "Suffer the little children to come unto me."

About 10 minutes later Cougar Myers's mama came in there, hunting a birthday present for her daddy. John let her come around behind the counter, and he showed her the bandana handkerchiefs and the pocket combs and the sock supporters and the Barlow knives and Aqua Velva and stuff. She picked her out a nice present for old man Myers, and John gift-wrapped it for her for free with some old Christmas paper he had left over.

She paid him and went out the door, and as he went to the register to ring up the sale, he looked heavenward again and said, "Honor thy father and thy mother."

Boy, by then, we were impressed with all that Scripture. It wasn't long afterward that we heard a big commotion outside the store. We looked out, and a brand-new bright blue pickup truck with a matching horse trailer had pulled up in front of the store. It had out-of-the-county license tags. Nobody knew that old feller.

Sure enough, he got out of the truck and came into the store. He had on a sheepskin coat, a big old 10-gallon hat, and pointy cowboy boots. He came a-struttin' in, walked up to the counter, and growled, "I want to buy me a horse blanket."

John said, "I'll see what I got." So he went to the back room, and he had three horse blankets there. They were all the very same kind, but each one was a different color. Naturally, John got the top one off the shelf and brought it out and laid it on the counter. The man said, "All right, how much is that?" John said, "Sir, that'll be $9.95."

That man yelled, "Nine ninety-five? Nine ninety-five? Buddy, I've got a $50,000 racehorse in that trailer out there, and I'm not about to put a cheap blanket like that on my horse! You can just forget it if you haven't got anything better." Old John said, "You want a better blanket." The man said, "Yeah, I want a better blanket."

John went to the back room again and took the next one down the line—same thing, just a different color—and brought it out and put it down on the counter. The man said, "All right, how much is that one?" John said, "Sir, that'll be $19.95."

The man said, "Buddy, I thought I told you I had a $50,000 racehorse out there, and no cheap stuff like that is going on the back of my horse!"

John said, "Sir, I aim to please. I think I got another one. I know what you want now."

So John took back that horse blanket and brought out the last one, carrying it as if it were some royal gem, and he laid it down real gentle in front of that man. Old John turned back one corner of the blanket, rubbing his hand over it, and he said, "Now, how is this?" The man said, "How much is that one?"

John said, "Sir, that's the best blanket in the house. That'll be $99.95."

The man said, "I'll take it." He whipped out the fattest wallet I've ever seen. Now, it might have been filled mostly with ones—I don't know. But he thumbed through there and pulled out a crisp $100 bill and laid it on the counter. He stuck that blanket under his arm and said, "Keep the change." Then he went out that squeaky screen door, jumped into his pickup truck, and took off.

There was dead silence. We couldn't believe what had just transpired. John stood behind the counter, holding that hundred-dollar bill in his hands. He looked over at us, and we looked at him. He waited. We reckoned he was waiting for some divine inspiration.

Finally he went over to the cash register. He looked toward heaven, rang that sale up, and said, "He was a stranger, and I took him in."

Jim Baker's Bluejay Yarn

———·•·——

Animal tales have always been a feature of North American folklore. Storytellers have given animals every human trait, including foolishness. Mark Twain, who was known as one who didn't suffer fools lightly, told this tale when he went on his lecture tours in the nineteenth century.

————

Animals talk to each other, of course. There can be no question about that; but I suppose there are very few people who can understand them. I never knew but one man who could. I knew he could, however, because he told me so himself. He was a middle-aged, simple-hearted miner who had lived in a lonely corner of California, among the woods and mountains, a good many years, and had studied the ways of his only neighbors, the beasts and the birds, until he believed he could accurately translate any remark which they made. This was Jim Baker. According to Jim Baker, some animals have only a limited education, and use only very simple words, and scarcely ever a comparison or a flowery figure; whereas, certain other animals have a large vocabulary, a fine command of language and a ready and fluent delivery; consequently these latter talk a great deal; they like it; they are conscious of their talent, and they enjoy "showing off." Baker said, that after long and careful observation, he had come to the conclusion that the bluejays were the best talkers he had found among birds and beasts. Said he:

"There's more *to* a bluejay than any other creature. He has got more moods, and more different kinds of feelings than other creatures; and, mind you, whatever a bluejay feels, he can put into language. And no mere commonplace language, either, but rattling, out-and-out book-talk—and bristling with metaphor, too—just bristling! And as for command of language—why *you* never see a bluejay get stuck for a word. No man ever did. They just boil out of him! And another thing: I've noticed a good deal, and there's no bird, or cow, or anything that uses as good grammar as a bluejay. You may say a cat uses good grammar. Well, a cat does—but you let a cat get excited once; you let a cat get to pulling fur with another cat on a shed, nights, and you'll hear grammar that will give you the lockjaw. Ignorant people think it's the *noise* which fighting cats make that is so aggravating, but it ain't so; it's the sickening grammar they use. Now I've never heard a jay use bad grammar but very seldom; and when they do, they are as ashamed as a human; they shut right down and leave.

"You may call a jay a bird. Well, so he is, in a measure—because he's got feathers on him, and don't belong to no church, perhaps; but otherwise he is just as much a human as you be. And I'll tell you for why. A jay's gifts, and instincts, and feelings, and interests, cover the whole ground. A jay hasn't got any more principle than a Congressman. A jay will lie, a jay will steal, a jay will deceive, a jay will betray; and four times out of five, a jay will go back on his solemnest promise. The sacredness of an obligation is a thing which you can't cram into no bluejay's head. Now, on top of all this, there's another thing; a jay can outswear any gentleman in the mines. You think a cat can swear. Well, a cat can; but you give a bluejay a subject that calls for his reserve-powers, and where is your cat? Don't talk to *me*—I know too much about this thing. And there's yet another thing; in the one little particular of scolding—just good, clean, out-and-out scolding—a blue-jay can lay over anything, human or divine. Yes, sir, a jay is everything that a man is. A jay can cry, a jay can laugh, a jay can feel shame, a jay can reason and plan and discuss, a jay likes gossip and scandal, a jay has got a sense of humor, a jay knows when he is an ass just as well as you do—maybe better. If a jay ain't human, he better take in his sign, that's all. Now I'm going to tell you a perfectly true fact about some bluejays.

"When I first begun to understand jay language correctly, there was a lit-tle incident happened here. Seven years ago, the last man in this region but me moved away. There stands his house,—been empty ever since; a log house, with a plank roof—just one big room, and no more; no ceiling—nothing between the rafters and the floor. Well, one Sunday morning I was sitting out here in front of my cabin, with my cat, taking the sun, and looking at the blue hills, and listening to the leaves rustling so lonely in the trees, and thinking of the home away yon-der in the states, that I hadn't heard from in thirteen years, when a bluejay lit on that house, with an acorn in his mouth, and says, 'Hello, I reckon I've struck something.' When he spoke, the acorn dropped out of his mouth and rolled down the roof, of course, but he didn't care; his mind was all on the thing he had struck. It was a knot-hole in the roof. He cocked his head to one side, shut one eye and put the other one to the hole, like a 'possum looking down a jug; then he glanced up with his bright eyes, gave a wink or two with his wings—which signifies gratification, you understand—says, 'It looks like a hole, it's located like a hole,—blamed if I don't believe it *is* a hole!"

"Then he cocked his head down and took another look; he glances up perfectly joyful, this time; winks his wings and his tail both, and says, 'Oh, no, this ain't no fat thing, I reckon! If I ain't in luck!—why it's a perfectly elegant hole!' So he flew down and got that acorn, and fetched it up and dropped it in, and was just tilting his head back, with the heavenliest smile on his face, when all of a sudden he was paralyzed into a listening attitude and that smile faded gradually out of his countenance like breath off'n a razor, and the queerest look of surprise took its place. Then he says, 'Why, I didn't hear it fall!' He cocked his eye at the hole again, and took a long look; raised up and shook his head; stepped around to the other side of the hole and took another look from that side; shook his head again. He studied a while, then he just went into the *de*tails—walked round and round the hole and spied into it from every point of the compass. No use. Now he took a thinking attitude on the comb of the roof and scratched the back of his head with his right foot a minute, and finally says, 'Well, it's too many for *me*, that's certain; must be a mighty long hole; however, I ain't got no time to fool around here, I got to 'tend to business; I reckon it's all right—chance it, anyway.'

"So he flew off and fetched another acorn and dropped it in, and tried to flirt his eye to the hole quick enough to see what become of it, but he was too late. He held his eye there as much as a minute; then he raised up and sighed, and says, 'Confound it, I don't seem to understand this thing, no way; however, I'll tackle her again.' He fetched another acorn, and done his best to see what become of it, but he couldn't. He says, 'Well, *I* never struck no such a hole as this before; I'm of the opinion it's a totally new kind of a hole.' Then he begun to get mad. He held in for a spell, walking up and down the comb of the roof and shaking his head and muttering to himself; but his feelings got the upper hand of him, presently, and he broke loose and cussed himself black in the face. I never see a bird take on so about a little thing. When he got through he walks to the hole and looks in again for half a minute; then he says, 'Well, you're a long hole, and a deep hole, and a mighty singular hole altogether—but I've started in to fill you, and I'm d—d if I *don't* fill you, if it takes a hundred years!'

"And with that, away he went. You never see a bird work so since you was born. He laid into his work . . . and the way he hove acorns into that hole for about two hours and a half was one of the most exciting and astonishing spectacles I ever struck. He never stopped to take a look any more—he just hove 'em in and went for more. Well, at last he could hardly flop his wings, he was so tuckered out. He comes a-drooping down, once more, sweating like an ice-pitcher, drops his acorn in and says, '*Now* I guess I've got the bulge on you by this time!' So he bent down for a look. If you'll believe me, when his head come up again he was just pale with rage. He says, 'I've shoveled acorns enough in there to keep the family thirty years, and if I can see a sign of one of 'em I wish I may land in a museum with a belly full of sawdust in two minutes!'

"He just had strength enough to crawl up on to the comb and lean his back agin the chimbly, and then he collected his impressions and begun to free his mind. I see in a second that what I had mistook for profanity in the mines was only just the rudiments, as you may say.

"Another jay was going by, and heard him doing his devotions, and stops to inquire what was up. The sufferer told him the whole circumstance, and says, 'Now yonder's the hole, and if you don't believe me, go and look for yourself.' So this fellow went and looked, and comes back and says, 'How many did you say you put in there?' 'Not any less than two tons,' says the sufferer. The other jay went and looked again. He couldn't seem to make it out, so he raised a yell, and three more jays come. They all examined the hole, they all made the sufferer tell it over again, then they all discussed it, and got off as many leather-headed opinions about it as an average crowd of humans could have done.

"They called in more jays; then more and more till pretty soon this whole region 'peared to have a blue flush about it. There must have been five thousand of them; and such another jawing and disputing and ripping and cussing, you never heard. Every jay in the whole lot put his eye to the hole and delivered a more chuckle-headed opinion about the mystery than the jay that went there before him. They examined the house all over, too. The door was standing half open, and at last one old jay happened to go and light on it and look in. Of course, that knocked the mystery galley-west in a second. There lay the acorns, scattered all over the floor. He flopped his wings and raised a whoop. 'Come here!' he says. 'Come here, everybody; hang'd if this fool hasn't been trying to fill up a house with acorns!' They all came a-swooping down like a blue cloud, and as each fellow lit on the door and took a glance, the whole absurdity of the contract that that first jay had tackled hit him home and he fell over backwards suffocating with laughter, and the next jay took his place and done the same.

"Well, sir, they roosted around here on the housetop and the trees for an hour, and guffawed over that thing like human beings. It ain't any use to tell me a bluejay hasn't got a sense of humor, because I know better. And memory, too. They brought jays here from all over the United States to look down that hole, every summer for three years. Other birds, too. And they could all see the point, except an owl that come from Nova-Scotia to visit the Yo Semite, and he took this thing in on his way back. He said he couldn't see anything funny in it. But then he was a good deal disappointed about Yo Semite, too."

The Killer Mosquitoes

Mosquitoes turn up all the time in North American folklore presumably because they are a common pestilence in almost every region of the country. They most often appear in the tall tales, but this story from Louisiana, with versions all over the South, is told to poke fun at foreigners who are not familiar with our critters.

There were once three Irishmen called O'Leary, O'Bleary, and O'Neary who decided to leave the old country and come to Louisiana. They'd heard about the rich, black, delta dirt and the great plantations. They figured they'd find some work, save their money, and start farming. They'd grow sugar cane and cotton, beans and rice, everything but potatoes—they were just sick and tired of eating potatoes. O'Leary, O'Bleary, and O'Neary took passage on a ship bound for New Orleans. After weeks at sea, the Irishmen arrived in Louisiana at last. They got off the boat and started walking around to see what they could find for themselves.

They kept to the river, looking for a plantation where they could find work. Before long they were lost in the middle of the river bottom. Everywhere there were only swamp woods as far as they could see. The *mousse* hung down from the trees like an old man's beard, and *boscoyo* [cypress] rose up from the water like knobby knees. Alligators snapped at them and cottonmouth snakes hissed. But they weren't afraid, for they'd heard about the strange creatures that lived in La Louisianne: fish with cat whiskers and big as a man; giant snapping turtles; *pichou*, the bobcat that screamed like a woman. They fancied they knew all they needed to know to get by, so on they tramped, deeper and deeper into the swamp.

The sun began to sink low, so they decided they better make camp for the night. They found a little sheltered piece of dry ground and settled down there. The sun set and darkness fell. The three Irishmen were so tired, they were soon fast asleep. They'd slept only a few winks when suddenly they woke up howling and slapping at their faces and arms. A high, whining sound whirred in their ears.

They were being attacked by some kind of tiny beasts with a bite like the stick of a needle!

"What is it?" hollers O'Leary.

"I dunno, but it bites like the devil!" O'Bleary yells.

"I can't see it," says O'Neary, "but I can hear it whinin' for our blood!"

All night long the Irishmen slapped and cursed at the little monsters. When morning came they were red-eyed and covered with itchy red bumps. At last they got a look at the beasts that had nearly eaten them alive. They didn't know what to make of the little bloodthirsty creatures. They had never heard of mosquitoes!

"We better get out of here before they come back with their mates and kill us for good," says O'Leary. O'Bleary and O'Neary agreed, and they hurried away as quickly as they could through the swamp.

Well, the three men didn't have a notion of where they were going, and they wound up on the river right back where they started. They'd been walking in a circle. They turned in the opposite direction and walked until the sun was low in the sky. A little deserted cabin lay before them, perched on the river bank. They thought it looked like a good place to spend the night.

The three Irishmen barred the door and pulled the shutters. "We'll be safe here from those creatures. They'll not bite us tonight," they said. They settled in, with stomachs growling and the three of them just itchin' all over. They were dog-tired, and pretty soon they fell fast asleep. O'Neary's snoring woke up O'Leary, and when he sat up he saw blinking lights buzzing about the room.

"Wake up, mates!" he shouts. "Those blood-suckin' devils are back!" The others woke up trembling. "They mean to kill us for sure!" hollers O'Neary. "Faith and begorra!" shouts O'Bleary. "Look! They brought lanterns so they could see us and suck us dry. Run for it, boys! Aaiieegghh!"

The three Irishmen were running so wildly to get out of that cabin that they broke the door down. They didn't know that the blinking, buzzing lights in the cabin were only harmless *mouches à feu*, fireflies.

O'Leary, O'Bleary, and O'Neary didn't stop running until they got back to New Orleans, where they took the first ship they could find back to Ireland. After that they never minded eating potatoes at every blessed meal. For at least at home they were safe from those whining, needle-nosed, lantern-carrying, blood-sucking, killer mosquitoes!

The Yankee Peddler and the Innkeeper

Two famous American characters are brought together in this tale of deception and fool-ishness. The Yankee Peddler makes a frequent appearance in stories from the Northeastern United States, not as a fool but as a clever bargainer who does his best to make fools of his customers. He finds an easy mark in the Dutchman, who, in nine-teenth-century Pennsylvania Dutch culture, was the object of many jokes the people told on themselves.

A Yankee peddler westbound with his team of horses and load of notions was held up at a Dutchman's Inn for almost a week because of a very severe storm. Rains had made the roads impassable and the streams were in a flooding state.

Finally after days of eating and sleeping and drinking at the Inn, and after demanding considerable service from the Dutch innkeeper, he asked that his horses be hitched and be made ready to depart.

Finally he asked the innkeeper, "How much is my fare?" and the Dutchman thinking a dollar a day enough, but seeing the man wasn't a regular customer, said, "$10.00."

The Yankee said, "Maybe it would be better if I paid you on the way back, then I could give you $20.00 for my stay and it would allow me time to make more sales and have more ready cash after I sell my supplies." But to this the Dutchman was suspicious and insisted on being paid cash THEN.

The Yankee paid him the $10.00 and the Dutchman, feeling that he had made a good profit, seeing that he charged him almost half again as much as he usually did to other people, said, "It's a custom for the innkeeper to offer a traveller a drink for the road," to which the Yankee said, "Fine." (This was a time honored custom, to be expected by the Yankees.)

The innkeeper handed the Yankee a mug of cider and the Yankee said, "This certainly would make fine wine if you put it through that new secret wine-making process." And the Dutchman thought, "If I could convert cider into good wine, I'd be rich and have hundreds more visitors, etc."

The Dutchman said, "Tell me how to make it." And the Yankee said, "It is new and valuable and I'll charge you $10.00 now and when I return, if the cider is wine, you will have to agree now to pay me an additional $50.00."

After the agreement was made, the Dutchman and Yankee went into the cellar, and the Yankee asked for a half-inch auger, bored a hole into one end of the barrel of cider and asked the Dutchman to place his thumb to this, and stretch his arm so he could cover the other hole also.

"Hold this position while I go up and get the spigots from my wagon."

With this he left the Dutchman, arms spread out holding the barrel with holes in it, and jumped in his wagon and left.

8

Love Stories

Woven into the fabric of many homespun North American folktales are recognizable elements from European fairy tales. More than any other type of tale, love stories inherit their themes from these ancient sources. Regional North American tellers have for centuries taken half-remembered stories, placed them in settings close to home, and rendered them in dialects from all over the continent. As the tellers adapt the stories to reflect their own surroundings, they change characters' names, add some details and omit others, and, in some cases, combine several stories into one. "Cinderella" is frequently used as the basis for a love story, and it is closely followed in popularity by "East of the Sun and West of the Moon" and "Beauty and the Beast."

In addition to Old World tales that have been altered to fit North American storytelling styles, several purebred American love stories are represented here. Just as with every other aspect of life, North Americans have developed their own peculiar way of courting each other and of talking about it later. Some of these stories are legendary. That is, they are probably based on real events that are either very funny or are significant to the culture group that keeps them alive. Other tales are pure romantic fiction.

The Girl That Married a Flop-Eared Hound-Dog

This remarkable American version of one of the world's most frequently repeated fairy tales was told to Marie Campbell by Uncle Tom Dixon of Kentucky in the 1930s. Readers will recognize in this tale elements of "East of the Sun and West of the Moon."

That old flop-eared hound-dog laying there on the hearth with his head to the fire 'minds me of a tale my foreparents used to tell of evenings gathered about the hearth. While we wait for Suzanne to call supper, I aim to tell you the old time tale called "The Girl That Married a Flop-Eared Hound-Dog." Musta looked pine-blank like that old hound-dog laying right there by the fire.

They was a man—a king maybe—that had a fine castle and lands that stretched from here to yonder. His wife died and left him all lonesome. One day when he was out in the woods, not hunting but just walking around nearly about to lonesome to death, a fine hound-dog with long flop-ears come up to him wagging its tail and acting friendly. The king thought maybe it had got lost from some folks hunting in his woods. So he sat down on a log and called the dog up to him and said to it, "What you doing here, flop-eared hound-dog? How come you got lost from hunting? What you want me to do for you?"

He never thought a breath about no answer. He was just making friends with a good hunting dog. But the flop-eared hound-dog set itself down in front of him and said, "I want to marry one of your girls; that's what I want, and I can take good care of her and keep her happy if she's a-mind to have me."

Well, the king was so addled in his mind with hearing a hound-dog speak out that way that he said, "Come along home with me, and I'll let you ask one of my girls will she marry you, and I'm willing if she is."

The flop-eared hound-dog asked the oldest girl first would she marry him. She flew mad and screeched and screamed, "No I won't marry no flop-eared hound-dog! I won't marry nothing but a natural man! Who ever heard tell of such an idea!"

Then the flop-eared hound-dog asked the middle girl would she marry him. And she had a bigger fit than the oldest girl done had. And she wouldn't marry him neither.

When he asked the youngest girl would she marry him, she said she would if she could come back home now and again to see her folks. She never 'peared to feel no shame about who she was marrying but asked a big passel of folks to the wedding just like she was going to marry a natural man. And she fixed a heap of fine wedding clothes.

Then the very minute of the wedding ceremony when the sisters had their eyes covered up with their hands, for they couldn't bear to see a flop-eared hound-dog stand up and marry their sister in front of a whole crowd of folks that never had no hint that she weren't marrying a natural man—well, that very minute the groom came in, and it weren't no flop-eared hound-dog no more but a good-looking young man dressed up in his Sunday clothes. A mean old witch had put him under a spell till some nice girl was willing to marry him of her own free will. He was so good-looking and rich that the oldest girl and the middle girl turned mighty jealous. And folks said it was the best wedding they been to that season.

After the wedding frolic was over, the bride and groom went to their fine home in some place a far piece off. I don't know where it was nor no more about it. It was just a fine big house and they lived happy together.

Then in a year and a day the girl hankered to go see her folks, and she wanted to stay there till she birthed her baby. Her man was willing for her to go on a visit to her folks, but he cautioned her not to tell his name to nobody even if they begged mighty hard. If she told that his name was Sunshine on the Dew, she wouldn't never see him no more.

Well, she had the baby at her old home place, and it was a mighty pretty boy baby. When it was two days old, in the night folks heard fairy music; and in the morning the baby was gone. Whoever had stole the baby left sweet cakes and wine at the head of the bed. But no trace of the baby.

The sisters blamed the baby's daddy and they tried to find out what his name was—but the youngest girl shut her mouth up tight and wouldn't tell. Her man came in a month's time and took her home with him.

Another year and a day passed by and the youngest girl hankered to visit her folks again and stay till she birthed her [next] baby. Her man cautioned her again not to tell his name to nobody or she wouldn't see him no more. When the second baby—a girl this time—was two days old, they was fairy music in the night. And the baby gone—nobody could guess where. Whoever had stole this baby had put sweet cakes and wine at the head of the bed like the time before.

The sisters blamed the baby's daddy again and tried to find out his name. But the youngest girl shut up her mouth tight and wouldn't tell. In a month's time her man come and took her back home with him.

Three times the youngest girl went home to visit her folks and stayed till she had birthed her baby—the last one another boy. Three times her man cautioned her not to tell his name or she wouldn't see him no more. But the sisters threatened her with her life if she wouldn't tell. So she said in a low whisper that his name was Sunshine on the Dew.

When the last baby was two days old the fairy music in the night came again. And the next morning—no baby—no sweet cakes nor wine at the head of the bed neither. And no man come to take her home with him no matter how long she waited.

After she waited some months for her man to come and he never showed up, she set out on foot to go to her married home. Nobody home when she got there. No sign of nobody. So she set out to travel till she found her man. She traveled all day till she had holes in her shoes. At nighttime she saw a little house in the woods. The door stood open and a fire was blazing in the fireplace. An old woman in a rocking chair by the hearth made her welcome. She said her man with three babies different sizes had been there three nights before. The old woman gave her a good supper and warm water to wash herself and a soft bed to her sides. In the morning she gave the girl some scissors that she said would cut by themselves whatever the girl wanted her cloth to be.

The second night at the same kind of little house an old woman made her welcome and said her man with three babies different sizes had been there two nights before. This old woman gave her a good supper and warm water to wash herself and a soft bed to her sides. In the morning she gave the girl a thimble that would sew by itself.

The last night another old woman in a little house made the girl welcome and told her her man with three babies different sizes had been there just the night before. The girl wouldn't stay for no supper nor no warm water to wash herself nor no soft bed to her sides. She wanted to hurry on and try to catch up with her man. The old woman tied up a snack to eat in a budget (small sack) and gave it to the girl along with a needle that would sew fine things by itself.

The girl went on till she came to a fine big house with a crowd of folks gathered about. It was her man fixing to marry again. But the girl swapped her magic sewing tools that could cut and sew fine things without no help from any person. She swapped them things to the other girl to give back her man to her. I don't call to mind the details and particulars of how it come about—but when the man that had been a flop-eared hound-dog saw his first woman, it all come over him again how he loved her with all his heart; and he gave the fine new house to the woman he wasn't going to marry, and took his babies three different sizes and the girl that had birthed him the babies and they went back to their own home place to live out all the days of their life.

The Algonquin Cinderella

The basic story of Cinderella is told in almost every culture on Earth, and some experts think that it is thousands of years old. Whether the Native American Algonquin tribes heard it from European settlers and altered it or generated their own version, we will never know. But this beautiful tale stands as one of the best renditions I have ever heard.

There was once a large village of the MicMac Indians of the Eastern Algonquins, built beside a lake. At the far end of the settlement stood a lodge, and in it lived a being who was always invisible. He had a sister who looked after him, and everyone knew that any girl who could see him might marry him. For that reason there were very few girls who did not try, but it was very long before any-one succeeded.

This is the way in which the test of sight was carried out: at evening-time, when the Invisible One was due to be returning home, his sister would walk with any girl who might come down to the lakeshore. She, of course, could see her brother, since he was always visible to her. As soon as she saw him, she would say to the girls:

"Do you see my brother?"

"Yes," they would generally reply—though some of them did say "No."

To those who said that they could indeed see him, the sister would say:

"Of what is his shoulder strap made?" Some people say that she would enquire:

"What is his moose-runner's haul?" or "With what does he draw his sled?"

And they would answer:

"A strip of rawhide" or "a green flexible branch," or something of that kind.

Then she, knowing that they had not told the truth, would say:

"Very well, let us return to the wigwam!"

When they had gone in, she would tell them not to sit in a certain place, because it belonged to the Invisible One. Then, after they had helped to cook the supper, they would wait with great curiosity, to see him eat. They could be sure that he was a real person, for when he took off his moccasins they became visible, and his sister hung them up. But beyond this they saw nothing of him, not even when they stayed in the place all the night, as many of them did.

Now there lived in the village an old man who was a widower, and his three daughters. The youngest girl was very small, weak and often ill, and yet her sisters, especially the elder, treated her cruelly. The second daughter was kinder, and sometimes took her side, but the wicked sister would burn her hands and feet with hot cinders, and she was covered with scars from this treatment. She was so marked that people called her *Oochigeaskw*, the Rough-FacedGirl.

When her father came home and asked why she had such burns, the bad sister would at once say that it was her own fault, for she had disobeyed orders and gone near the fire and fallen into it.

These two elder sisters decided one day to try their luck at seeing the Invisible One. So they dressed themselves in their finest clothes, and tried to look their prettiest. They found the Invisible One's sister and took the usual walk by the water.

When he came, and when they were asked if they could see him, they answered: "Of course." And when asked about the shoulder strap or sled cord, they answered: "A piece of rawhide."

But of course they were lying like the others, and they got nothing for their pains.

The next afternoon, when the father returned home, he brought with him many of the pretty little shells from which wampum was made, and they set to work to string them.

That day, poor little Oochigeaskw, who had always gone barefoot, got a pair of her father's moccasins, old ones, and put them into water to soften them so that she could wear them. Then she begged her sisters for a few wampum shells. The elder called her a "little pest," but the younger one gave her some. Now, with no other clothes than her usual rags, the poor little thing went into the woods and got herself some sheets of birch bark, from which she made a dress, and put marks on it for decoration, in the style of long ago. She made a petticoat and a loose gown, a cap, leggings and a handkerchief. She put on her father's large old moccasins, which were far too big for her, and went forth to try her luck. She would try, she thought, to discover whether she could see the Invisible One.

She did not begin very well. As she set off, her sisters shouted and hooted, hissed and yelled, and tried to make her stay. And the loafers around the village, seeing the strange little creature, called out "Shame!"

The poor little girl in her strange clothes, with her face all scarred, was an awful sight, but she was kindly received by the sister of the Invisible One. And this was, of course, because this noble lady understood far more about things than simply the mere outside which all the rest of the world knows. As the brown of the evening sky turned to black, the lady took her down to the lake.

"Do you see him?" the Invisible One's sister asked.

"I do, indeed—and he is wonderful!" said Oochigeaskw.

The sister asked:

"And what is his sled-string?"

The little girl said:

"It is the Rainbow."

"And, my sister, what is his bow-string?"

"It is The Spirit's Road—the Milky Way."

"So you *have* seen him," said his sister. She took the girl home with her and bathed her. As she did so, all the scars disappeared from her body. Her hair grew again, as it was combed, long, like a blackbird's wing. Her eyes were now like stars. In all the world there was no other such beauty. Then, from her treasures, the lady gave her a wedding garment, and adorned her.

Then she told Oochigeaskw to take the wife's seat in the wigwam: the one next to where the Invisible One sat, beside the entrance. And when he came in, terrible and beautiful, he smiled and said:

"So we are found out!"

"Yes," said his sister. And so Oochigeaskw became his wife.

La Cenicienta Huasteca

It is possible that the story of Cinderella was brought to southwestern North America from Spain, where it has always been popular. This Mexican version characteristically changes the main setting for the story from a fancy ball to the church. "La Cenicienta" is Spanish for Cinderella; "Huasteca" is probably derived from Aztec.

Maria la Cenicienta was a girl who worked for a woman who had a daughter. She had to do all the housework and besides was compelled to labor at night carding wool. However, there was a little lamb that helped her. And this story tells us that the woman learned about this and ordered the lamb killed. Also, she called this girl, La Cenicienta, and told her to take the stomach of the lamb to the river and wash it and prepare it for *menudo*. While she was at the river preparing the meat for *menudo* some fish came and carried the little stomach away. La Cenicienta began to cry.

Then a fairy woman appeared and told her to weep no more. She said that near by La Cenicienta would find a small house and in the house was a baby crying and some large *tinajas* (large earthen jars) turned upside down.

"Sing to the baby and put it to sleep," she said; "then turn the *tinajas* upright."

La Cenicienta did as that fairy woman ordered. She found the small house and the baby crying. She sang and the little one went to sleep. Then she turned a *tinaja* upright, and immediately a golden star fixed itself upon her forehead and she was dressed in fine clothes. She turned another *tinaja* and there found the *menudo* meat prepared for cooking.

When she returned home the woman and the girl wanted to know how she got the fine clothes and the star. La Cenicienta told them what had happened at the river.

Envy entered the hearts of the woman and the girl, and they took the clothes from La Cenicienta. Then the woman had another lamb killed and sent her daughter to the river with the stomach of the animal.

"Do as La Cenicienta did," she said. "You will get more beautiful things."

The daughter took the meat to the river and while she was washing it, some fish came and carried the little stomach away. Then the girl pretended to weep. A fairy woman came to her and said:

"Weep no more. Go to the little house near here. You will find a baby crying. Sing it to sleep. Then the *tinajas* you see in the house are to be turned upright."

That girl went to the small house, and she whipped the baby hard. She turned a *tinaja*, and the *moco* of a *guajolote* (a turkey-cock's comb) attached itself to her forehead. She went home and wrapped a cloth about her head to hide the *moco*.

Later, the woman and her daughter went to mass. La Cenicienta was in the kitchen weeping and working when a fairy woman came to her and asked why she was sad.

"I wanted to go to mass," said La Cenicienta, "but they wouldn't let me." And then the fairy woman gave her a wand of *virtud*. "When you wish with your heart for something that is good, touch the star on your forehead with this wand and your wish will come true," she said.

Immediately La Cenicienta wished for elegant clothes and golden shoes and a carriage *mejor que ninguno* with a span of fine horses.

She went to mass. Everyone was amazed, and a prince fell in love with her.

When later the woman and her daughter came home, they found La Cenicienta in her ashy clothes working in the kitchen as usual. They told La Cenicienta of the miracle that they had seen at mass.

"The miracle was I," said La Cenicienta.

They laughed and mocked and said the star on La Cenicienta's forehead was taking the salt from her brain.

The following Sunday the woman and daughter went to mass, and as before left La Cenicienta home. However, this time La Cenicienta did not weep. She used her wand of *virtud* as she had done before, and behold she was at mass as beautiful as the most beautiful fairy.

When La Cenicienta left the church she lost one of her golden shoes near the door. The prince found it and went to the home where the woman lived with her daughter. He said he intended to marry the girl whose foot would fit that shoe. The woman's daughter crammed her big foot into the shoe. The prince put her in the carriage and was on his way to his palace when a little dog began barking and saying, "*Moco de guajolote va en coche y estrella de oro está en casa* (the turkey-cock's comb goes in the carriage, and the star of gold is in the house)." The prince was puzzled and went back to the house where the woman lived. He found the beautiful servant La Cenicienta. The golden shoe fitted her foot. They were married, *y fueron muy felices.*

Fabiano and Reyes

This dramatic tale, which is told in the Hispanic Southwest in North America, clearly has roots in the romantic fairy tales of Europe's Middle Ages. As the European ancestors of modern Hispanics crossed paths with the Indian populations of the American Southwest, tales such as "Fabiano and Reyes" were given more homely settings, though the notion of royalty was retained. This blending of the Old and the New Worlds produces a story of extraordinary love, and serves as a caution, as well.

Once there lived two kings and their wives who were very good friends. When one of the queens gave birth to her first child, the neighboring king and queen were asked to be godparents, and they named the baby boy Fabiano. Two years later the other queen gave birth to a baby girl, and she and the king, in turn, invited their friends to be godparents, and they named the girl Reyes.

Fabiano and Reyes grew up like brother and sister, and they loved each other very much. When they were growing up they would visit each other, spending one week in one palace and the next in the other. And later when they went to study at school Fabiano always took care of Reyes, because he cared for her as if she were his sister.

Fabiano grew to be a very handsome young man, one without equal in the region. When he was only fifteen he began writing love notes to his many girlfriends, and he shared all his secrets with Reyes because she was his confidante. When he showed her a letter from a girl whose heart he had broken he would say, "My dear Reyes, I only want a beautiful girl. If I had to marry an ugly girl I'd rather be blind."

And Reyes, who didn't consider herself a beautiful girl, would bow her head in shame and answer, "Fabiano, you deserve the most virtuous woman on this earth, one who is as beautiful as you."

Time passed and Fabiano continued his flirtations, and he always told Reyes everything, including his dislike for ugly girls. When school was over they returned home, and they still visited each other as before—one week in one palace and the next in the other.

In those days the kings often entertained people by holding big fiestas at their palaces. There were dances, bullfights and many other diversions. And as usual, Fabiano and Reyes were always together. Fabiano always found the most beautiful girls to dance with, and when he introduced them to Reyes he would always whisper, "I'll never marry an ugly girl, better to be blind than that!"

One summer, after the dances had come to an end in the palace of Fabiano's family, the entertainment was moved to the palace of Reyes' father. Her father had vowed to outdo his compadre—he was going to bring singers and bull-fighters from across the sea!

And so it was at a dance at Reyes' home that Fabiano found a pretty American girl. When he introduced her to Reyes he said, "Look, I have finally found my sweetheart. This is the kind of girl for me, is she not a beauty?"

"I agree," Reyes answered courteously. "Also, the woman who marries you should be the most virtuous woman in the world."

The following night Fabiano saw that Reyes was not dressed in her silk dress and jewelry; instead she had made a very simple linen dress for herself.

"Reyes!" Fabiano exclaimed, "Why aren't you dressed in your silk dress! That simple linen dress doesn't become a rich princess who has all the virtues of the world."

"Fabiano," she answered, "a woman as ugly as myself doesn't deserve to wear silk and fine apparel. I should wear only the most simple dress."

"I will be ashamed," he said, "for you to be seen with my American sweetheart; she will be dressed in her best silks and you in simple linen."

"Oh, she deserves the best," Reyes answered. "She is a lovely woman. But I don't deserve silk as I am ugly. So I will dress in a simple manner."

The following night, which was the last night of entertainment at the palace of Reyes' father, the singers who had been invited failed to arrive. Fabiano, who was eager to show off his new sweetheart, waited for them all afternoon, but there was no sign of the singers. Finally a servant arrived with the message that there had been a shipwreck and the singers had drowned.

Reyes grew very worried. "I don't want my father to be ashamed in front of his guests because he has no entertainment," she said. "Perhaps I can take their place."

"Oh, no!" Fabiano objected. "It would be a disgrace to have you, a princess, sing in public!"

Nevertheless Reyes decided to sing for the sake of her father. Even as Reyes began to sing Fabiano continued to insist that she should not. It wouldn't look right, he said, for such a handsome man as he to be seen with a plain and common singer.

But Reyes sang and when Fabiano heard her he was astonished. Never had he heard such a beautiful voice. He then became so enamored of Reyes that he didn't know what to do. When Reyes finished singing Fabiano was immediately at her side telling her how beautifully she had sung, but Reyes reminded him that she was an ugly woman and unworthy of his attention.

That evening when the festivities were concluded, Fabiano could hardly bear to leave. He had fallen completely in love with Reyes. The next day he told his parents that they should go and arrange for him to have Reyes' hand in marriage. The king and queen were overjoyed to hear of this plan.

But Reyes refused the offer by sending back a pumpkin, which according to the custom of that time meant a refusal. She also sent a letter in which she told Fabiano that she didn't deserve a man like him. She reminded him he had often derided ugly women, and since she was not beautiful and didn't wish him to be blind he should marry someone else. Fabiano waited a month but then became impatient and sent a friend to again ask Reyes to marry him. The friend went to Reyes but she explained that a marriage with Fabiano was impossible because of his conceit. It was true, she loved Fabiano, but as things were, the situation was impossible.

When Fabiano heard Reyes' answer he was brokenhearted. To try to forget his love he left his parents and moved to a foreign country. But he couldn't forget Reyes and every week he wrote her of his love.

Now it so happened that one afternoon Fabiano went hunting. He fired at a rabbit and the gun exploded. The gunpowder burned his eyes and blinded him. To make matters worse, while Fabiano was recovering from the accident his parents died, and shortly afterwards he heard that Reyes' parents had died also.

Later, when Fabiano returned home, he found himself alone. He had kept all of the letters he had written to Reyes but had never sent in a small box, but since he was now blind he was unable to read them as he used to. Now his only companion was a friend who came to visit him. His friend saw that Fabiano was very sad because he was alone and blind. One afternoon when he was visiting Fabiano, the friend inquired about Reyes.

"Has Reyes come to see you?" he asked.

"No," Fabiano answered, "she doesn't come to see me because of the way I treated her, but I know that without her I will die. She doesn't know that I truly love her and that she is my only consolation in life."

Then the friend went to see Reyes, and she asked about Fabiano.

"As you know, he is home, and he is blind, but you are such a hard woman it seems you have forgotten you grew up together."

"You are wrong, sir," Reyes answered. "The love I have for Fabiano cannot be destroyed by death itself."

"He doesn't know that," the friend said. "He thinks you don't love him. His life is very difficult. Because he is blind, his servants take advantage of him and feed him only when they want to. The food is poorly prepared and he is neglected. He needs someone to care for him. Would you be willing to be his nurse?"

"I will be Fabiano's nurse on one condition," Reyes answered, "and that is if you swear not to tell him it is I. I still believe he fell in love with me only because he heard me sing. Perhaps this way I will discover if he truly loves me."

"You have my word that I won't tell him anything," the friend said, "and you can see for yourself if his love is real."

The friend went back to Fabiano and asked him if he could bring a nurse to care for him. "Yes," Fabiano agreed, "but bring me a nurse who can read, one who will care kindly for me and see that I am fed."

So the friend brought Reyes to Fabiano's palace, and she was so overjoyed to see him again that she turned away and wept secretly. Then with great care she prepared his bath, and after he had bathed she helped him dress in the clothes of a prince. She fed him well and took good care of him because she loved him very much.

One day after she had been there a month Fabiano asked her for a favor.

"Nurse," he asked, "can you keep a secret?"

"I believe I can," Reyes answered.

"Then go to the storage room near my bedroom. There you will find a small box. Bring it to me. But remember, this is a secret only you and I will share."

Reyes brought the box and when Fabiano opened it she saw it was full of his old love letters to her. He asked her to read the letters and when she read them Fabiano grew very sad and his eyes grew wet with tears. Reyes, too, wept silently, but because Fabiano was blind he could not see the tears which rolled down her cheeks.

The next day Fabiano's friend came to visit and he found Reyes in the kitchen, her eyes red from crying. He asked Reyes what was the matter.

"Yesterday I discovered that Fabiano's love for me is real," she said, "and I cried all night after reading the letters he wrote to me."

"What do you plan to do?" the friend asked.

"I must put aside the mistakes of the past and marry Fabiano," she answered. "I have always loved him, and I love him even more now and want to care for him."

The friend was overjoyed. He immediately went to Fabiano and said, "My friend, I believe you should be married. You have many good years of life left; perhaps you should consider marrying this good woman who is your nurse."

Fabiano sighed. "Who would love a blind man?" he said. "And although the nurse is a good woman, the only love in my heart is for Reyes."

"Then I shall go and ask her for you," the friend said.

Fabiano shook his head. "She refused me when I was young and hand-some. Why should she accept me now that I am blind?"

"I will ask her anyway, and we shall see if she loves you or not!" the friend insisted.

For a moment hope stirred in Fabiano's heart. "Oh, if Reyes would marry me I would give you half of all I own, my friend!"

So the wedding was arranged, and the next day the friend and his wife, who were to be the witnesses, brought Reyes to Fabiano.

As they left for the church, Fabiano, who still didn't know that it was Reyes who had been his nurse, called for the nurse and told her to prepare a ban-quet table for the wedding feast.

Then the wedding party went to the chapel and Fabiano and Reyes were married. When they returned everyone was happy and excited. Fabiano called his nurse to come and serve them. Only then did his friend turn to him and tell him that the nurse who had served him so loyally all that time was Reyes herself: "Don't call for your nurse, for she is in truth Reyes. She is the bride at your side!"

Fabiano then took Reyes in his arms and understood at last that the real beauty of a woman lies in her soul.

A Bunch of Laurel Blooms for a Present

The theme from "Beauty and the Beast" begins this Kentucky story, and "The Frog Prince" ends it. But in "The Frog Prince," the princess is usually angry at the frog and throws him against the wall, which brings about a magic transformation. Here, we are given a stronger, braver heroine who takes the decisive step to release her lover from the spell.

Brought you some laurel buds to make a flowerpot to pretty up your house. Mary always loved laurel blooms the best when they were still little, knobby, pink buds, kinda square-shaped. Giving you a bunch of laurel blooms puts me in mind of an olden tale about a girl that wanted laurel blooms for a present.

It starts with a man going off from home a far piece to tend to some business, and he asked his three girls what they wanted him to bring them back for presents. The oldest girl said she wanted him to bring her back a green silk dress. The middle girl said she wanted him to bring her a pair of gold beads. The youngest girl wanted him to bring her a bunch of laurel blooms for a present. Maybe they had moved down to the level country from the mountains, and she was used to seeing laurel blooms back where they used to live. I don't know. The tale don't say.

The man bought the green silk dress and the pair of gold beads as soon as he got to the far-off place. But he waited about the laurel blooms till he was ready to start back home, so they wouldn't get all wilted. Then he couldn't find any laurel blooms. He looked and he looked. After a time he saw some laurel blooms on the edge of a woods. Seemed like they didn't belong to nobody, so he picked some to give his youngest girl for a present.

After he picked the laurel blooms, an old witch came out of the laurel bushes and said they belonged to her, and she didn't aim to let nobody pick them. She said he had already picked some, and he would have to die. He told her the flower blooms were for a present to his youngest girl. Then the old witch said he could live if he would give his youngest girl to her.

He would rather die than do that. He begged the old witch to let him go home and give the presents to his girls. She said he could do that. He gave the green silk dress to the oldest girl and the pair of gold beads to the middle girl. They put on their finery and primped in front of the looking glass. He gave the laurel blooms to the youngest girl, and she hugged his neck and kissed him. Then she put her present of flower blooms in a flowerpot of water to keep them fresh. Her sisters made fun of her for asking for nothing but flower blooms when she coulda had fine things to wear.

The man told his girls he had to go to the witch, and the youngest girl ran off in the night and went in his place to save him from the old witch. The old witch put her to live in a nice little house with an upstairs. A good supper was fixed and on the table waiting. The youngest girl saw two places at the table. Then in came the biggest toad-frog she ever did see.

It sat down in one chair, and she sat down in the other chair, and they ate supper together. The toad-frog washed up the dishes and told her to rest from the long journey. She went upstairs and found a room with a nice bed and lay down to sleep. In the night she could see by the candle the big toad-frog climbing into her bed. She went back to sleep, and in the morning when she woke up, he was gone. He had breakfast ready when she went downstairs, and all the time he cooked and kept house. He treated her kind and good, but she couldn't like his warty old skin and his toad-frog eyes. Living with a man-size toad-frog would give a girl the creeps, it seems like to me. But she learned to love his kind and helpsome ways, though not his looks.

He picked laurel blooms every day and brought them to her for a present. She felt like she could live out her days with him, if only he looked like a natural human. One night she woke up thinking about it. In the moonlight she could see a handsome young man laying in the bed beside her and the warty old frog skin hanging on a bed post.

She eased out of bed, got the warty

old frog skin in her hands, and tipped downstairs. She flung the warty old frog skin into the fireplace and watched it crackle and burn. Then she went back to bed and slept sound till morning.

It was a handsome young man woke her up next morning. He told her he could stay a man now. Burning up the warty old frog skin had lifted the witch's spell on him. They lived there amongst the laurel blooms together in the nice little house with an upstairs.

Her sisters were jealous all their lives for her having such a handsome man that would cook the breakfast, and give her a house with an upstairs. Maybe they learned their lesson about being greedy and wanting costly presents and ending up with not as much as the youngest sister that asked for nothing more than a bunch of laurel blooms.

The Toadfrog

Herewith an inevitable, all-American takeoff on the fairy tales that play so big a part in North American love stories. It comes from the Ozark Mountains and, like the previous story, has elements of both "The Frog Prince" and "Beauty and the Beast."

One time there was a pretty girl walking down the street, and she heard somebody say, "Hi, Toots!" But when she looked around there was nobody in sight, just a little old toadfrog setting on the sidewalk.

So then the pretty girl started to walk on down the street, and she heard somebody say, "Hello, Beautiful!" But when she looked around there was nobody in sight, just this little old toadfrog.

So then the pretty girl started to walk on down the street, and she heard somebody say, "You got anything on tonight, Baby?" But when she looked around there was nobody in sight, just this little old toadfrog setting on the sidewalk.

The pretty girl looked down at the little old toadfrog. "I know it ain't you a-talking," she says.

"It's me, all right," says the toadfrog. "I'm a handsome young man, by rights. But I'm turned into a toadfrog now, because an old witch put a spell on me."

The pretty girl studied awhile, and then she says, "Ain't there anything you can do to break the spell?"

The toadfrog says there is only one way, and that is for a pretty girl to let him sleep on her pillow all night. The pretty girl thought it was the least she could do, to help this poor fellow out. So she took the little old toadfrog home and put him on her pillow when she went to bed.

Next morning the pretty girl's father come to wake her up, and he seen a handsome young man in the bed with her. She told her father about the little old toadfrog, and the witch that put a spell on him, and how it all happened. But the old man didn't believe the story, any more than you do!

Old Black-Oak Knows Best

Sometimes it takes a "supernatural" effort to win the girl. The teller of this tale, Mr. Frank Payne, of Missouri, claimed he heard it first in 1904. Other versions have the boy hiding in church and waiting for his girl to come and pray for a husband.

One time there was a pretty girl named Josie, and her folks was well fixed but they had trouble with the law, so the town boys didn't come around much. There was a young farmer name of Pete wanted to go with her, but Josie wouldn't do it because she figured them high-collar town boys was better. She give old Gram French two dollars for a charm, but it didn't do no good. Finally Gram told her to hang the charm on the old black-oak at midnight, and then say a little rhyme.

When Josie come to the old black-oak she done just like Gram told her, and then set down to see what happened. Pretty soon she heard a voice away up in the air a-mumbling. Josie was kind of scared, but she stood still a minute and listened. There was some more mumbling, and then the voice says, "You got to marry Pete." Josie run for home when she heard that and never told the folks nothing.

The next night she went back to the old black-oak and done just like Gram told her, and then set down to see what happened. Pretty soon she hears some more mumbling up in the air, and then the voice says, "You got to marry Pete." Josie went home and thought about it a long time.

The third night she went back to the old black-oak and done just like Gram told her, and then set down to see what happened. Pretty soon she heard something a-mumbling up in the air, and then the voice says, "You got to marry Pete." Josie went home just like she done before, and never slept a wink all night.

Next day she went and told Gram French what happened. "If you heerd the same thing three nights a-runnin', you better go ahead an' marry Pete," says Gram. "What's the use to marry a fellow like that?" says Josie. "Why, he ain't got a pot to cook in, or a window to throw it out!" Gram just set and looked at her awhile. "Old black-oak knows best," she says. "It takes more'n pots an' windows to make a good husband." Gram didn't say no more, and Josie didn't return no answer.

Josie told the folks she knowed all the time it was Pete a-talking out of the old black-oak, and she says Gram French must have put him up to it. But Pete just grinned, and he never did admit nothing. Him and her got hitched in the dark of the moon, all right. But the neighbors say they done about as good as any other married folks.

Hard of Hearing

Persuading the girl to look twice at him is sometimes the easy part of a young man's courtship. Dealing with her father might prove the greatest challenge of all. "Jonathan" in the following story is an old slang term referring to a man from the New England states.

————•◦•————

A young Jonathan once courted the daughter of an old man that lived "down east," who professed to be deficient in hearing, but, forsooth, was more captious than limited in hearing, as the sequel will show.

It was a stormy night in the ides of March, if I mistake not, when lightning and loud peals of thunder answered thunder, that Jonathan sat by the old man's fireside, discussing with the old lady (his intended mother-in-law) on the expediency of asking the old man's permission to marry "Sal." Jonathan resolved to "pop it" to the old man the next day. Night passed, and by the dawn of another day, the old man was found in his barn-lot, feeding his pigs. Jonathan rose from his bed early in the morning, spied the old man feeding his pigs, and resolved to ask him for Sal.

Scarce had a minute elapsed, after Jonathan made his resolution, ere he bid the old man "good morning." Now Jonathan's heart beat; now he scratched his head, and ever and anon gave birth to a pensive yawn. Jonathan declared that he'd as lief take thirty-nine "stripes" as to ask the old man; "but," said he aloud to himself, "however, here's go it, a faint heart never won a fair girl," and addressed the old man thus:—

"I say, old man, I want to marry your daughter."

Old Man—"You want to borrow my halter. I would loan it to you, Jonathan, but my son has taken it and gone off to the mill."

Jonathan—putting his mouth close to the old man's ear, and speaking in a deafening tone—"I've got five hundred pounds of money!"

Old Man—Stepping back as if greatly alarmed, and exclaiming in a voice of surprise— "You have got five hundred pounds of honey, Jonathan? Why, it is more than all the neighborhood has use for."

Jonathan—(Not yet the victim of despair, and putting his mouth to the old man's ear, bawled out)—"I've got gold."

Old Man—"So have I, Jonathan, and it's the worst cold I ever had in my life." So saying, he sneezed a "wash up."

By this time the old lady came up, and having observed Jonathan's unfortunate luck, she put her mouth to the old man's ear, and screamed like a wounded Yahoo:

"Daddy, I say Daddy—you don't understand; he wants to marry our daughter."

Old Man—"I told him our calf halter was gone."

Old Lady—"Why, daddy, you don't understand—he's got gold!—he's rich!"

Old Man—"He's got a cold and the itch, eh! What's he doing here with the itch, eh!" So saying the old man aimed a blow at Jonathan's head with his walking cane—but happily for Jonathan, he dodged it. Nor did the rage of the old man stop at this, but with angry countenance, he made after Jonathan, who took to his heels; nor did Jonathan's luck stop here, he had not got out of the barn yard, nor far from the old man, who run him a close race, ere Jonathan stumped his toe, and fell to the ground, and before the old man could "take up," he stumbled over Jonathan and fell sprawling in a mud hole. Jonathan sprung to his heels, and with the speed of a John Gilpin, cleared himself. And poor Sal! she died a *nun. Never had no husband.*

Farmer Smith and Ma'am Jones

Courtship among the conservative and reserved residents of New England had a style all its own. It is entirely possible that this story is based on a real incident, the retelling of which became a popular way to describe the unique character of New England dwellers.

Widower Smith's wagon stopped one morning before widow Jones' door and gave the usual country signal, that he wanted to see somebody in the house, by dropping the reins, and sitting double, with his elbows on his knees. Out tripped the widow, lively as a cricket, with a tremendous black ribbon on her snow white cap. Good morning was said on both sides, and the widow waited for what was further to be said.

"Well ma'am Jones, perhaps you don't want to sell one of your cows, no how, for nothing, any way, do you?"

"Well there, Mr. Smith, you couldn't have spoke my mind better. A poor, lone woman like me, doesn't know what to do with so many creatures, and I should be glad to trade if we can fix it."

So they adjourned to the meadow. Farmer Smith looked at Roan—then at the widow—at Brindle—then at the widow—at the Downing cow—then at the widow again—and through the whole forty. The same call was made every day for a week, but Farmer Smith could not decide which cow he wanted. At length, on Saturday when widow Jones was in a hurry to get through with her baking for Sunday—and "ever so much" to do in the house, as all farmers' wives and widows have on Saturday, she was a little impatient—Farmer Smith was as irresolute as ever.

"That 'ere Downing cow is a pretty fair creature"—but he stopped to glance at the widow's face and then walked round her—not the widow, but the cow.

"That 'ere short horn Durham is not a bad looking beast, but I don't know"— another look at the widow.

"The Downing cow I knew before the late Mr. Jones bought her." Here he sighed at the allusion to the late Mr. Jones, she sighed, and both looked at each other. It was a highly interesting moment.

"Old Roan is an old milch, and so is Brindle—but I have known better." A long stare followed this speech—the pause was getting awkward, and at last Mrs. Jones broke out—"Lord Mr. Smith, if I'm the one you want, do say so!"

The intentions of widower and the widow Jones were duly published the next day as is the law and custom in Massachusetts; and as soon as they were "out published," they were married.

Strawberries

Storyteller Gayle Ross draws upon her native Cherokee myths and legends for many of her performances. This magnificent ancient love story is also an origin myth about the reason for the creation of "love berries."

Long ago, in the very first days of the world, there lived the first man and the first woman. They lived together as husband and wife, and they loved one another dearly.

But one day, they quarreled. Although neither later could remember what the quarrel was about, the pain grew stronger with every word that was spoken, until finally, in anger and in grief, the woman left their home and began walking away—to the east, toward the rising sun.

The man sat alone in his house. But as time went by, he grew lonelier and lonelier. The anger left him and all that remained was a terrible grief and despair, and he began to cry.

A spirit heard the man crying and took pity on him. The spirit said, "Man, why do you cry?"

The man said, "My wife has left me."

The spirit said, "Why did your woman leave?"

The man just hung his head and said nothing.

The spirit asked, "You quarreled with her?"

And the man nodded.

"Would you quarrel with her again?" asked the spirit.

The man said, "No." He wanted only to live with his wife as they had lived before—in peace, in happiness, and in love.

"I have seen your woman," the spirit said. "She is walking to the east toward the rising sun."

The man followed his wife, but he could not overtake her. Everyone knows an angry woman walks fast.

Finally, the spirit said, "I'll go ahead and see if I can make her slow her steps." So the spirit found the woman walking, her footsteps fast and angry and her gaze fixed straight ahead. There was pain in her heart.

The spirit saw some huckleberry bushes growing along the trail, so with a wave of his hand, he made the bushes burst into bloom and ripen into fruit. But the woman's gaze remained fixed. She looked neither to the right nor the left, and she didn't see the berries. Her footsteps didn't slow.

Again, the spirit waved his hand, and one by one, all of the berries growing along the trail burst into bloom and ripened into fruit. But still, the woman's gaze remained fixed. She saw nothing but her anger and pain, and her footsteps didn't slow.

And again, the spirit waved his hand, and, one by one, the trees of the forest—the peach, the pear, the apple, the wild cherry—burst into bloom and ripened into fruit. But still, the woman's eyes remained fixed, and even still, she saw nothing but her anger and pain. And her footsteps didn't slow.

Then finally, the spirit thought, "I will create an entirely new fruit—one that grows very, very close to the ground so the woman must forget her anger and bend her head for a moment." So the spirit waved his hand, and a thick green carpet began to grow along the trail. Then the carpet become starred with tiny white flowers, and each flower gradually ripened into a berry that was the color and shape of the human heart.

As the woman walked, she crushed the tiny berries, and the delicious aroma came up through her nose. She stopped and looked down, and she saw the berries. She picked one and ate it, and she discovered its taste was as sweet as love itself. So she began walking slowly, picking berries as she went, and as she leaned down to pick a berry, she saw her husband coming behind her.

The anger had gone from her heart, and all that remained was the love she had always known. So she stopped for him, and together, they picked and ate the berries. Finally, they returned to their home where they lived out their days in peace, happiness, and love.

And that's how the world's very first strawberries brought peace between men and women in the world, and why to this day they are called the berries of love.

Lovers' Retreat

Among the romantic tales of love in North American folklore there are many stories of star-crossed lovers who, for reasons of birth or parental condemnation, have had to take risks in order to be together. "Lovers' Retreat" is one of many legends that give names to places in North America.

Many years ago, in the northern part of Texas, lived a small band of Indians among whom were a young brave and a young maiden lost in love. For the sake of convenience, we shall call the young brave Running Elk and the maiden Laughing Water. She was the daughter of old Chief White Eagle, but in the veins of the warrior lover there was no royal blood, and the father refused to allow the marriage that both of the lovers so greatly desired.

The refusal was not, however, based primarily on the difference in rank. Running Elk was an ideal young brave. He was the best hunter in the band; no other could run so swiftly, ride so skillfully, or shoot an arrow so truly as he. His bravery had been tried more than one time. In a battle he had once, single handed, fought and killed six of the enemy. Many a chieftain would have been proud to claim such a warrior for son-in-law. Indeed, Chief White Eagle was pleased with the suitor, but his tribe was a weak tribe and he wanted his daughter to marry into a strong tribe. Such an alliance he regarded as necessary against powerful enemies.

After many pleadings with the old chief and as many refusals, the lovers saw that there were but two courses left to them. They could give up all hope of marriage and let the negotiations that were already under way for the marriage of Laughing Water into a powerful tribe proceed; or they could run away and seek united refuge in a strange tribe. They chose the latter course.

It was dark midnight when Laughing Water met Running Elk at the outskirts of the Indian village. He had two ponies ready, and the lovers were on their way immediately. They rode during the remainder of the night and almost all the following day. Late in the afternoon they saw a cloud of moving dust rising perhaps an hour's ride behind them. The pursuers were gaining ground rapidly.

The runaways were now at the edge of a strange, mountainous country. Their horses were tired and further journey on them meant capture, then torture. Running Elk called a halt, and when the girl had dismounted, he tied a thorny stick to the tail of each horse, gave the horses a slash with the thong of buffalo hide that he used for a bridle, and saw them disappear down a draw. Then he and the maiden set out on foot, selecting rocks and hard gravel for a path. Their tribesmen would be baffled by the trail for a little time at least.

After the couple had traveled in this way for what seemed to them a long while, they reached the top of a mountain covered with cedar, walnut, and scrub oak. All at once they came upon a wide crevice. They turned their direction and were as suddenly confronted by another crevice, narrow and forty or fifty feet deep. This they descended, taking care not to loosen rocks or earth.

The two Indians were surprised to find that this break led to a network of such passages, the widths of which varied from a foot to twenty or thirty feet. The walls were of solid rock and rose to a height of from forty to sixty feet. On the tops of these rocks had formed a soil that sustained a variety of vegetation. A greenish moss covered the sides of the rocks and against them clung straggling vines; from the tops and from niches along the sides, prickly pears hung; here and there a tree grew up out of the bottom of the fissures and swept its branches over the tops of the cliffs. A cold spring trickled from the bottom of one of the rock walls.

The lovers knew that there must be a cave somewhere amid such surroundings. They began to search for it, and had searched only a little while when they came to a small mountain lake. It was at a kind of gateway between mountain and plateau, and on the mountain side was the cave. It opened into the lake, its floor well above the level of the water, and extended back into the enormous boulder.

Running Elk swam to the mouth of the cave and climbed in, and with his senses as alert as those of the panther explored the darkness. He found that the recess ran back some twenty feet and that it was clear of harm. He swam back to the shore, got his beloved, and returned to the cave. The two had not been hidden ten minutes when they heard their tribesmen making camp by the water.

Presently a few of the young bucks went into the lake for a swim. One of them discovered the mouth of the cave and called to his companions. They all came to him and began to talk of exploring the place.

Huddled close to each other in the remotest part of the cave, the lovers waited. Though they were themselves in pitchy darkness, they could see the world outside; however, dusk was approaching. Then they saw one of the bucks raise his body into the edge of the cave. He paused, fixed himself, and reached down to give a hand to a companion. Just then the lovers heard a wild shouting. They recognized the voice of their Medicine Man. He was screaming to the braves to come away from the cave, and telling them that all caves with their openings in or just above water were inhabited by evil spirits. The braves left the cave with frenzied strokes and soon the silence told that all the Indians had deserted the region of the lake. Again the lovers breathed freely.

But they would not leave their refuge until they were sure of safety. All that night, all the next day, and all the next night, they remained in hiding. Then they left in search of a friendly tribe to take up with, and the story generally goes that they found hospitality and security.

The white man has changed the looks about the picturesque region where the couple wandered and hid; but the cave and lake where they evaded their pursuers bears in memory of them the name of Lovers' Retreat.

Poke-o'-Moonshine

Another legend that lends its name to a landmark, "Poke-o'-Moonshine," with its tragic ending, is more typical of the tales of lovers who are denied the right to be together.

One of our few satisfying mountain names is Poke-o'-Moonshine, or Peekamoonshine, in the Adirondacks. In this lonely height is a cave with a crack in the roof through which, in certain phases of the moon, a ray of light will enter; and this peek or peep or poke of moonshine has given a name to the mountain itself. In 1757 a young Huguenot noble, François du Bois, came to America to join his regiment in Canada. He came the more willingly because he knew that his sweetheart, Clemence La Moille, would presently follow him, for her father had incurred the dislike of certain political enemies and had been virtually banished from the kingdom. And, true enough, it was not long ere Emil La Moille and his daughter left their home, forever. From New Rochelle, where they lived for a little time, they went northward with an Indian guide and eventually settled in a lovely valley, east of Lake Champlain, on the bank of that river now called La Moille. Clemence found a way to let her lover know their whereabouts. He ascended the lake at that time with Montcalm's force, which some days later attacked the English near Lake George, and no doubt he cast a longing eye at the peaceful hills that walled Champlain on its eastern side, for somewhere among them his lady awaited him.

Possibly he did not then imagine that in a few days he should be seeking her, a disgraced and heart-sick soldier, but so it fell out. Truth is, he had little stomach for his business. He was less in love with war than with Clemence; being Protestant, he could not sympathize heartily with the scheme of a Catholic government against a Protestant people; and especially he loathed the brutalities that the Indians committed under permission of his fellow officers. The horrible massacre that followed the French victory on Lake George ended his endurance. He stole away from camp at night, found a canoe, and in a few days he had reached the La Moille cabin, weak, discouraged, but with no jot of his love abated. He did not dare to meet the father. Exile though he was, the old man still revered his France and loved his old profession of arms. When he learned that this proposed son-in-law was a deserter he would spurn him indignantly from his presence.

But with the girl it was otherwise. Du Bois gained audience with her, and with pity for his mental and bodily suffering mingled with her love she sheltered him. The French army would soon be returning toward the St. Lawrence, and he might be seen, chased, captured, and imprisoned, if not shot. Clemence lived almost as free a life as an Indian, and she was a willful girl withal. It was an easy matter to absent herself for a day or two from home. In a night journey across the lake the young couple reached a trail leading into the fastness of the Adirondacks, and there Clemence left François, after directing him how he should reach Poke-o'-Moonshine, and promising to join him so soon as she could replenish their ammunition and recover some of her belongings.

A few days later she kissed her father and said she was going upon the lake. She never returned. Her dog reached home that evening with a letter in his collar, but rain or dew had made it illegible. Years afterward old La Moille, while hunting in the mountains, took shelter from a storm in the grotto of Poke-o'-Moonshine. The tempest lasted so long that he gave up the thought of leaving it that night, so he made himself comfortable and went to sleep. In the small hours he awoke to see a slender ray of moonlight falling through a chink in the rock. It rested on a scrap of gold lace from a military coat, and on a necklace—his daughter's. Was he dreaming? He reached out and took the pearls into his hand. They were real. Had the cave become the tomb of the young pair? Had they fallen victim to bears or panthers? It will never be known. But the cross that stood at the cave door for years after has banned all shadows, and the figures that glide over Lake Onewaskra by moonlight are said to be François and Clemence.

A Tale of Love

———·—·———

Perhaps the most endearing of all North American traditional tales, this one is not about human love at all. Yet this story, which is perennially popular in Mexico, evokes all the themes so popular in folk legend.

———·———

It was that time when the swallows return. They leave on the feast day of San José and come back on the feast day of San Juan. They say that many cross the ocean but few return, because they are eaten by the Moors.

They waste no time, once on land, but begin immediately to gather mud and build their nests. Most of them choose the eaves of houses and barns, but one young and especially pretty swallow chose the belfry of a little church.

In the churchyard there was a large mesquite tree where a pitacochi came and sang every day. One morning, when the swallow stuck her neck out to hear better, he noticed her and began to sing as he had never sung before. It was truly love at first sight.

From then on the two birds spent every moment together. In the mornings, they would circle low around the village and then fly away into the countryside. And in the evenings, they would rest on the branches of the mesquite and he would serenade her. Indeed, the little swallow made a wonderful summer for the pitacochi.

Time flew by and the green leaves turned to gold. One day, as they sat on a branch of the mesquite, the pitacochi noticed how sad the swallow's eyes were and how she bent her head.

"What's the matter?" the pitacochi asked. "Why are you so sad?"

The little swallow was silent for a moment, then looked up at him. "The time for us to leave is almost here and I wish I didn't have to go. It will hurt me to leave you," she said, bending her head down again.

"That's right," said the pitacochi. "I'm so in love that I had forgotten you have to leave." The pitacochi tried to comfort her. "You can stay here with me. I'll take care of you."

The swallow looked up at him again. "We must all go away together," she told him. "If I stay here, I will surely die."

"Then I'll go with you," said the pitacochi.

Though his decision made the little swallow happy, she still tried to change his mind. "You'll never make it," she said. "We have to fly clear across the ocean and you're too heavy." But despite all her pleading, the pitacochi was determined to go with her.

Swallows always carry two small twigs in their beaks, when they fly over the sea, so they can rest on the waves when they become tired. And so, when the feast day of San José arrived, the swallow had two little twigs ready for the pitacochi. When they reached the edge of the sea, they stopped on a cliff top to rest, and once more the swallow tried to persuade the pitacochi to change his mind.

"It's best for you to remain here," she said. "If you should have to turn back, I'll never stop worrying about you."

In the distance the flock made crooked little lines against the blue horizon.

"You wait here," said the swallow, "and if God grants, I'll return and we'll be together again."

The pitacochi looked out at the mighty sea. "We'd better catch up with the rest," he said.

The land kept sinking deeper each time the swallow turned around, "Drop your twigs in the water," she would tell the pitacochi when she noticed him getting tired. They would stop to rest for a while and then start up again. But after many tries, the pitacochi lost all hope.

"You're right," he cried. "I cannot make it. I'm not good for anything. I wish I were dead." He tried to make the swallow catch up with the flock.

"We're not too far out yet," he said. "You must go on."

"No," said the swallow. "If I let you go back alone, I will surely die of grief."

The two birds slowly made their way back to shore. When they were on the cliff top once again, they began to weep.

"Wait for me," the swallow told the pitacochi, "and pray to God that I can return."

They embraced each other for the last time and the little swallow spread her wings and took off. "Adiós," she called as she swooped out toward the sea.

The pitacochi stood on the cliff watching, with tears rolling from his eyes, until he could no longer see the fading form of his love.

Summer came once more and it was time again for the swallows to return. When they arrived, they began as usual to build their nests in the eaves of houses and barns. The pitacochi waited and waited for the little swallow to return. But he was still sitting alone in the mesquite tree when the stars came out that evening.

And so it was every summer until one day, he waited no more.

9

Of Ghosts, Witches, and the Devil

North America was and is fertile ground for the growth of spine-tingling tales. From the earliest times the spirit world has infused every aspect of life for Native Americans, giving rise to an elegant supernatural tradition. Early European settlers, whose belief in the existence of witches and devils was highly developed, confronted a continent where unimaginable stretches of wilderness provided the perfect atmosphere for supernatural lore. Later, African slaves brought tribal traditions that blended with Christianity to form voodoo and other forms of "black magic."

Although the twentieth century has been hard on people's belief in the supernatural, tales about witches and demons are popular to this day. Ghost stories are different in that they are most often legendary in nature. That is, they are the result of people really seeing a ghost, or at least thinking they did. There are thousands of such tales in North America. They are usually regional, involve an identifiable landmark, and sometimes recount the lives and deaths of real people. For example, I can find published accounts of the Hessian soldier who haunts the basement of my own Revolutionary War–era house. I have not yet made his acquaintance, but I know several previous residents who say they've felt his benign presence on dark and stormy nights.

Choosing from among the tales in this most popular folktale genre, I have tried to represent several regions and culture groups in North America. This chapter, then, offers a variety of supernatural encounters—some legendary, some cautionary, and some that have been handed down just to give you the creeps.

The Haunted House

This is the essential ghost story, containing everything a tale needs to spook the innocent listener. It also provides the satisfaction of knowing that justice is done in the end. "The Haunted House" was recorded in Wise County, Virginia.

One time a preacher went to see if he could put a haunt to rest at a house in his settlement. The house had been haunted for about ten years. Several people had tried to stay there all night, but they always would get scared out by the haunt.

So this preacher took his Bible and went to the house—went on in, built himself a good fire, and lit a lamp. Sat there reading the Bible. Then just before midnight he heard something start up in the cellar—walking back and forth, back and forth. Then it sounded like somebody was trying to scream and got choked off. Then there was a lot of thrashing around and struggling, and finally everything got quiet.

The old preacher took up his Bible again, but before he could start reading, he heard footsteps coming up the cellar stairs. He sat watching the door to the cellar, and the footsteps kept coming closer and closer. He saw the doorknob turn, and when the door began to open, he jumped up and hollered, "What do you want?"

The door shut back easy-like, and there wasn't a sound. The preacher was trembling a little, but he finally opened the Bible and read awhile. Then he got up and laid the book on the chair and went to mending the fire.

Then the haunt started walking again and—step!—step!—step!—up the cellar stairs. The old preacher sat watching the door, saw the doorknob turn and the door open. It looked like a young woman. He backed up and said, "Who are you? What do you want?"

The haunt sort of swayed like she didn't know what to do—then she just faded out. The old preacher waited, waited, and when he didn't hear any more noises, he went over and shut the door. He was sweating and trembling all over, but he was a brave man and he thought he'd be able to see it through. So he turned his chair to where he could watch, and he sat down and waited.

It wasn't long before he heard the haunt start up again, slowly—step!—step!—step!—step!—closer, and closer—step!—step!—and it was right at the door.

The preacher stood up and held his Bible out before him. Then the knob slowly turned, and the door opened wide. This time the preacher spoke quiet-like. He said, "In the name of the Father, the Son, and the Holy Ghost—who are you and what do you want?"

The haunt came right across the room, straight to him, and took hold of his coat. It was a young woman about twenty years old. Her hair was torn and tangled, and the flesh was dropping off her face so he could see the bones and part of her teeth. She had no eyeballs, but there was a sort of blue light way back in her eye sockets. And she had no nose to her face.

Then she started talking. It sounded like her voice was coming and going with the wind blowing it. She told how her lover had killed her for her money and buried her in the cellar. She said if the preacher would dig up her bones and bury her properly, she could rest.

Then she told him to take the end joint of the little finger from her left hand, and to lay it in the collection plate at the next church meeting—and he'd find out who had murdered her. And she said, "If you come back here once more after that—you'll hear my voice at midnight, and I'll tell you where my money is hid, and you can give it to the church."

The haunt sobbed like she was tired, and she sunk down toward the floor and was gone. The preacher found her bones and buried them in the graveyard.

The next Sunday the preacher put the finger bone in the collection plate, and when a certain man happened to touch it, it stuck to his hand. The man jumped up and rubbed and scraped and tore at that bone, trying to get it off. Then he went to screaming, like he was going crazy. Well, he confessed to the murder, and they took him on to jail.

After the man was hung, the preacher went back to that house one midnight, and the haunt's voice told him to dig under the hearthrock. He did, and he found a big sack of money. And where that haunt had held on to his coat, the print of those bony fingers was burned right into the cloth. It never did come out.

Marie Jolie

When she was a child in Louisiana, J. J. Reneaux heard this Cajun story from her grandmother, and now she incorporates it into her storytelling performances. An encounter with the Devil is the subject of hundreds of North American folktales, and elements of this tale are common in many of them.

Down in the bayou country there was once a beautiful girl named Marie. She was so pretty, so *jolie*, that all the people called her Marie Jolie. She was as sweet as sugar cane, but if you did her wrong, look out, for that girl could show a temper as hot as cayenne pepper.

Now, Marie Jolie grew to be of a marrying age, but to her maman's disappointment, she wasn't yet of a mind to be married. First she wanted to have adventures and see the big world. So she found something wrong with every young man who came to court her. This one was too short; that one was too tall; the next one had the ears of an *éléphant*.

After a while her maman got impatient with Marie, for she worried that her daughter would wind up an old maid—a terrible fate in those days. So Maman said, "Marie Jolie, it is time for you to take a husband. You can't pick one to suit you, so me, I'm gonna do it for you. We gonna have us a contest. You see this pumpkin? I'm gonna get M'su Carencro, the buzzard, to put it on the highest, skinniest branch of that big cypress tree out there in the swamp. *Chère*, the man who can fetch that pumpkin down without fallin' in the water is gonna be your husband!"

"Well, Maman," said Marie, "if it's got to be, I s'pose that's as good a way as any of choosin' a man."

The contest was held the following week. Men came from parishes far and near, each one more eager than the last to win the hand of Marie Jolie. But one, a tall, dark, handsome man, stood out from the crowd. "Ooh, Maman," said Marie, "I hope he gets the pumpkin! He's a good lookin' devil for true."

One after the
other, the men tried to climb
the great cypress, but they all ended up
spitting swamp water. At last the good
lookin' stranger's turn came. Quick as
lightnin' he scaled that tree like a cat,
snatched the pumpkin, and landed with his boots on dry
land. Before she knew it, Marie Jolie was a married woman.

She climbed proud as could be into her husband's
wagon, and they started driving down the road. It wasn't
long, however, before she noticed that things were getting
strange. The path was growing darker and darker, and her
new husband uglier and uglier.

Suddenly a fearsome man appeared beside the path.
"Gimme my tie and collar that I lent ya!" he called out. Marie's
husband took off the tie and collar. "Here then," he said, "take
back your ol' tie and collar!"

A little further down the road, they met another man. He said, "Gimme
back my coat that I lent ya!" "Take your ol' coat," said her husband. Yet a third
man appeared and demanded his trousers; a fourth demanded his hat. Her husband stopped the wagon, disappeared briefly into the swamp woods, and returned
just as well dressed as before.

Finally, a fifth man, fiercer than all the others together, his face hidden in
the shadow of his tall hat, appeared before them and pointed a long, bony finger.
"Give me the horses that I lent ya!" he roared. "Go to the devil, then," said her
husband with a wicked laugh, "and take your ol' horse with ya!"

He watched as the man led the animals away, and then he turned to his
wife and hissed, "Girl, get down and hitch y'self to the wagon, and pull us home!"
Marie Jolie could feel her temper rising. She was gonna tell him a thing or two!
But a terrible change had come over her husband. His icy glare and ugly scowl
frightened her. She thought she had better do as he said—at least for a little while.

She climbed down, hitched herself to the wagon, and began to pull with all her strength.

At last they arrived at her husband's *cabane*. It was a gloomy lookin' place, set way back in the swamp woods. "Marie Jolie," said her husband, "I must leave. While I am gone, you will stay here, and my maman will take good care of you." And he disappeared in a burst of flames and smoke.

Marie was scared for true. She begged her new mama-in-law, "Please, Belle-mère, tell me why my husband is so strange!"

Belle-mère, who was a kind woman at heart and felt worse than anybody about how her son had turned out, sadly shook her head. "Oh, *chère fille!*" she said. "You've made a terrible match. You have gone and married M'su Diable, the devil himself!"

Marie couldn't believe her ears. "Old woman, you are only jealous. You just want to break up my marriage!"

"You do not believe me, *'tite fille*? Come with me," the old woman whispered. She led Marie Jolie inside the house to a secret door. She unlocked it with a big brass key, and the heavy door creaked open. There inside that dim room Marie saw the devil's other wives—each one hanging from a hook.

Now Marie Jolie knew the truth. "Oh, please. Belle-mère," she cried. "You gotta tell me how I can escape! How can I get out of here?"

"Girl, do you not see what became of the others who tried to escape? Stay with me, little one. I will keep you comp'ny and ease your suffering," Belle-mère pleaded. "Do not bring down the terrible wrath of my son, the devil!"

But Marie Jolie was growing angry, and in her anger she grew bold. "No," she insisted, "I will not be the devil's wife! If you won't help me escape, I'll find a way on my own!"

Belle-mère sighed. "The devil knows many tricks. He can change into fire and smoke and ride the wind. You cannot outrun him, but maybe—if you are brave enough—you can outsmart him. Even the devil cannot defeat a strong heart. But if your courage fails, he will destroy you!"

Marie was determined. "My heart is strong, and my mind is made up," she said. "M'su Diable will not destroy me!"

"All right then," said Belle-mère, "here is what you must do. M'su Diable will return in the deepest night, at three o'clock, the soul's hour. He hates dawn and the rising sun. In its light he cannot hide his true self, so he sleeps. His spy, L'Gaim, the rooster, keeps watch. If he catches you tryin' to escape, he will crow. Tonight you must feed L'Gaim three bags of corn instead of one so that he will oversleep. At sunrise go and gather six dirty eggs. They will protect you. Do not take the clean eggs, for they are bad luck. Then, *chère*, run as quick-quick as you can away from this place!"

Marie did as she was told. Rooster overslept, and she got the six dirty eggs. She tiptoed out, soft-soft, but the gate hinge squeaked. and L'Gaim woke up crowin' full-throat. "M'su Diable, M'su Diable, Wake up! *Vite-vite!* Your wife is gettin' away!"

Marie ran for her life as M'su Diable came screaming after her. She had not gone far when she turned and saw a cloud of smoke and fire approaching. She took one dirty egg and threw it over her shoulder. BOOM! It exploded right in the devil's path, and a fence of wood as high and wide as the eye could see sprang up. M'su Diable snorted and stomped in fury and flew back to his *cabane*. When he returned he had his magic golden ax. The ax chopped through the fence at once, and the devil was again hot on the trial of his runaway wife.

Marie grabbed a second dirty egg and heaved it straight at the devil. CRACK! It flashed like a bolt of lightning, and a fence of brick sprang up as high and wide as the eye could see. The devil cursed and spat, but his magic ax smashed the brick to bits.

Marie took aim and flung the third dirty egg. It shattered like thunder, and a fence of stone sprang up as high and wide as the eye could see. The devil shrieked and set his ax to ripping through the wall, and soon the cloud of fire and smoke again threatened to destroy her.

Marie took the fourth egg and hurled it through the air. The earth shook with its force, and a fence of iron sprang up as high and wide as the eye could see. But it too was little trouble for M'su Diable's fearsome magic.

Marie ran as fast as she could, but M'su Diable was almost upon her. She grabbed the fifth egg and pitched it straight into the fireball behind her. A wall of flames roared to the sky, and a deep bayou appeared before the devil. The water stopped him cold. But suddenly a great gust of wind blew the evil cloud of smoke and fire over the bayou, and the waters began to boil.

Marie's blood ran cold as ice when she looked back this time. For M'su Diable had dropped his disguise, and now she saw the ol' devil himself as he truly is. His forked tail whipped wildly about, his cloven hooves raised clouds of dust, and his goat beard flapped wickedly in the wind. The bright sun glinted off his sharp, curved horns, and his beady eyes burned like hot coals. Crusty red scales covered his body. For true, M'su Diable looked a whole lot like a boiled crawfish!

Only one dirty egg remained, and Marie threw it with her last ounce of strength. But her hand trembled, so that she completely missed her mark. The egg fell at her own two feet and exploded. The earth rumbled and cracked. A mighty river came rolling by. It was the Mississippi. Marie was trapped. How could she ever swim such a wide, dangerous river?

But wait—wasn't that old Grandmaman Cocodrie [the alligator] sunning herself over there in the shallows? Marie cried out to the gator. "*Te prie, Grandmaman, traversez moi! Grandmaman, te prie sauvez ma vie! Aidez moi, Cocodrie!* Grandmother, I pray you, carry me across. Grandmother, I pray you, save my life! Help me, Old Cocodrie!"

Grandmaman Cocodrie, always on the lookout for an easy meal, swam up to Marie without a moment's hesitation. "Maybe I will carry you across," she growled. "But tell me, what makes you think I won't eat you up?"

"Grandmaman," said Marie, "I'd rather be your supper than be the devil's wife!"

"Climb on my back, *'tite fille*, I like your courage!" said the old alligator, and she carried Marie quickly and safely to the other side.

Just then, M'su Diable came runnin' up to the bank. In his most charming voice he called out, "*Traversez moi, Grandmaman, traversez moi! Belle, belle Cocodrie!* Carry me across, old Grandmother, carry me across! Beautiful, beautiful Cocodrie!"

"Climb on my back, M'su. I'll give you a ride for sure!" said the ol' gator with a snap of her jaws. M'su Diable stepped onto her scaly back, holding his forked tail out of the muddy water, and Grandmaman Cocodrie swam out into the deep river.

Things were looking awfully bad for Marie, with M'su Diable closing in on her. But if there was anything that Grandmaman Cocodrie hated, it was a mean ol' devil on her back, and suddenly, way out where the water was swiftest and darkest, she dived. M'su Diable didn't have a snowball's chance in August. M'su Diable, of course, can't swim a lick—not much water down where he comes from. The Ol' Muddy took that devil kickin' and sputterin' all the way downstream to New Orleans. Some say he washed up in the French Quarter, right smack dab in the middle of Bourbon Street—but then, that's another story altogether.

As for Marie Jolie, she lived to be *une très vieille femme*, a very old woman. She had many adventures before her black hair turned snow white. People began to call her Marie Esprit, the spirited one. When they asked why she never married again, she'd just smile and say, "You know, *chère*, once you been married to one devil, there's no need to go out and look for another one!"

Sammy and His Fiddle

The following legend surrounds a man who lived in the Pine Barrens region of New Jersey during the first half of the nineteenth century. Though near the densely populated, supersophisticated Northeast region of the United States, the Pine Barrens have a history of deep-woods isolation, and the lore of the place is steeped in mystery.

Folk writers have long been fascinated with the ancient legend in which an old man bargains with the devil—his soul for a return to youth. It has appeared in many forms, in many lands, including two operatic versions.

The Southern Jersey Pinelands story tellers have their own version of this tale. It concerns the Giberson family, who were pioneers in the Ocean County and Little Egg Harbor regions of the Pines. Many of the Gibersons still reside in the area.

Samuel Gordon Giberson, one of the well-known clan who lived deep in the woodlands of Ocean County during the middle 1800s, was known throughout the area as "Fiddler Sammy Buck." Every door was open to him and his fiddle. Sammy had two joys in life: to play for the social gatherings of his Pines neighbors and to enjoy a nip or two, preferably two, in the taverns of the area.

One night at a small backwoods inn near New Gretna, Sammy and another character by the name of Bill Denn began swapping tales over a few bolts of Jersey Lightnin' (Pineland applejack) and doing a bit of bragging. Eventually a dispute arose as to who was the better fiddler and dancer.

They decided on a contest. Sammy played for Denn while the latter displayed his dancing skill, and Denn played fiddle for Sammy. As the night progressed, so did the drinking and dancing until finally Sammy boasted, "I can beat you or any man I ever seed dancin' and fiddlin'. Could even beat the devil in a showdown."

The contest ended inconclusively, with both participants exhausted. Sammy weaved out of the tavern and along the road to his shack. As he approached a bridge he stopped for a nip from his flask, as a precaution against the morning damps. A dark figure blocked his way.

"Sammy Giberson?" asked the stranger.

"Yeh," replied the tired and slightly tipsy Sammy.

"I hear you think you can beat me dancing and fiddling!" said the figure on the bridge.

Considering this a challenge, Sammy replied, "I can beat anybody. Who are you?"

"The devil. Start playing!"

According to the tale repeated many times in the woodlands, Sammy took out his fiddle and started a tune. The devil began dancing. The more he danced the wilder became the music and the steps. Then it was Sammy's turn. The contest continued to dawn.

Apparently an understanding was reached in which the devil promised Sammy to teach him tunes that no one else knew or could play, including an "air tune," and Sammy would become the greatest fiddler the Pines had ever known, or would ever know.

Giberson continued to delight the Pinelands with new and fancy fiddling, including tricks of playing he had never attempted before. He'd fiddle with the instrument above his head, behind his back, even on the ground. One of his favorite tricks to astonish listeners was to remove violin strings one by one until only a single one remained. Sammy could play as expertly and as beautifully upon the single string as upon the normal four. He was always well supplied with refreshment during these performances, the termination of which varied according to Sammy's mood of the moment.

Following Sammy's encounter on the bridge that one early morning, listeners detected something different about their favorite musician. He was not only playing strange tunes but given to telling tales of a close association with a creature he called the devil. According to the Pines people, Sammy would disappear on moonlight nights and from the deep woods would come the sounds of not one, but two fiddles! These became known as the devil duets.

Sammy Giberson soon began to feel his oats and play games on his duet partner, every so often slipping in a well-known hymn tune while they were playing. At this, the devil was forced to stop fiddling and vanish.

No one knows for sure the final outcome of this strange relationship. Sammy continued playing for the Pinelanders, especially the much requested "air tune," which Giberson would inform one and all he "just picked outta the air." This he would not perform unless well fortified with his special brew and then, according to stories told by listeners, he would rise to the heights of a Paganini. Although many tried to copy the "air tune," none could master it. Sammy would ignore requests for this melody until a late hour. As soon as he played it, he would end his performance, pack his fiddle, and disappear into the woodlands.

Eventually Sammy died. According to some reports he is buried in a Little Egg Harbor Township woods cemetery. To those with livelier imaginations, Sammy still roams the Pines. Recalling the legend that the devil never gave anything without demanding something in return, many believe that Satan finally collected Sammy as payment for his fiddle lessons.

The fiddle itself was locked in its black box and put upon an attic shelf. From time to time, some say, it would break into melody of its own accord, an added embellishment to the folklore that has sprung up around Sammy. Whether that is true or not, we do know that the fiddle eventually vanished.

However, those who frequent Pineland trails during brisk autumn evenings when the leaves begin to turn swear they still hear the sounds of Sammy and his fiddle playing the "air tune."

Or is it just the night winds among the trees?

Tom Dunn's Dance on Rag Rock

———•–•–•———

The following tale resembles "Sammy and His Fiddle," except that it is a much older story with a Puritan flavor. There are dozens of folktales in North America that follow the theme set down in literary form as the stories of Doctor Faustus, or "The Devil and Daniel Webster." Some tales, like Sammy's, give no real moral lesson, and other's, like Tom Dunn's, offer an unforgettable lesson about resisting temptation.

———•–•———

Rag Rock, in which Wabanowi had his long sleep, was a home of sprites and demons down to the nineteenth century. Thomas Dunn knew this, and on ordinary nights he would have taken all manner of long cuts around it, for he had no fondness for things not of this world, whether they were ghosts or gospels. But on the night of his dance, having been to a husking-bee where he had "kept his spirits up by pouring spirits down," and having found so many red ears that he was in a state of high self-satisfaction, for he had kissed his pretty partner twenty times, he spunked up and chanced it straight across the hill. As he approached he saw a glow among the trees and heard a fiddle going—going like mad. He buffeted his way through the thicket to see who of his towns-people were holding a picnic in the moonshine and dancing to such sacrilegious music; for there was dancing; he could hear the shuffle of feet. In a minute he had reached the edge of a grade lighted by torches and found there a richly dressed and merry company tripping it with such spirit as he had never seen before. He dearly liked to shake a leg in a jig or reel, and a chance like this was not to be withstood. He entered the ring, bowing and all a-grin, and was welcomed with a shout. On a hummock of moss sat a maid without a partner, a maid whose black eyes snapped with mischief, whose cheeks and lips were rosy, and whose skirt, raised a trifle higher than common, showed a pair of marvelous neat ankles. The invitation in her smile and sidelong glance were not to be resisted. Tom caught her by the waist, dragged her to her feet, and whirled off with her into the gayest, wildest dance he had ever led. He seemed to soar above the earth. After time he found that the others had seated themselves and were watching him. This put him on his mettle, and the violin put lightning into his heels. He feated it superbly and won round on round of applause. He and the girl had separated for a matter of six feet and had set to dance each other down. As he leaped and whirled and cracked his heels in the air in an ecstasy of motion and existence Tom noticed with pain that the freshness was leaving his partner's face, that it was becoming longer, the eyes deeper and harder. This pain deepened into dismay when he saw that the eyes had turned green and evil, the teeth had projected, sharp and yellow, below the lip, the form had grown lank and withered. He realized at last that it was the demon crew of the hill with which he was in company, and his heart grew so heavy that he could barely leap with it inside of him, yet leap he must, for he was lost unless he could keep up the dance till sunrise or unless a clergyman should order him to stop— which was not a likely thing to happen. So he flung off his coat, hat, vest, and tie and settled into a business jog. The moon was setting. In two hours he would be free, and then—a cramp caught him in the calf, and with a roar of "God save me!" he tumbled on his back.

The cry did save him, for a witch cannot endure to hear the name of God. He saw a brief vision of scurrying forms, heard growling, hissing, and cursing in strange phrases, realized for a second that a hideous shape hung threatening over him, was blinded by a flame that stank of sulphur, then he saw and heard no more till daylight. If he was drunk, and imagined all this, how can one explain the two portraits of the witch he danced with? They were etched in fire on the handle of his jack-knife, one as she appeared when he met her, the other as she looked when his eyes were closing. A fever followed this adventure. After he had regained his health Tom took to himself a wife, joined the church, forsook all entertainments, drank tea, and became a steady workman. He recovered his peace of mind, died a deacon, and was rewarded by having a cherub with a toothache sculptured on his gravestone.

Whickety-Whack, Into My Sack

Like Maud Long, who told "Jack and the Giants' New Ground" in Chapter 6, Ray Hicks grew up in the southern Appalachian Mountains, where the Jack Tales were a main feature of his childhood. He is among the handful of people in the second half of the twentieth century who can tell the Jack Tales from memory. "Whickety-Whack" is a favorite, and one that he particularly enjoys telling.

Well, Jack went into the army and stayed thirty years. And at that time, all you got when they discharged you was two loaves of bread. And when they discharged Jack, they give 'im two loaves of bread, and he headed off into the woods, tryin' to git home.

When he got into a little old town, he met a beggar who was a-beggin' fer somethin' to eat. So Jack—he was what they called good-hearted—give 'im one of them loaves of bread.

Jack went on and hadn't went but jist a little ways 'til he met another beggar, and he was a-beggin' for somethin' to eat. So Jack took out the second loaf, cut it in half, and give it to the second beggar.

Well, Jack went on down the road a little ways and got to studyin' that he'd cheated that last beggar. He'd give the first beggar a whole loaf. So Jack run back and overtook 'im and says, "I cheated you. I met a beggar before you and I had two loaves, and I give 'im a whole loaf. Here's the other half of yours."

So the beggar took it and thanked 'im. "Being you're so honest," the beggar says, "I'm a-goin' to give you somethin'." And he pulled out a sack. "Take this sack with you. If anything gits to botherin' you or you need anything, just say, 'Whickety-whack, into my sack.'"

And then he says, "Here's a drinkin' glass. Take it along. If anybody is sick, git the glass a third or half full of water. If the blubbers goes to the bottom, that person's a-goin' to die. If they come to the top, he's a-goin' to live."

Jack thanked 'im and went on his way. But he hadn't walked too fer outa town 'til he come to some woods, and he seed twelve wild turkeys a-sittin' up in a tree.

"Bedad," he says, "right here is a good time to try this sack out."

So Jack eased as close as he could—them turkeys were awful wild—and he got the sack between his legs, a-holdin' it, and he looked up at those turkeys and said, "Whickety-whack, into my sack."

And he said it was a sight to watch them twelve turkeys crowd down into that sack. Twelve big ones. And he shet it up, slung it across his back, and went on down the road 'til he came to another little old town. It was a-gittin' late up into the night, he was hungry and tired, and he seed he had to stay over.

So Jack went into a hotel and showed them folks the turkeys, and he made a deal with 'em. They kept 'im all night for them turkeys, and Jack got fifteen cents to boot.

Well, the next mornin', he started out and purty soon made it home. He went to a-workin' on his cabin, repairin' his old home place, to live in it 'til he got to where he could do better.

In a few days, he heerd that there was a man in that settlement who had a big farm, and it was hainted. Ghosts were 'bout to run 'im off his place. So the farmer put the word out that if there was any man in that country that could whip them ghosts, he'd deed' 'im the house and land, give 'im a clear title to it.

So Jack went out the next day, inquirin' and findin' out about it, and finally he found the man. Jack took 'im up on it, and the man gave Jack a fryin' pan and some vittles. Jack got settled in at the house, and when it got dark, he fixed 'im some supper and eat and laid down aside the fireplace to take 'im a nap.

He hadn't laid there but jist a few minutes 'til he heerd somethin' a-comin' down the stairs. He shook his head and said, "What do you reckon that is?" And directly, they come down and it was six little black devils and each had a sword apiece, a bag of money apiece, and a deck of playin' cards apiece. They rousted Jack up and begin to beggin' 'im to play cards.

Well, they got to playin', and finally at three games, Jack had lost all but a nickel of the fifteen cents he got in his boot fer them twelve wild turkeys on his way home from the army. But Jack watched careful and purty soon got one pot, and he began to gain, and directly, Jack broke them six little black devils. He had all of their money in his pocket.

So them little devils said, "We'll jist kill you and take it back." So, they got to makin' at Jack with their swords, and Jack was dodgin' 'em. And they thought they had 'im, but Jack happened to think of his sack. So when them little devils got to puffin' for wind and begin to give down a little, Jack grabbed his sack, jerked it open—it had a drawstring on it—and said, "Whickety-whack, into my sack."

Jack said it was somethin' to see them six little devils stuff themselves down in that sack. He jist shet it up, throwed it over in the comer, and laid down to finish his nap.

The next mornin', the farmer come up, jist a-knowin' certain that Jack was gone. He'd done buried fifty men who'd tried. "You're a-livin' and they ain't a scratch on ya," the man said. "What happened here last night?"

Jack says, "It's a-layin' over there in that sack. It's six little black devils shet up in there."

The man says, "As much trouble as them devils have been to me, I won't be satisfied until I see 'em beat up on a blacksmith's anvil. There's a fellow down yonder in the holler who runs a blacksmith shop. Will you go with me?"

Jack says, "Yes, I'll go."

So him and Jack went down there and got the man that run the blacksmith shop to hammer them devils up on the anvil. And when he begin to hammer, so many sparks flew outa them little devils that it set the blacksmith shop on fire and burnt it down.

Well, anyhow, Jack got the deed to the land and begin to stay there and work on the place.

But then, the king's daughter got sick and death was on 'er. And he'd had all of the doctors beheaded 'cause they couldn't cure his daughter. So the king put out an advertisement that if any man, just any community country man, could cure 'er, the money, the gold and silver, wouldn't be a-lackin'.

So Jack took that drinkin' glass and his sack and begin to hunt up the old king to see 'im and see if he could do 'er some good. So he went to the king's house and hollered 'im out.

And the king says, "What're ya here for!"

Jack says, "I hear that you had out word that if any man could cure your daughter the money wasn't a-lackin', and if he couldn't cure 'er, you'd behead 'im."

And so the king says, "Yeah, but you don't look like you could do a job like that."

"Well, bedad," Jack says, "I might look like that, but you said *anybody*."

So the king says, "That's right. I'll have to give ya a try."

Well, they took Jack into the room where the king's daughter lay sick, and Jack sent the king to git his special glass a third or half filled with water. And the king brought it to 'im, and Jack looked, and, sure enough, the blubbers went to the bottom. Death was on 'er.

So Jack got his sack down beside 'er bed and said, "Whickety-whack, come into my sack." And Death went down in that sack, and Jack shet it up. And the girl, the king's daughter, went to jumpin' over the floor, a-praisin'.

The king offered to pay Jack, but he wouldn't take nothin'. He said, "I didn't come for wealth. I come to save your daughter."

Jack went on back home and got some boys to climb a tree, a big poplar in the yard, and take that sack with Death in it and tie it way up on a big limb.

Well, years passed and one day, Jack decided he'd take a little walk down the road. And he hadn't went but a little ways 'til he heerd somethin' a-comin' 'round the turn. Rickety-rack. Bumpety-bump. Rickety-rack. Bumpety-bump. And he looked beyond the curve, and he saw it was an old woman who'd jist went to bones and hide. Her bones was a-creakin' as she walked, and her nose was a-bumpin' her knees.

Jack says, "Howdy do, ma'am."

"Howdy do," she says. "Law me, I can't git around no more. I'm so poor. I've jist went to bones and hide. It seems like I've been a-livin' a million years. And I can't die. I've heerd that some rascal has Death tied up in a sack, and we can't die."

Well, that made Jack think. And after a while, he went back home and tried to climb that poplar tree to git the sack. But he had gotten so poor 'imself that he had to git a younger boy to go up that poplar. So that boy got that sack and brought it down to Jack, and they said when Jack opened it, he was the first one that fell dead.

And that was the end of Jack in that tale.

The Grouse Girl

This haunting tale of the creature who sheds her skin to become human was recorded on Kodiak Island in Alaska. It has many versions around the world, the best known being the tale of the Silkie, a seal who frequents the islands near Ireland, Scotland, and Canada, and who, if caught, becomes the prisoner of whoever holds the skin.

Two men, the older lame and unattractive, the younger sound and handsome, lived by themselves in a barrabara far from other human beings. When they arose in the morning, they drank some oil—to keep hunger away the rest of the day—and then went out hunting; one to the hills, and the other to the beach. In the evening one returned with seal meat, while his partner brought bear meat. Many years they lived in this manner without seeing or even knowing that other people existed.

After the usual breakfast one morning, the older man went to the beach to hunt, and the younger man to the hills, and in the evening both returned loaded with seal and bear meat respectively. By rubbing together two sticks of wood, they soon had a fire over which they cooked some meat, and, after eating, put on their parkas and sat outside on the barrabara, with their faces toward the sea. While sitting there, a grouse appeared and lit on the barrabara, near the younger man, and commenced pecking. "Why does the grouse come here?" the man asked, and pushed her away. She flew up, but returned a moment later to the place occupied before. Seeing her there again, the handsome fellow said to the other one: "What is the matter with the bird? Her home is on the hills, and yet she is bothering here." He drove her off, but she, not discouraged, came back to him. "What does she want?" he exclaimed impatiently, and forced her away rather roughly. When she descended the fourth time, it was by the side of the lame man who took her in his hand, began stroking her, and finally decided to keep her as his pet. Before retiring, the lame man made a nest for the bird near him, and then all turned in for the night.

The next morning the men went hunting as usual. As they approached the barrabara in the evening, they were greatly surprised to see smoke coming out of it, and on entering to find it clean, a warm supper waiting for them, and a pair of new leather suspenders hanging over the lame man's bed. "Somebody has been here to-day," said the younger man; and although they looked outside and inside, they found no one. The grouse was on her nest, her head hidden under her drooping wings, and looked altogether tired. Perceiving her condition, the lame man remarked: "The bird has had nothing to eat or drink the whole day; she must be both hungry and thirsty."

This little excitement did not prevent them from enjoying their supper, nor did it disturb their sound sleep during the night; and the next morning they proceeded with their daily occupation. As the evening before, they found their home in order, the meat cooked, and a pair of new *torbarsars* (shoes made of seal-skin) hanging where the garters had hung the day previous. The grouse was on her nest, her head under the drooping wings, but no one else was to be found, although they searched a long time. After eating their supper, the older man fed and played with the grouse, and then they all went to sleep.

On account of the stormy weather, the several days following the men remained at home. During that time the bird tried once more to gain the good grace of the handsome man, but he treated her roughly, and would not let her come near him, and she avoided him after this. The first favorable day the two men went in different directions to hunt. As soon as the younger man was out of sight, the lame man squatted down, saying: "I will watch to-day and see who cleans and cooks for us, and makes torbarsars for me." Slowly and cautiously he crawled back quite close to the barrabara and waited. The morning passed without giving him a clue, but towards evening he saw smoke coming out of the smoke hole. He crept still closer, and heard footsteps within. While he lay there, guessing who it might be, a young and beautiful girl stepped out. Her face was white, hair and eyebrows black, the parka was of white grouse feathers, and the leggings of the fur seal torbarsars were white with various trimmings. He gazed at her, and when she went in, he followed her, watched her a moment at her work, and then seized her.

"Ai-Ai-Y-a-h!" she exclaimed. "You scared me. Let me go." Instead he drew her fondly to him, and when he did so, her face reddened with blushes.

"I will not let you go," he said; but when he noticed a grouse skin on the nest, he freed her, and although she begged to have the skin back, he took it outside, and hid it.

The handsome man was both scared and amazed, but he asked no questions. Since it was customary for a newly married man to stay at home with his wife for a certain time, it was a long time before the old man went out hunting again. When he did so, he always returned before his partner, and generally found a pair of torbarsars or some other present waiting for him; but the younger man found nothing.

Though the younger man asked no questions, and knew not who the girl was and where she came from, he did a great deal of thinking. It puzzled him to know why the girl preferred a lame, old man to him a young, handsome man. She did not like him, he knew, for she never made anything for him, while the lame man had presents forced on him. He finally decided to take matters in his own hands, and make the girl his wife. One night, when the married couple were asleep, he arose and killed the lame man. Going back to his bed, he called to the girl to leave her dead husband and be his wife. This she refused to do. "You cannot go away from here," he said; "you will have to be my wife."

"I will never be your wife," she answered; and getting up, she searched for the grouse skin among her husband's things and found it in his tool bag. This she hid under her parka. When he called her again, saying, "Come, you are my wife," she replied: "I came here to be your wife, but you did not take me. Three times I came to you, and three times you chased me away. The last time you hurt me. I will not be your wife now." While speaking, she pulled out the grouse skin, shook it three times, and, when she had finished, pulled it on herself and flew out through the smoke hole, leaving a young, sound, and handsome man wifeless and partnerless.

Aunt Tucky

———•—•———

This is one of the creepiest tales I have ever heard. Witches have long been known to shed their skins when they go out haunting at night, and tradition has it that the way to catch them is to make it impossible for them to get back in. Storyteller Harriet Lewis heard this African American tale as a child from a woman in her community who claimed to know it for the truth.

———•—

Back when I was a girl, there was a woman lived way back on the Cypress Bayou, away from everybody else. She had a shabby little cabin. To the front, she had two plank boards for steps and a rough board door. Across the back, there was a porch built out over the edge of the bayou. She was a couple of miles above us on the right fork of Linton Road and about a quarter-mile down the first dirt trail to the right. She was a witch-woman; everybody said so.

She had a bunch of children out at the little place—which was passing strange since she wasn't married. We thought maybe she stole them. Anyhow, she would never let them around other people, church, school, or nothing. She just kept them out there working them, and teaching them witch-woman ways.

We all knew that if a man had a fight with someone, all he had to do was walk down that dirt path to Aunt Tucky's place—that's her name, Aunt Tucky. He could walk up those two wooden steps, rap on the board door and call out, "Aunt Tucky, Aunt Tucky!" The door would crack open. The old woman would peer out and snap, "What you want?"

That man could tell her how he was mad at whoever. He could say, "I want you to give him a whammy. Put a bad spell on him!"

And from behind the door, Aunt Tucky would say, "Cross my palm with money." One bony hand would stretch out, palm up, fingers waiting. (It did not take much. Two bits would do.)

When that quarter was placed in Tucky's hand, she pulled it in. Still behind the door, she'd say, "Name the man." After the name was named, business was done. That man on the doorstep could go on home.

Within five days, guaranteed, something would happen to the one named. It could be that the man would be cutting firewood to sell for Christmas money. He could be cutting with a brand new axe or a trusty old one. Didn't matter. His axe was going to break! Old or new, it would break. And he'd have to spend all his money on a new one! Bad luck! Or, that man's best, favorite coon-hunting dog—perfectly strong and healthy—would be turning around to take a nap. That dog would fall over, *blap!* Dead on the ground! A friend gone and lots less meat on the table 'til he's replaced. Bad luck from Aunt Tucky! Or one of the feller's children—run those fields, climb those trees, swim that bayou—one of them would fall off his own back porch. The child would break all four legs! Yes! Four legs. I said that to show you *double* bad luck! That man would have to take off work, take the child to the doctor. See, he lost money from his work, and lost money on the doctor. Double bad luck from Aunt Tucky the witch-woman.

We all knew about hexes and spells, but some people claimed there was more. Some heard that at the moment the sun set and the night breeze began, Aunt Tucky could shed her skin. She could slip out of her skin and become like a spirit or a ghost or a haunt. The children whispered that Tucky could catch the night wind and ride it across the bayou waters, sifting herself through the moss and stirring the foggy, black water. Going who-knows-where and doin' who-knows-what! All night, until the dawn. Then she'd ride the wind across her back porch and call, "Skin, my skin. Let me in." Tucky would slide back into her skin. She'd walk back into the house just as if she'd been on God's green earth all along. That is what she'd do back in those woods, and nobody around to see!

One summer evening, Tucky called her children together and told them she was going away. "You big ones take care of the little ones," she said. "Sit by the fireplace, keep the front door locked. If anybody comes knocking on the door and calling 'Aunt Tucky,' don't open the door. Just answer them and say, 'Ain't no Aunt Tucky here!' They will think they got the wrong place and go away. Stay here, sit still. Watch for me and wait. I'll be back."

Then she called one of the big children to come to the back porch with her. Aunt Tucky told the child to pick up the skin when Tucky shed it. Most important, the child had to hang the skin on the nail on the wall next to the porch. That was so Aunt Tucky could get back in it easy.

Tucky began to moan, "Skin, my skin. Let it begin." She simmered; she glowed. Her old brown skin slid down to the porch floor. Aunt Tucky was like a spirit or a haunt! Floating up and out, lighter than a spider's silk thread, she hitched to the night wind and rode away across the dark bayou waters.

The poor child did what she was told. So Aunt Tucky's skin, all wrinkled up, was hung on the nail on the back porch wall: and the children sat inside by the fireplace waiting. But Aunt Tucky did not come back the next morning. They all got hungry; the little ones cried. Still the big ones made them stay put because Tucky had told them to stay. They's scared of her. So, they waited through another day and night. The big ones were so hungry they wanted to cry, too.

When the sun rose proud-high, on the third day, the big ones took the little ones by the hand saying, "Come on! We're going somewhere where people take care of their children—where people care about being with their families." They walked out that wooden front door, down those two plank steps, to the road, and to the first neighbor's house they could find. Before those children could finish telling her about being hungry and Aunt Tucky being gone, that good neighbor-woman was already cooking. She filled those empty stomachs with biscuits and white gravy 'til they were full satisfied. Then she told them to go back to their cabin place. Aunt Tucky would be looking for them if she had come back, you see. "But I'll come check on you before the day is over," she promised. So they went back to sit still, and watch and wait.

The neighbor lady took some of her egg money, caught a ride to town and bought a ham and a big bag of salt. How she got all that out to Aunt Tucky's before dark, I don't know. But she did. Late in the day, the neighbor-lady came down the path. She called to the children—not knocking—so they let her in. Seeing that Tucky hadn't come back, she fried them some ham. They ate, then sat by the fireplace again, watching the neighbor-lady in Aunt Tucky's house. She told the big ones that she wanted to show them how to use the salt to cure ham. That could wait 'til tomorrow though. She needed to start home before dark.

"But," she said, "we've got to do something about this salt before I go. It would be rock hard if that damp air off the bayou gets to it over night!"

She began looking for a bucket with a lid, a jar or canister with a top. But she couldn't find anything. She went to the back porch. She looked up the porch—nothing. She looked down the porch—nothing. Bare, clean, empty, nothing! When she turned to go back into the house, the woman spotted something hanging on the wall by the door. The children heard her say, "Here! This old hide-y-side-y thing will do!" And she lifted Aunt Tucky's skin from the nail on the wall.

The little children were scared. What should they do? What should they say? The big ones decided they should do exactly what Aunt Tucky told them. They did not say one word. They just sat still and watched and waited. They kept quiet and watched out the back door as the neighbor lady shook out the skin. She opened it wide at the top and began to scoop salt into it. They watched the lady fill the brown hidey-skin bag with the white salt, then take off a shoelace to tie tight 'round the neck of it. They kept quiet as she leaned the salt-filled skin against the back porch wall, brushed off her hands, and came back inside. She told them the sun was going down and she had to go. She'd be back tomorrow, and she told them to lock the doors after she left.

Doors locked, the children waited quietly. It was that night that Aunt Tucky returned from wandering the bayou. Her voice moved across the porch, calling, "Skin, my skin. Let me in."

But something was wrong! The salt! The salt poured into Aunt Tucky's skin had dried and shrunk the skin! The hide was shriveled so that Aunt Tucky could not fit. Also, the knot of shoelace at the throat top was pulled tight. Being a spirit-thing, Tucky couldn't force the knot undone! Aunt Tucky forced the breeze across the porch again; her voice was anxious.

"Skin, skin, always lucky. Welcome home your Aunt Tucky."

Nothing happened.

Again and again they heard her beg, "Skin, my skin. Let me in."

But she could not get in.

Tucky whipped up a fury wind and began to howl and moan. She rode the wind full force, battered the front door—*blam! blam! blam!*—calling, "It's Aunt Tucky-y-y, it's Aunt Tucky!" But the children had been told what to do when someone knocked against the door. They huddled close, and shouted, "Ain't no Aunt Tucky! No Tucky here. No Tucky here. Go away!"

Tucky went some kind of mad! She started trying to tear down the house. She'd make those children help her get back her skin. She whipped the wind 'round the house, rattled the cracked windows, shook walls. She pulled shingles from the roof. Those poor children sat waiting and watching. Tucky and the wind seemed to be shaking the house apart.

Through the night Aunt Tucky's voice called, "Skin, my skin. Let me in-n-n. It's-s-s Aunt Tucky . . . y!" Through the same night, the big ones and the little ones held each other close waiting and waiting and hoping.

Their hope came through the east window. They saw the sky lighten to gray, then the earth edged with pink. Tucky's voice seemed to fade; the wind slowly went away. A beautiful golden ray of sunlight reached up from the east and glorified the cloudless morning! The night wind began to weaken. The night air had to go back to the foggy bayou and its shadow places. And Aunt Tucky had to ride away with it.

Soon as there was light enough, the big ones took the little ones by the hand and explained, "Aunt Tucky ain't never coming back. We're going to find a place where people care about their children, where people come home to their families. And we'll stay there." So they went out and down the Linton Road where they found good people. Several families took those children in and cared for them. Raised them.

Even today, people can go up Linton Road and out on that dirt path to the little cabin. It's still there and in fair shape. Nobody lives there though. I hear that if a person can walk out on the porch just at sunset, the evening breeze will begin to stir from across the bayou as dark comes. I've heard some say that on that porch just at dark . . . if they are very still, and will watch and wait, they'll see the moss move. They can feel the night wind, and they can still hear a thin old voice saying, "Skin, my skin. Let me in." That witch-woman can't come back and she can't leave here, either. To this day, it's still Aunt Tucky.

The Yellow Ribbon

This story, with its can't-miss shock value, is a classic among schoolchildren all over North America. Folklorist Maria Leach reports that the tale is quite old and is told in many parts of Europe, as well as in North America.

John loved Jane. They lived next door to each other, and they went to first grade together, and John loved Jane very much. Jane wore a yellow ribbon around her neck every day.

One day John said, "Why do you wear the yellow ribbon?"

"I can't tell," said Jane. But John kept asking, and finally Jane said maybe she'd tell him later.

The next year they were in the second grade. One day John asked again, "Why do you wear the yellow ribbon around your neck?" And Jane said maybe she'd tell him later.

Time went by, and every once in a while John asked Jane why she wore the yellow ribbon, but Jane never told. So time went by.

John and Jane went through high school together. They loved each other very much. On graduation day John asked Jane please to tell him why she always wore the yellow ribbon around her neck. But Jane said there was no point in telling on graduation day, so she didn't tell.

Time went by, and John and Jane became engaged, and finally Jane said maybe she would tell him on their wedding day.

The wedding day came, and John forgot to ask. But the next day John asked Jane why she wore the yellow ribbon. Jane said, "Well, we are happily married, and we love each other, so what difference does it make?" So John let that pass, but he still did want to know.

Time went by, and finally on their golden anniversary John asked again. And Jane said, "Since you have waited this long, you can wait a little longer."

Finally Jane was taken very ill, and when she was dying John asked again, between sobs, "*Please* tell me why you wear the yellow ribbon around your neck."

"All right," said Jane, "you can untie it."

So John untied the yellow ribbon, and Jane's head fell off.

The Ghost of Jean Lafitte

Every region of North America has its legends of famous ghosts. In Louisiana, the pirate Jean Lafitte haunts the bayou where it is believed he buried his treasure before he died.

A young, war-weary Confederate soldier was making his long way back home, following the snaking path of a bayou, when a terrible storm fell upon him. The wind wailed as thunder boomed and rain fell like needles. The soldier saw that he had better find shelter, so he left the bayou and began to wander through a thicket. He soon became lost in the blinding rain.

The soldier came to an abandoned house in the middle of nowhere. The door stood open. He called out but nobody answered, and since it was nearly dark he went inside to escape the howling wind. He struck a match and found dry firewood left behind by some other lost soul. The young man quickly made a fire and settled down for the night. He was dead tired from his journey, and he soon fell into a heavy sleep.

Sometime in the deep of the night he waked with the strange feeling that he was not alone in the house. And there by the light of the dying fire, he saw the ghostly figure of a man standing in tall, muddy boots. His arms were folded across his chest and a pirate's cutlass hung at his side.

The man pointed at him and says, "Come with me."

"Who—who are you?" whispers the soldier.

"I am Jean Lafitte," he wails. "*Viens avec moi!* Come with me, save my soul, help me!"

The man disappeared into thin air without another word. The soldier's heart was pounding hard, but he told himself it was only a dream. He stoked the fire and lay back down. The apparition had unsettled him, and now he jumped at every creak and groan of the old house, until at last his tired body gave in to sleep.

The fire had died down when the soldier again waked with a start. A strange, icy draft of wind whistled through the room and the ghostly pirate appeared once more before him.

"Help me, free my soul," the pirate's spirit pleads.

The young man could barely speak for fear. "Wh—what do you wa— want from m—me?" he asks.

"I am condemned," wails the ghost, "a slave to my treasure—bought with human tears and broken hearts. Now I must pay the price of my fortune. My soul is bound to my blood money. Take my treasure and set me freeeee!"

The young man could feel himself being lifted against his will and forced to follow the ghost of Jean Lafitte. The spirit brought him to a secret room. There, with a wave of the pirate's hand, the boards in the floor disappeared to reveal a huge chest, spilling over with treasure. The room was lit up by the shining glow of silver, jewels, and golden coins.

Jean Lafitte stretches out his hands, crying, "Take it! Take my treasure. Help me save my soul!"

The spirit's hands were gory, and bloody tears dripped from his burning eyes. He reached out, closer, closer, until the young man felt the bloodstained fingers grasp his arm like an icy claw—it was the touch of death itself. The soldier's terror rose beyond the power of the spirit's spell and he broke away, running like a madman into the stormy night. The wind tore at him and booming thunder shook the ground. He crashed through the thorny thicket in the blinding rain. Behind him he could hear the ghost crying in the wind, "Take my treasure. Ohhhhh, help meee!"

The young man lived to tell the story, and he warned all who would seek the treasure to beware. The pirate's bloody curse, he would say, follows whoever takes the treasure. To this day, when a storm booms down the bayou, many believe that the wailing wind carries the pitiful cries of the ghost of Jean Lafitte. For his spirit is condemned to wander forever through the dark night, begging, pleading for somebody to take his cursed treasure and free his tortured soul at last.

The Weeping Woman

———•••———

In the Southwestern United States, and in Mexico, the reigning queen of ghosts is La Llorona, the weeping woman. So many tales exist about the origin of her presence that looking at a few of them provides a fascinating look at the folk-process at work.

———•••———

I.

A long time ago, an Indian couple was to be married, another ordinary marriage as it may appear. But as time went on, the economic status of the family went from fair to very poor. When the couple had its first baby, a boy, the father knew he couldn't feed him, so after thinking about what was best for the child, he went to the river, and after asking God for forgiveness, he dropped the child in the river. The husband believed he was doing the right thing and repeated his feat as each child was born. Each time the town's people heard the wife screaming, "Ay, my hijo" [Oh, my son] in an eerie tone.

When her last son was born [all previous ones were boys], she was determined to have him live. She went down to the river, and after her husband dropped the boy, she went after him. Since she wasn't skilled in the art of swimming, she drowned along with her son.

Nobody thought much of it after the death, but one foggy night, one of the farm workers saw the ghostly figure of a woman and child in the river. The woman screamed in her high pitched voice, "Oh, my son." After that night, the ghost appeared on the water and the nearby land. The husband couldn't sleep because he heard these eerie sounds. Finally the husband, knife in hand, jumped into the river and tried to kill the woman. After his unsuccessful try, his body was never found.

After the story was spread around, people reported seeing her in different places. But the local people said that she appeared only on rainy, foggy nights.

II.

La Llorona hated men, especially men who have two or more women. She appears to them dressed in a white robe and makes a pass and when they follow her they are always found drowned, sometimes in the canal, but sometimes they will be in the street. They always die with their eyes open like they were looking up at something and couldn't stop.

III.

There was a woman who had gone out into the fields one day to help her husband with the crop. She left her children unattended. When she came home that evening, she found all of her children dead. Somehow they had poisoned themselves. When she saw this, she went out of her mind and killed herself. Since a suicide cannot be admitted to heaven, the Llorona was condemned to wander the earth.

IV.

When she was born, she was a twin. She and her sister were so identical, that when they were baptized, the other one was baptized twice. La Llorona was never baptized. She married when she was nineteen and had a son and a daughter. But she did not love them, so she drowned them in a ditch. When she died and went before God, He punished her by having her cry and search throughout the world for her children until the day the world ends. Then she will be pardoned. They say that she appears where there are lakes and ditches, and her weeping and wailing can be heard.

V.

Well, my friends told me there once lived this lady who had a bunch of kids. Well, you see, she couldn't feed these kids. So she decided to kill them. She took them to the river and told them they were going to go swimming. They believed her. She drowned them. And God punished her for this. So He said, "You will always cry when a person puts a broom in the corner and it's raining." She regretted what she had done. But every time someone puts a broom in the corner when it rains at night, she has to go out and kill someone.

La Llorona Teaches a Hippie a Lesson

In most stories about sightings of La Llorona there is one common feature: She usually appears to people who are in danger of straying from the straight moral path. First-person accounts are often given by people who had been drinking, had been contemplating stealing, hadn't been to church in a while, or were guilty of some other misdemeanor, until the sight of La Llorona convinced them to leave their evil ways behind.

There are many stories here in Chimayo about La Llorona. This is one of my favorites.

Back about 1970, the first hippies moved here. Some of them were okay, but some of them were very disrespectful. This story concerns one of the disrespectful ones, who was also a thief.

This hippie was named after some animal or bird—the hippies used names like that. He was named "Bear," or "Crow." I can't remember. Maybe it was "Mole." No, now that I think of it, "Mole" was someone else's name—a friend of his, I think. I'll call him "Bear" for the purposes of this story. He had a wife who also had a strange name like "Sunshine" or "Ocean" or something like that, and a couple of little children who ran around with runny noses and no pants or shoes. They bought a little piece of land that no one else would want and built a house that was all underground, with boards over the top for a roof. It was a terrible place to live. At least, my husband and I thought so. But who am I to judge? *"Cada chango a su columpio"*—each monkey to his own swing.

Now, this "Bear" was from California and had a very rich family, so he never had to work and he didn't have any respect for people who worked hard.

The first trouble we had with "Bear" was when he would go riding horses across our pasture and leave the gates open so the cows would get out and my poor husband would spend days chasing them back into the pasture. This caused a lot of trouble for us, believe me. A couple of people even shot in his direction, but he didn't pay any attention. He thought the land belonged to everyone and there shouldn't be any fences, but my husband says, "Good fences make good neighbors."

The other thing we all thought was strange was that this hippie had some idea he was an Indian. We would see him riding his horse along the arroyo and all he wore was this little leather thing like Tarzan, with beads and feathers around his neck and moccasins.

People tried to ignore this "Bear," but soon they started to notice signs that something had been in their gardens. At first it was like the skunks do when they get at the corn, with all the ears broken off. Then, other vegetables started to disappear and some fruit, too. We soon realized it wasn't a skunk—not the four-legged kind, anyway.

Nobody had caught "Bear" stealing, but people knew it was him anyway. As we say up here in the north, *"Cuando el sartén chilla, algo hay en la villa"*— "When the frying pan sizzles, something's up in the village."

So, this stealing went on through the summer and then, that fall—in October, I think—it all stopped. We had a long summer that year with no frost in September, so there was still food in many gardens. One of the best gardens belonged to Mrs. Martinez and she told me this story.

Late one night in this particular October, when the moon was almost full and the leaves were dry and rustling on the trees, Mrs. Martinez could not sleep. She has sciatica, *pobrecita*, so she was up at her table late, drinking *atole* and looking out the window. Hearing a noise, she looked closer and saw this "Bear" in her garden with a sack and all of a sudden she realized that he was taking her carrots! He was wearing his Tarzan costume and had smeared himself with something dark like mud, probably so he couldn't be seen.

The wind was blowing that night, so there were noises from the loose tin on Mrs. Martinez' roof and the tree branches. Now, you should know that Mrs. Martinez' garden is right below the Martinez *acequia*, which is the big one that runs through the plaza, and it is well known that La Llorona likes the ditches.

So, as Mrs. Martinez was watching this "Bear" through her window, she heard the wind really start to howl louder and louder. Then she realized that it was not just the wind—it was the cry of La Llorona! She saw this "Bear" straighten up all of a sudden after bending over the carrot patch, and even through the mud on his face, she could see his eyes get big. Across the ditch came floating La Llorona, tall like she is, and all dressed in black, increasing her howling by the minute. The "Bear" dropped poor Mrs. Martinez' carrots and began to run. He was so scared he ran right into the fence and fell down. He tried to get up, but his body failed him and so he scrambled along on all fours.

All along the road, as "Bear" ran, the howling continued and all the porch lights came on and the dogs began to bark. Everyone saw "Bear," running as fast as he could, his Indian braids standing out straight behind him as he ran for his life.

After that night, this "Bear" took his family to live somewhere else. He is probably still stealing because, as we all know, "*La zorra mudara los dientes pero no las mientes*"—"The fox may lose its teeth but not its ways."

But, thanks to La Llorona, this doesn't happen in our village anymore.

A Pretty Girl in the Road

Readers will instantly recognize the story of "the vanishing hitchhiker." This tale is ever-popular, usually features a car and two boys, and often includes the detail of the girl's borrowing a sweater that is later found draped over her gravestone. This simple rural version is from Missouri.

One time there was a fellow a-riding along and it was getting dark and coming on to rain besides. He seen a girl a-standing beside the road, where a old house had burnt down but the chimney was still there. She was a tall slim girl with a poke bonnet on, but he seen her face plain. He stopped and says if you are going somewheres I will give you a ride, because my horse carries double. She says her name is Stapleton, and her folks live down the road a piece. So then she jumped up behind him light as a feather. Pretty soon he spurred the horse a little, so she had to put her arms round his waist.

They rode on about a mile and he found out her first name was Lucy, and she wasn't married neither. He could feel her breath on his neck while they was a-talking, and he liked it fine. He got to thinking this was the kind of a girl he'd like to marry up with, because he liked her better than any girl he ever seen before.

So they rode another mile and it was pretty dark by this time, and they come to a graveyard. And there was a big house with lights in the windows just a little way off. She says that's where my folks live, but I'd better get down here. He figured she was going to take a short cut home, so her paw wouldn't know she had been riding with a stranger. Folks was awful particular about what their daughters done in them days. The girl jumped off and walked over to the gate. He says, "I'll be seein' you pretty soon," but Lucy just waved him goodbye and went into the graveyard.

The fellow waited awhile so she would have time to get home, and then he rode up in front of the big house. Soon as the dogs begun to bark an old man come out, and he says, "My name is Stapleton." He says the fellow is welcome to have supper with them and stay all night, as they have got plenty of room. And then he hollered a boy out of the barn to take care of the traveler's horse.

They had a mighty good supper, but there wasn't nobody at the table, only Judge Stapleton and his wife. The fellow kept looking for Lucy to show up any minute, but she never come. So after while he went to bed in the spare room. It was a fine shuck mattress too, but he didn't sleep very good.

Next morning after breakfast they got to talking, and the Judge says him and his wife just moved here a year ago. "We used to live two miles down the road," he says, "but our house was lightnin'-struck and burnt plumb down. There ain't nothing left now but the old chimney." The fellow says yes, he seen that chimney when he rode by there last night. "I didn't mind losing the house," says the Judge, "only our daughter was sick in bed. We carried her out to the gate, but the shock was too much for her, and she died that same night."

The fellow just set there, and the Judge went on a-talkin' about what a fine girl his daughter was, and how him and the old woman was pretty lonesome nowadays. "We buried her in that little graveyard," says the Judge. "You can see her stone from the front gallery. There ain't a day goes by, rain or shine, that my wife don't walk over there an' set by the grave awhile."

Everything was mighty still for a minute, and then the traveler says, "What was your daughter's name?" It sounded kind of funny, the way he said it, but he was obliged to know.

"Her name was Lucy," says the Judge.

The Spectre Bride

———·•·———

The major supernatural element of "The Spectre Bride," a tale told among Osage tribes in the early part of this century, is remarkably similar to that of numerous versions of "the vanishing hitchhiker."

———·———

Fighting Buffalo, a young hunter of the Osages, left camp on the Nickanansa to sell his furs in St. Louis and to buy there some ornaments worthy to be worn by Prairie Flower, the girl who had promised to marry him, on his return. This journey, eighty or ninety years ago, was a matter of toil and difficulty, so that he was absent for about three weeks, during which time he had no news of affairs at home. When he regained the Nickanansa and had neared the site of his village he quickened his pace, for there were no lodge peaks above the earth waves of the prairie, no wisps of smoke to promise the comfort of supper. Not greatly wondering at this, as he knew and shared the migratory habits of his people, he looked about to find some picture-writing that should guide him to the new village of the tribe, and was pleasantly surprised on seeing at a distance the figure of a young woman, seated among the ashes and refuse of the vanished camp, and bent, as if weeping. The pleasure of this discovery was in the recognition of the girl. It was Prairie Flower. He ran forward eagerly, and would have embraced her, but she turned her head sadly, and would not look at him.

"I have jewels and ribbons for you, my bride," he said, tossing off his pack.

She gave a little sob.

"Where are our people?" he asked.

"Gone. Gone to the Wagrushka."

"But you are here, alone."

"I was waiting for you."

"Then we will go to our people at once, and to-morrow we shall be married; and you will be the most beautiful of all the girls; yes, in all the flat country."

She still averted her face. "I will carry your pack," she said. Among

Indians the burdens that are not borne by horses are usually carried by women, so that this was quite the thing to do. Fighting Buffalo laughed a little as his sweetheart picked up the bundle, for it was filled with gifts that would make her happy. But why did she hide her face? and now that they had started on the march for the Wagrushka, why did she gather her cloak about her in that fashion, and cover her head, like the head of a corpse that is ready for burial? "There's no accounting for women's tempers," thought the hunter. "She will be more kind tomorrow." Plodding on through the tall grass, she following silently in his footsteps, seldom speaking, and then but quietly, they came at sunset to the new camp of the Osages and saw the blue smoke curling pleasantly above the tepees. The girl stopped. "It is better that we should not enter the camp together. You know that is the custom only with married people. I will wait for a time beneath this tree."

Fighting Buffalo ran on ahead, aroused the village with a joyful shout, and called greetings to his relatives, while yet a quarter of a mile away. Tomorrow Prairie Flower would be his wife, and he was happy. As he went nearer he was chilled by a boding. The people were sad and silent. Even the children desisted from their play. "What ails you all?" he asked. "Has any one died since I left you?"

There was no answer. Then he addressed his sister: "Feather Cloud, go back and tell Prairie Flower to come to us."

His sister recoiled. "Do not speak like that," she murmured, with a sidelong glance toward her parents, as if she feared they might have heard her brother's words.

"Tell me, what has come over every one? Why have you moved? Why will you not bring my bride to me?"

"Prairie Flower is dead, and is buried beneath that tree."

"This is poor fun, if you intend to joke. She came with me from the Nickanansa, and brought my pack as far as that tree. Faugh! I will go after her myself."

He walked hastily back in the twilight, his people following at a distance. His pack lay at the tree-foot, on a new grave. With a choking cry he pressed his hands upon his heart and fell on the mound, dead.

Acknowledgments

CHAPTER 1

"The Boy of the Red Sky" adapted from "The Boy of the Red Twilight Sky" by Cyrus Macmillan from *Canadian Fairy Tales*, The Bodley Head.

"What Makes Brer Wasp Have a Short Patience" from *Afro-American Folktales* edited by Roger D. Abrahams. Copyright © 1985 by Roger D. Abrahams. Reprinted by permission of Pantheon Books, a division of Random House, Inc.

"Oppossum Steals Fire" from *The Mythology of Mexico and Central America* by John Bierhorst. Copyright © 1990 by John Bierhorst. Reprinted by permission of Morrow Junior Books, a division of William Morrow & Company, Inc.

"Light" from "Tales from Kodiak Island" collected by F. A. Golder in *The Journal of American Folklore*, Volume 16: April–June 1903.

"Ojeeg, The Summer Maker" from *Myths and Legends of the Mississippi Valley and the Great Lakes* edited by Katherine B. Judson. Copyright 1914 by A. C. McClurg & Company, Chicago.

"Powerful Changed" from *Mules and Men* by Zora Neale Hurston. Copyright 1935 by Zora Neale Hurston. Renewed 1963 by John C. Hurston and Joel Hurston. Reprinted by permission of HarperCollins Publishers, Inc.

"The Star Husband" by Lynn Moroney from *Best Stories from the Texas Storytelling Festival* published by August House Publishers, Inc. Copyright © 1995 by Lynn Moroney. Reprinted by permission of Lynn Moroney, Oklahoma City, OK.

"The Dog-Rib Legend of Ithenhiela" from *The Journal of American Folklore*, Volume 16, 1903.

"Man, the Burro, and the Dog" from *Cuentos: Tales from the Hispanic Southwest* selected and adapted by Jose Griego y Maestas, retold by Rudolfo A. Anaya. Copyright © 1980 by the Museum of New Mexico Press. Reprinted by permission of The Museum of New Mexico Press.

"Possum, Turtle, and the Wolves" by Doug Elliott. Reprinted by permission of Doug Elliott, 3831 Painter Gap Road, Union Mills, NC 28167. Doug Elliott is a naturalist, an herbalist, and a storyteller. He has written several books and produced a number of award-winning recordings, including one of "Possum, Turtle, and the Wolves."

"Getting Common Sense" from *Anansi and Miss Lou* by Louise Bennet, Sangster's Book Stores, Ltd., Kingston, Jamaica.

"Ouiot and Frog" from *The Journal of American Folklore*, Volume 19, 1906.

CHAPTER 2

"How to Tell a Story" from *How to Tell a Story and Other Essays* by Mark Twain. Copyright 1897, 1898, 1899 by Harper & Bros., New York.

"Ab Yancey's Squirrel Hunt" from *Ozark Mountain Folks* by Vance Randolph. Copyright 1932 by Vanguard Press, Inc.

"Tall Hunting Tale" from *South from Hell-fer-Sartin: Kentucky Mountain Folk Tales* by Leonard W. Roberts. Copyright © 1964 by the University Press of Kentucky. Reprinted by permission of Edith R. Roberts, Stanville, KY.

"The Dog Who Could Walk on Water" from *Cajun and Creole Folk Tales: The French Oral Tradition of South Louisiana* collected and annotated by Barry Jean Ancelet. Copyright © 1994 by Barry Jean Ancelet. Reprinted by permission of Barry Jean Ancelet and Garland Publishing Inc.

"Old Gawge and the Ninety and Nine" by Walter H. Martin in *Sun Up*, September 1932.

"Uncle Swain" adapted from "Local Character Anecdotes Down East" by Catherine Peck in

The North Carolina Folklore Journal, Volume 39, No. 2 (Spring 1993). Used by permission of Catherine Peck.

"The Trained Trout" from *The Tame Trout and Other Fairy Tales* narrated by Ed Grant of Beaver Pond, Maine, chronicled by Francis I. Mauls. Published in 1904 by Maine Woods and Woodsman Printing.

"A Trip to the Moon" from *Storytellers: Folktales and Legends from the South* edited by John A. Burrison. Copyright © 1989 by the University of Georgia Press. Reprinted by permission of the University of Georgia Press.

"The Snake-Bit Hoe Handle" by Doc McConnell as it appeared within *Homespun: Tales from America's Favorite Storytellers* edited by Jimmy Neil Smith. Copyright © 1988 by Doc McConnell. Reprinted by permission of Doc McConnell, Rogersville, TN.

"Uncle Billy Hallock's Yarn" from the *New York Folklore Quarterly*, Volume 9, No. 1 (Spring 1953). Reprinted by permission of the New York Folklore Society, P. O. Box 130, Newfield, NY, 14867.

"I Wish I Could Tell a Lie" from *The American Imagination at Work: Tall Tales and Folk Tales* edited by Ben C. Clough. Copyright 1947 by Alfred A. Knopf, Inc. and renewed 1975 by Ben C. Clough. Reprinted by permission of Alfred A. Knopf, Inc.

"Remarks Made at the Hatchet Club" from *Library of Wit and Humor by Mark Twain and Others, with the Philosophy of Wit and Humor* edited by Melville D. Landon. Published in 1898 by Star Publishing Company, Chicago.

"Billy Earthquake" as it appeared within *An American Glossary, Being an Attempt to Illustrate Certain Americanisms upon Historical Principles* by Richard H. Thornton, Vol. II. Published in 1912 by J. B. Lippincott Company, Philadelphia. This story was originally published in a Florida newspaper, circa 1840.

"The Purple Blossom of Gingham Mountain" from "Old Man Enright's Love" in *Wolfville Days* by Alfred Henry Lewis. Published in 1902 by Frederick A. Stokes, Company, New York.

"California" from *Forty-Niners* by Archer Hulbert. Copyright 1931 by Archer Butler Hulbert, by permission of Little, Brown & Company.

CHAPTER 3

"Annie Oakley Makes Her Name" from *The Female Hero in Folklore and Legend* by Tristram Potter Coffin. Copyright © 1975 by Tristram Potter Coffin. The Seabury Press, Inc.

"Grinning the Bark off a Tree" published in *Sketches and Eccentricities of Colonel David Crockett of West Tennessee* in 1833 by J. & J. Harper, New York.

"The Colonel Swallows a Thunderbolt" as it appeared in *Davy Crockett, American Comic Legend* selected by Richard M. Dorson. Published in 1939 by Rockland Editions, New York. This story was originally published in the 1854 *Crockett Almanac* by Cozans, New York.

"David Crockett Meets a Bear" from *The American Imagination at Work: Tall Tales and Folk Tales* by Ben C. Clough. Copyright 1947 by Alfred A. Knopf, Inc. and renewed 1975 by Ben C. Clough. Reprinted by permission of the publisher.

"Mike Fink Meets David Crockett" from *The American Imagination at Work: Tall Tales and Folk Tales* edited by Ben C. Clough. Copyright 1947 by Alfred A. Knopf, Inc. Renewed 1975 by Ben C. Clough. Reprinted by permission of Alfred A. Knopf, Inc.

"The Ballad of Casey Jones" as it appeared in *Erie Railroad Magazine*, Volume 28 (April 1932), No. 2, p. 12.

"Johnny Appleseed" from *Rosella Rice's Recollections*, reprinted for the Ohio Valley Folk Research Project of the Ross County Historical Society, Chillicothe, Ohio, by Dave Webb from *History of the Ashland County Pioneer Historical Society*, Ashland, OH.

"A Folktale of Johnny Appleseed" from "Frontier Preacher and Planter" by Iantha Castillo in *The Missouri Historical Review*, Vol. XIX, No. 4, July 1925.

"The Cherry Tree Legend" from *The Life of George Washington* by Mason Locke Weems, 1806. Weems was an itinerant preacher and book peddler who published *The Life and Memorable Actions of George Washington* in 1800.

"Belle Starr's Horse Race" from *Ozark Tales and Superstitions* by Philip W. Steele. Copyright © 1983 by Pelican Publishing Company, Inc. Reprinted by permission of the publisher.

"Belle's Arrest" from the *Dallas News,* June 7, 1886, as published in *Legendary Ladies of Texas.* Francis Edward Abernathy, ed. Dallas: E-Heart Press, 1981.

"Judge Roy Bean's Necktie Justice" from *Vinegarron: The Saga of Judge Roy Bean* by Ruel McDaniel. Copyright 1936 by Ruel McDaniel. Southern Publishers, Kingsport, TN.

"Wild Bill Hickock's Duel with Dave Tutt" from "Wild Bill" by Ward Nichols in *Harper's New Monthly Magazine*, Vol. XXXIV (February 1867), No. CCI.

"Stackalee" from *The Rainbow Book of Folktales and Legends* by Maria Leach. Copyright © 1958 by Maria Leach. Reprinted by permission of HarperCollins Publishers, Inc.

"The Ballad of Stackalee." Onah L. Spencer. From *Direction*, Vol. IV (Summer, 1941), No. 5, pp. 14–17. Copyright 1941, by Direction, Inc.

CHAPTER 4
"The Birth of Paul Bunyan" from *Paul Bunyan* by Esther Shepherd. Copyright 1924, renewed 1952 by Esther Shepherd. Reprinted by permission of Harcourt Brace & Company.

"Babe the Blue Ox" from *Paul Bunyan Swings His Axe* by Dell J. McCormick. Copyright 1936 by Caxton Printers, Ltd. Reprinted by permission of the publisher.

"Pipeline Days" abridged from *Foller de Drinkin' Gou'd*, Publications of the Texas Folklore Society, 1928. Reprinted by permission of the Texas Folklore Society.

"Paul's Popcorn" from *Tall Tale America: A Legendary History of Our Humorous Heroes* by Walter Blair. Copyright 1944, renewed 1972 by Walter Blair. Reprinted by permission of Coward, McCann & Geoghegan, a division of The Putnam & Grosset Group.

"Paul Bunyan Takes Care of Mosquitoes" from *Paul Bunyan: Last of the Frontier Demigods* by Daniel Hoffman. Copyright 1952, renewed 1980 by Daniel Hoffman. Published by Temple University Publications and reprinted by permission of Daniel Hoffman.

"Cal Bunyan's Ireland, Jerusalem, Australia & Southern Indiana Railroad" from *The Signalman's Journal*. Reprinted by permission of the Brotherhood of Railroad Signalmen, Mount Prospect, IL.

"The Birth of John Henry" from *John Henry* by Roark Bradford. Copyright 1931 by Roark Bradford. Published by Harper & Bros., New York.

"The Ballad of John Henry" collected, adapted, and arranged by John A. Lomax and Alan Lomax. Copyright 1934, renewed Ludlow Music, Inc., New York. Used by permission of The Richmond Organization, New York.

"Annie Christmas" by Catherine Peck. Used by permission of Catherine Peck.

"The Saga of Pecos Bill" as it appeared in *A Parade of Heroes* by Tristram Potter Coffin. Copyright © 1978 by Tristram Potter Coffin. Published by Bantam Doubleday Dell.

CHAPTER 5
"Looking For Trouble" from *Bo Rabbit Smart for True* by Priscilla Jaquith. Text copyright © 1981 by Priscilla Jaquith. Reprinted by permission of Philomel Books.

"The Bird That Was Ashamed of Its Feet" by Gayle Ross as it appeared in *Best Stories from the Texas Storytelling Festival* published by August House Publishers, Inc. Copyright © 1995 by Gayle Ross. Reprinted by permission of Gayle Ross, Fredericksburg, TX.

"A Boy and His Donkey" from *Cuentos: Tales from the Hispanic Southwest* selected and adapted by Jose Griego y Maestas and Rudolfo A. Anaya. Copyright © 1980 by Museum of New Mexico Press. Reprinted by permission of the publisher.

"Brer Possum's Dilemma" by Jackie Torrence from *Jackie's Tales*, by Jackie Torrence, 1998 (New York: Avon Books).

"The Red Rag Under the Churn" by Alice Childs from *American Speech*, Vol. V, December 1929, No. 2.

"The Two Wagoners" from *Cuentos: Tales from the Hispanic Southwest* selected and adapted by Jose Griego y Maestas and Rudolfo A. Anaya. Copyright © 1980 by Museum of New Mexico Press. Reprinted by permission of the publisher.

"Annancy and the Yam Hills" adapted from *Annancy Stories* by Pamela Colman Smith. Published in 1899 by R. H. Russell, New York.

"Words of Wisdom" from *Cuentos: Tales from the Hispanic Southwest* selected and adapted by Jose Griego y Maestas and Rudolfo A. Anaya. Copyright © 1980 by Museum of New Mexico Press. Reprinted by permission of the publisher.

"The Golden Rain" from *Tales from the Cloud Walking Country* by Marie Campbell. Copyright © 1958 by Indiana University Press. Reprinted by permission of the publisher.

"Why Men Have to Work" from *Black Folktales* by Julius Lester. Copyright © 1969 by Julius Lester. Reprinted by permission of Grove/Atlantic.

"A Bundle of Troubles" collected by W. E. Hennessee of the Writer's Program of the Works Progress Administration in the State of North Carolina, in *Bundle of Troubles and Other Tarheel Tales* edited by W. C. Hendricks. Copyright 1943 by Duke University Press. Reprinted by permission of Duke University Press.

"The Robe" from *The Weeping Woman: Encounters with La Llorona* edited by Edward Garcia Kraul and Judith Beatty. Copyright © 1988 by Edward Garcia Kraul and Judith S. Beatty. Reprinted by permission of Judith Beatty, Santa Fe, NM.

CHAPTER 6

"Brother Rabbit Breaks Up a Party." Adapted from *Nights With Uncle Remus* by Joel Chandler Harris.

"Tío Conejo and the Hurricane" by Mary Ann Brewer, adapted from *Best Stories from the Texas Storytelling Festival* published by August House Publishers, Inc. Copyright © 1995 by Mary Ann Brewer. Reprinted by permission of Mary Ann Brewer, Richardson, TX.

"Coyote Tricks the White Man" from *Kiowa Apache Tales* edited by J. Gilbert McAllister. Publications of the Texas Folklore Society, 22, 1949. Reprinted by permission of the Texas Folklore Society.

"Big John the Conqueror" from *Stetson Kennedy: Palmetto Country*. Copyright 1942 by Stetson Kennedy. Published by Duell, Sloan & Pearce.

"Jack and the Giants' New Ground" as it appeared in *Folklore on the American Land* by Duncan Emrich, Little, Brown & Company, 1972.

"The Boy That Was Foolish-Wise" from *Tales From the Cloud Walking Country* by Marie Campbell. Copyright © 1958 by Indiana University Press. Reprinted by permission of Indiana University Press.

"The Arkansas Traveler" as it appeared in *Great American Folklore* compiled by Kemp Battle. Compilation copyright © 1986 by Kemp Battle. Published by Doubleday & Company, Inc.

"The Yankee Finishes His Meal" as it appeared in *Great American Folklore* compiled by Kemp Battle. Compilation copyright © 1986 by Kemp Battle. Published by Doubleday & Company, Inc.

"Razor-Strop Trade" originally published by *Cyclopaedia of Commercial and Business Anecdotes* by Frazar Kirkland, Vol. II, p. 555. D. Appleton and Company, 1864.

"How Pedro Urdemalas Got Into and Out of Heaven" from *Life on the King Ranch* by Frank Goodwyn. Copyright 1951 by Frank Goodwyn. Published by A & M University Press, 1983. Reprinted by permission of Frank Goodwyn, Silver Spring, MD.

"Bobtail and the Devil" from *South from Hell-fer-Sartin: Kentucky Mountain Folk Tales* by Leonard W. Roberts. Copyright © 1964 by the University Press of Kentucky. Reprinted by permission of Edith R. Roberts, Stanville, KY.

· ACKNOWLEDGMENTS ·

CHAPTER 7

"The Three Sillies" originally titled "The Foolish Bride" from *Storytellers: Folktales and Legends from the South* edited by John A. Burrison. Copyright © 1989 by the University of Georgia Press. Reprinted by permission of the publisher.

"Two Tales of Foolish John" from "The Legend of Foolish John" by Marie Theriot and Marie Lehaye in *Southern Folklore Quarterly*, Vol. BII, September 1943, No. 3. Copyright 1943 by the University Press of Kentucky. Reprinted by permission of the publisher.

"Fido est Mort (Fido Is Dead)" from *Cajun and Creole Folktales: The French Oral Tradition of South Louisiana* by Barry Jean Ancelet. Copyright © 1994 by Barry Jean Ancelet. Reprinted by permission of Garland Publishing, Inc.

"The Devil and the Lord Dividing Souls" from *Storytellers: Folktales and Legends from the South* edited by John A. Burrison. Copyright © 1989 by the University of Georgia Press. Reprinted by permission of the publisher.

"Pat and the Devil" from *The Journal of American Folklore*, Volume 31, January–March 1918.

"The Riddle Test" from *Folklore from Nova Scotia* collected by Arthur Huff Fauset. Reprinted by permission of the American Folklore Society from *The Journal of American Folklore*, 38:148, 1925.

"Jean Sotte and the Riddle" from *Louisiana Folktales* collected and edited by Alcée Fortier. Published in 1895 by Houghton Mifflin Company.

"Jean Sot and Bull's Milk" from *Cajun Folktales* by J. J. Reneaux. Copyright © 1992 by J. J. Reneaux. Reprinted by permission of August House Publishers, Inc.

"The Mule Egg" by Doc McConnell as it appeared in *Homespun: Tales from America's Favorite Storytellers* edited by Jimmy Neil Smith. Copyright © 1988 by Doc McConnell. Reprinted by permission of Doc McConnell, Rogersville, TN.

"The $50,000 Racehorse" by Hannah McConnell Gillenwater from *More Best-Loved Stories Told at the National Storytelling Festival*, 1992, selected by the National Association for the Preservation and Perpetuation of Storytelling. Copyright © 1992 by Harriet McConnell Gillenwater. Reprinted by permission of Harriet McConnell Gillenwater, Rogersville, TN.

"Jim Baker's Bluejay Yarn" from *A Tramp Abroad* by Mark Twain. Published in 1907 by Harper & Bros., New York.

"The Killer Mosquitoes" from *Cajun Folktales* by J. J. Reneaux. Copyright © 1992 by J. J. Reneaux. Reprinted by permission of August House Publishers, Inc.

"The Yankee Peddler and the Innkeeper" from *Pennsylvanian Republican*, York, PA, March 23, 1942.

CHAPTER 8

"The Girl That Married a Flop-Eared Hound Dog" from *Tales from the Cloud Walking Country* by Marie Campbell. Copyright © 1958 by Indiana University Press. Reprinted by permission of Indiana University Press.

"The Algonquin Cinderella" from *World Tales: The Extraordinary Coincidence of Stories Told in All Times in All Places* by Idries Shah. Copyright © 1979 by Technographia, S. A. and Harcourt Brace & Company. Reprinted by permission of Harcourt Brace & Company.

"La Cenicienta Huasteca" from the Publications of the Texas Folklore Society. Used by permission of the Texas Folklore Society.

"Fabiano and Reyes" from *Cuentos: Tales from the Hispanic Southwest* by Jose Griego y Maestas and Rudolfo A. Anaya. Copyright © 1980 by Museum of New Mexico Press. Used by permission of the publisher.

"A Bunch of Laurel Blooms for a Present" from *Tales from the Cloud Walking Country* by Marie Campbell. Copyright © 1958 by Indiana University Press. Reprinted by permission of Indiana University Press.

"The Toadfrog" and "Old Black-Oak Knows Best" from *The Devil's Pretty Daughter and Other Ozark Folk*

Tales by Vance Randolph. Copyright © 1955 by Columbia University Press. Reprinted by permission of Columbia University Press.

"Hard of Hearing" from *The Yankee Blade*, March 1, 1851 (Vol. X).

"Farmer Smith and Ma'am Jones" by H. Hastings Weld from *Burlington Daily Free Press*, May 19, 1948.

"Strawberries" by Gayle Ross from *Homespun: Tales from America's Favorite Storytellers* edited by Jimmy Neil Smith. Copyright © 1988 by Gayle Ross. Reprinted by permission of Gayle Ross, Fredericksburg, TX.

"Lovers' Retreat" from the Publications of the Texas Folklore Society, Number III, 1924. Reprinted by permission of the Texas Folklore Society.

"Poke-o'-Moonshine" from *American Myths and Legends* by Charles M. Skinner. Published in 1903 by J. B. Lippincott, Philadelphia.

"A Tale of Love" from *Mexican Folk Tales* translated and edited by Anthony John Campos. Copyright © 1977 by the Arizona Board of Regents. Reprinted by permission of the University of Arizona Press.

CHAPTER 9

"The Haunted House" from *American Folktales and Songs* by Richard Chase. Copyright © 1956 by Richard Chase. Reprinted by permission of Dover Publications, Inc.

"Marie Jolie" from *Cajun Folktales* by J. J. Reneaux. Copyright © 1992 by J. J. Reneaux. Reprinted by permission of August House Publishers, Inc.

"Sammy and His Fiddle" from *Pine Barrens Legends, Lore and Lies* by William McMahon. Copyright © 1980 by William McMahon. Reprinted by permission of Middle Atlantic Press.

"Tom Dunn's Dance on Rag Rock" from *American Myths and Legends* by Charles M. Skinner. Published in 1903 by J. B. Lippincott Company, Philadelphia.

"Whickety–Whack, Into My Sack" by Ray Hicks from *Voice of Appalachia* by Ray Hicks, 1998 (Winston Salem, NC: John F. Blair). By permission of Lynn S. Salsi, Box 3404 Greensboro, NC 27410. Lynn Salsi is Ray Hicks' biographer.

"The Grouse Girl" from *The Journal of American Folklore* collected by E. A. Golder. Published in 1903 by Houghton Mifflin Company.

"Aunt Tucky" by Harriet Culbertson Lewis from *Best Stories from the Texas Storytelling Festival* published by August House Publishers, Inc. Copyright © 1995 by Harriet Culbertson Lewis. Reprinted by permission of Harriet Culbertson Lewis, Benton, LA.

"The Yellow Ribbon" from *The Rainbow Book of American Folk Tales and Legends* by Maria Leach. Copyright © 1958 by Maria Leach. Reprinted by permission of HarperCollins Publishers, Inc.

"The Ghost of Jean Lafitte" from *Cajun Folktales* by J. J. Reneaux. Copyright © 1992 by J. J. Reneaux. Reprinted by permission of August House Publishers, Inc.

"The Weeping Woman" from *Legendary Ladies of Texas* edited by Francis Edward Abernathy. Copyright © 1981 by the Texas Folklore Society. Reprinted by permission of the Texas Folklore Society.

"La Llorona Teaches a Hippie a Lesson" from *The Weeping Woman: Encounters with La Llorona* compiled and edited by Edward Garcia Kraul and Judith Beatty. Copyright © 1988 by Edward Garcia Kraul and Judith S. Beatty. Reprinted by permission of Judith Beatty, Santa Fe, NM.

"A Pretty Girl in the Road" from *The Devil's Pretty Daughter and Other Ozark Folktales* by Vance Randolph. Copyright © 1955 by Columbia University Press. Reprinted by permission of the publisher.

"The Spectre Bride" from *American Myths and Legends* by Charles M. Skinner. Published in 1903 by J. B. Lippincott Company, Philadelphia.